Eros and Anteros: The Medical Traditions of Love in the Renaissance

Eros and Anteros: The Medical Traditions of Love in the Renaissance

Edited by

Donald A. Beecher
and
Massimo Ciavolella

University of Toronto Italian Studies 9

Dovehouse Editions Inc.

1992

Canadian Cataloguing in Publication Data

Main entry under title:
Eros and Anteros: The Medical Traditions of Love in the Renaissance

(University of Toronto Italian Studies ; 9)
Includes bibliographical references.

ISBN 1–895537–09–6 (bound) — ISBN 1–895537–08-8 (pbk.)

1. Lovesickness. 2. Philosophy, Renaissance. 3. Medicine—15th–18th centuries. 4. Lovesickness in literature. 5. European literature—Renaissance, 1450–1600—History and criticism. 6. Italy—Intellectual life—1268–1559. 7. Italy—Intellectual life—1559–1789. I. Beecher, Donald II. Ciavolella, Massimo, 1942– . III. Series.

RC543.E76 1992 128'.4 C92–090516–1

For orders or trade information:

Dovehouse Editions Inc.
1890 Fairmeadow Cres.
Ottawa, Canada
K1H 7B9

For information on the series:

University of Toronto Italian Studies
c/o The Department of Italian
University of Toronto
Toronto, Canada, M5S 1A1

Typeset by the HUMANITIES PUBLISHING SERVICES, University of Toronto

TABLE OF CONTENTS

Foreword

Our conviction in commissioning the articles for this volume is that a full measure has not yet been made of the extent to which ideas and philosophical systems originating in Medieval and Renaissance medicine escaped the medical establishment and were transferred into humanist and popular treatises, and informed the imaginative writing of that age. This collection is devoted, in particular, to exploring a variety of loci where medical philosophy provided the foundations for discussions of erotic love and the social management of erotic desire. Subsumed in Renaissance culture, perhaps more than is generally appreciated, is a complex pattern of notions concerning the humours, love, the diseased imagination, and the pathological vulnerabilities of the body due to love. This medico-literary nucleus emerges through poetic awareness of lovesickness as a dimension of intense desire, through stories in which the threat of disease is a motivating component, and through treatises that take for granted the clinical reality of eroto-melancholia and eroto-mania.

The following collection is by no means a history of the phenomenon which, in effect, remains to be written, although many of its pieces are beginning to appear. Rather it is an attempt to gather statements dealing with several of the main texts expressing these ideas—works by Ficino, Wier, Bodin, Fregoso, Equicola, Tasso, Campanella, della Porta, and Burton. To be sure, there are many more that might have been included. Moreover, it was our desire to cover a number of formats and rhetorical contexts through which these ideas find expression: medical treatises, treatises on witchcraft, studies of folly and madness, *trattati* proposing and opposing neoplatonic love, memory and physiology books, treatises on jealousy, utopian literature, love poetry, and treatises on melancholy, with their complex reflections on temperament, love, and humoural diseases. It can be but a sampling, but one sufficient to hint at the historical evolution of the founding ideas and the rich diversity of their expression during this dynamic cultural period—one characterized by the cross-fertilization of ideas from country to country and from discipline to discipline. The scope of the volume could easily have been doubled had we searched for only a few more representative studies of imaginative works of art in which erotic love, threatening melancholy or clinical expression, serves as a principal motif. This motif may be found in all the major national literatures, and from the earliest *novelle* to *The Sorrows of Young Werther*, with many outstanding examples from the sixteenth and early seventeenth centuries. Nevertheless, we believe that in the fourteen articles chosen and prepared for this volume there is a valid scope and comprehensiveness. It is our hope that these contributions will extend the base for further scholarship in this expanding area of research in the Renaissance history of ideas.

D.A. Beecher & M. Ciavolella

Acknowledgments

We would like to express our gratitude to the Social Sciences and Humanities Research Council of Canada for their financial contribution to the publication of this book.

We would also like to thank Gary Pinder and John Butler for their collaboration in the preparation of this volume for press.

Mary Frances Wack

From Mental Faculties to Magical Philters: The Entry of Magic into Academic Medical Writing on Lovesickness, 13th–17th Centuries

In Chaucer's *Canterbury Tales* the Wife of Bath proudly explains the stratagems she used to snare her fifth husband, the Oxford clerk Jankyn. As they dallied in the fields while her fourth husband was out of town, she recalls, "I spak to hym and seyde hym how that he, / If I were wydwe, sholde wedde me." Partly in erotic flattery and partly in self-excuse, she accuses him of having enchanted her: "I bar hym on honde he hadde enchanted me — / My dame taughte me that soutiltee."[1] Her false charge of love magic simultaneously announces her desire for Jankin and hides her erotic initiative under the guise of victimization. Her strategy, as their marriage shows, worked.

If, however, her ruse had backfired and either of them—clerk or would-be clerk—had sought to undo the enchantment, authoritative medical books of the sort found at Oxford would have offered remarkably little help.[2] Constantine, Avicenna, al-Rāzī and other authors studied in the medical schools say nothing about magical causes and cures of love. Though late medieval academic physicians enthusiastically debated the disease's causes, they ignored charms, philters, fascination, and other occult means of engendering passionate love.

As one medical commentator remarked, the causes of the disease of love are hard to understand. The common academic view, nonetheless, held that an imbalance of humors and a misfunctioning of the mental faculties of imagination and estimation (judgment) were responsible for the disease. Between the late thirteenth and the early seventeenth centuries, however, the language of mental faculties in academic treatises made room for new debates on philters, fascination, charms, and demonic causes of lovesickness.[3]

For example, the late sixteenth-century physician Jean Aubery in *L'antidote d'amour* asks not only "si par les yeux on peut enchanter et induire à l'amour?," but also "si le particulier amour se forme par philters," and whether figures, characters, numbers and charms can also cause a love that requires cure. In addition, he asserts that the devil and his ministers can represent images and species of things to "les âmes idiotes" who are deceived into mistaking shadows for substances.[4] Jacques Ferrand and Daniel Sennert, eminent physicians of the early seventeenth century, question whether insane love or erotic melancholy (the terminology varies) may be caused by philters or other occult means.[5]

How do we account for the insurgence of magic, fascination, and witchcraft into discussions of the causes of lovesickness? To trace this altered arena of causality—an epistemological shift, if you will—requires examining the relationship of academic medicine to its social and intellectual contexts. More specifically, it involves charting the negotiations that took place among the discourses of natural philosophy, medicine, and theology, and tracking some of the interchanges of elite and popular cultures. Even this ambitious program does not exhaust the relevant possibilities.[6] The remainder of this essay, therefore, can only sketch a highly generalized picture of why magic, broadly defined, became an acceptable topic in medical writing on lovesickness between the fourteenth and early seventeenth centuries.

Before proceeding further into a necessarily complicated exposition, let me summarize my conclusions. In the Middle Ages, academic medical writing on lovesickness, because of its adherence to the Aristotelian-Galenic system of causal explanation, by and large repressed talk of magic. This repression was part of the profession's general strategy of distancing itself from *empirici*, *vetulae*, and other unlearned healers. Since magic did not fit the epistemological framework of humors and mental faculties, it was generally ignored in academic medicine. However, an important change surfaced in the late thirteenth and fourteenth centuries, when theorists of lovesickness, explaining how the sight of beauty may cause the disease of love, adopted the language of visual *species*. Attention to visual *species*—images of objects that mediated between the world and the mind—entailed deepened interest in the powers of the imagination. The imagination, in turn, was increasingly linked in the fourteenth century to magic and demonic witchcraft. In the fifteenth century these developments converged with the emphasis on the occult powers of sight in revived Neoplatonism and with the renewal of learned magic as part of the larger recovery of classical literature. Finally, the invention of printing accelerated the preoccupation with both ancient and contemporary magic among physicians. Printing allowed the educated elite to attempt to correct popular "errors," which paradoxically required them to give the errors voice, so to speak, in their learned printed works. By the sixteenth century, then, all the elements were in place for learned disquisitions on lovesickness that elegantly adduced classical precedents for love magic, scrupulously debated whether charms work, and condescendingly rejected susperstitious popular ideas about amatory magic while reserving to the devil the power to induce insane love.

The early modern developments stand in sharper relief if we first consider the context of the medieval medical writers' peculiar silence about amatory magic. Magic, and especially love magic, was everywhere in the Middle Ages. Indeed, it has been omnipresent in Western history from antiquity to the twentieth century. In matters so important as wanting to be loved, or desiring another's sexual submission, magic beckons when all else fails. Plato calls Eros a magician and "pharmacist" (*goes kai Pharmakeus*, *Symposium* 202e), "subtile enchanteur et sorcier" in Ferrand's paraphrase.[7] Pliny's recipes for love charms exemplify ancient and medieval techniques for compelling love. For example, hairs from the muzzle of a hyena, when applied to a woman's lips, act as a love charm and its anus, worn as an amulet on the left arm, is so powerful a charm that, if a man wearing it but espies a woman, she at once follows him.[8]

Despite canon law's proscription of magical practices that might turn people's minds toward love or hate, in the medieval period even the powerful magic of the eucharistic Host was enlisted for amatory purposes.[9] If a woman held the consecrated Host in her mouth while kissing her husband or lover, she could bind him to her forever. The Host was also used in brewing the *poculum amatorium*. The *Minnetrank* of Tristan and Isolde, though lacking, as far as we know, any eucharistic ingredients, nonetheless belongs to the same well-documented category of love philters used by desperate lovers throughout the medieval and early modern periods.[10]

Penitentials and lay-folks' catechisms, unremitting in their efforts to eradicate from the populace all forms of magic and superstition including amatory magic, reveal the tenacity of those beliefs.[11] Instructions for parish priests in fourteenth-century England included this question for parishioners in the confessional: "Hast thow made any sorcery / To gete wymmyn to lyge hem by?"[12] In William Langland's long, complex poem, *Piers Plowman*, which draws on this kind of popular catechetical material, the figure of Lechery lists his schemes for seducing women. They include composing songs, and sending out old bawds "To wynne to my wille wymmen with gyle, / By sorserie sum tyme and some tyme by maistrie."[13] That these examples can easily be multiplied shows how pervasive amatory magic—or the fear of it— was among the populace.

But love magic was not restricted to folk practices or to popular culture. It also was part of the intellectual world of the educated elite and of the great nobles. In the middle of the eleventh century Anselm of Beste composed a *Rhetorimachia* (1047–50). Several episodes of love magic appear in this strange treatise. In one, the lover must keep vigil for three nights with a cock and a cat, then burn them to produce a powder that has great power over girls and married women. As Edward Peters has concluded, the treatise is important for what it tells us of credible charges about magic and witchcraft among the work's educated audience.[14]

In the fourteenth century, amatory magic entered the realm of political strategy among the nobility. In 1316 Mahaut of Artois was accused of using sorcery on her son-in-law Philip V in order to restore his affections for her daughter. Edward III's mistress Alice Perrers was accused in 1376 of using love magic on the aged king. For the years 1386–88 Froissart chronicles an intrigue in the House of Foix centering on a supposed love powder which was, in reality, a potent poison. Here again, the important point is not the historical accuracy of the charges, but the fact that love magic was a plausible accusation in elite circles.[15]

Strangely, however, nothing of amatory magic's ubiquity is reflected in the medical treatises on lovesickness in circulation from roughly 1070–1300. The entire artillery of scholastic causality was sometimes applied to the question of lovesickness, yet in the bewildering catalogue of antecedent, conjunct, coadiuvant, formal, efficient, material, and final causes, magic and witchcraft are notably absent. The Arabic medical treatises that stimulated a renewed Western interest in love as a disease were informed by Galenic-Aristotelian rationality. Magic had no place in this system because it could not be accounted for in rational, causal terms; magic is magic because its workings are occult. Anxious to secure the status of medicine as *scientia* as well as *ars*, the physicians of the medieval universities avoided what could not be explained within that epistemological framework. For the writers on lovesickness, such material unworthy of notice included the amatory magic practised by the unlearned populace.[16] The combined pressure of literary examples of love magic (from Vergil and Ovid), popular practices, and pastoral doctrine on magic could not break through this intellectual bulwark against the irrational and the merely empirical, against "the foolish practices of old women."

Though exclusion was the primary way that elite medicine differentiated itself from popular ideas on the subject of compulsive love, there is some evidence for the "controlled appropriation" of popular notions.[17] In the case of Peter of Spain (later Pope John XXI) two different approaches to the medical problem of love—one academic in the strict sense and one oriented toward treatment of the poor—show that while some popular ideas entered Latin medical writing, they were nonetheless still excluded from the rational-causal discourse of the classroom.

Peter included two detailed scholastic expositions of lovesickness around 1250 in his *Questions on the Viaticum.*[18] His accounts of the disease's causes are highly technical elaborations of the interactions of faculty psychology and physiology; not a word on magic creeps in. However, tradition ascribes to him another treatise in which popular ideas about love magic do appear. The *Thesaurus pauperum*, designed for those who could not afford expensive medical care, significantly enough has no chapter on *amor hereos*, which was, according to most thirteenth and fourteenth century physicians, a disease of the nobility. Nonetheless, it does contain the following malodorous recipe for those who would be rid of love caused by *maleficium*: "Item si quis maleficiatus fuerit ad nimis amandum aliquem uel aliquam, merda illius, quem diligit, recens, ponatur mane in subtellari dextro amantis et calciet se; quam cito fetorem sentiet, soluetur maleficium. Experimentator."[19]

Two explanations are possible for the presence of this recipe (a form of aversion therapy?) against magically caused love in the *Thesaurus pauperum* and the absence of magic in the questions on lovesickness in the *Viaticum* commentary. On the one hand, "nimis amor" in the *Thesaurus pauperum* may have been viewed as quite a different matter than *amor hereos.* That is, Peter may have drawn a nosological disinction between the two and thought that they required different causal explanations. *Amor hereos* afflicts the nobility who have the leisure and wealth to suffer from it; the populace may suffer from maleficium causing excessive love, but they do not contract the academically sanctioned disease of lovesickness.

On the other hand, conventions of audience or genre may have dictated the means for curing excessive love. University medical students listening to lectures on the *Viaticum* required a technical explanation of love in the terms of scholastic Aristotelianism; the general populace did not need and could not profit from such elaborate rationalizing. The *Thesaurus pauperum* offered them a remedy for love in their own terms, those of magical-empirical pharmacology.[20]

The same bifurcation of medical views of love along class lines appears in a fifteenth-century Latin *Dialogue between a Rustic and a Nobleman.*

The nobleman of the dialogue explains that the rustics, when they suffer from a natural illness, believe themselves to be "maleficiatos." Thus, when the rustic is invaded by "amor ereus," which according to Avicenna is a disease resulting from excessive and immoderate love, he believes himself to be "infected" (*inficiatum*) and "per mulieris exercitia secreta molestatum."[21] While the nobleman recognizes his malady as the "naturalis infirmitas" of lovesickness, the hapless rustic has no other model of explanation for his sleeplessness, restlessness, and sighs than magical attack. This dichotomy of explanatory models along class lines supports Peter Burke's thesis that for the majority, "popular culture was the only culture"; the elite minority, however, had access to both popular culture and the "great tradition." They were "amphibious, bi-cultural."[22] Unlike the author of the *Dialogue*, who juxtaposes the two traditions of lovesickness even as he distinguishes them, Peter of Spain channels them into separate forms of medical writing according to audience.

If these distinctions of disease, of audience, and of social class truly obtained in Peter of Spain's writings, it is also the case that they collapsed in the Renaissance. *Amor hereos* was no longer separated from love caused by magical means, and the beliefs of popular culture were given voice in academic treatises. How can we account for this change?

I suggest that the emergence of visual species in causal analyses of *amor hereos* in the late thirteenth and fourteenth centuries placed lovesickness in a fertile nexus of debates on imagination and magic in natural philosophy and theology. The language of *species* allowed a cross-fertilization among disciplines that resulted in magic's becoming acceptable to the physicians of love. In the interest of expository clarity, the main lines of development may be laid out as follows, though there are many crosslinks between them. For Aristotelians and others concerned with material and efficient causality, attention to vision and imagination enabled medical discourse on love to be linked to beliefs on the imaginative nature of magic and diabolical witchcraft. For the Neoplatonically inclined, the power of sight to infect and to fascinate took on new importance in explanations of lovesickness. In short, lovesickness and magic, whose effects seemed obvious but whose causes were obscure, became readily connected topics. Both challenged the ability of intellectual systems to explain unusual phenomena, and the power of both seemed to spring from a common ground in the imagination.[23]

In the thirteenth and fourteenth centuries, the problems associated with *species in medio* were at the heart of interlocking controversies in optics, psychology, epistemology and philosophy.[24] According to medieval visual theory, *species* were likenesses of objects that mediated between the material world and the mind. A widely-quoted dictum explained that "the stone itself is not in the mind, but rather the *species* of the stone." The mind's faculties—the internal senses as well as the intellect—exercised their functions on the images of things rather than on things themselves.

At the same time that intellectuals were debating the role of *species* in perception and cognition, writers on lovesickness adopted the term to explain more precisely than their predecessors had how beauty, or the sight of a beautiful form, could cause *amor hereos.* Guglielmo de' Corvi (or Brescia), a doxographer of *amor hereos* who quoted or alluded to almost everything on the subject available around 1275, claimed that the *causa primitiva* of lovesickness is the *aspectus rei* having the form of a beautiful woman. This sight kindles the heart just as the sun ignites straw through the intermediary of a lens.[25] The Florentine physician Dino del Garbo, in glossing the line "Vèn da veduta forma che s'intende" of Guido Cavalcanti's canzone "Donna me prega," specifies that the impression of a *species* causes love.[26] In his commentary on the ninth book of Rāzī's *Liber ad almansorem*, the Montpellier master Gerard de Solo (early fourteenth century) remarked that the principle cause of lovesickness is a pleasurable object imprinting its *species* on the imagination and the estimation.[27]

From the visual *species* impressed in the imagination it is but a short step in the fourteenth century to the complex controversies over the powers of the imagination, including the possibilities of action at a distance, the transitive effects of magic, and the relation of mind and body.[28] Both Aristotle (*De motu animalium*) and Avicenna (*De anima* IV.4) had indicated that the imagination has the power to cause alterations in the body and to induce health. Relying on these authorities, scholastic physicians and natural philosophers debated such phenomena as fascination, incantations, and demonic illusions in the context of the powers of the imagination and their relation to visual *species.*[29] The natural philosopher Nicole Oresme was among the most prominent writers who concerned themselves with these issues.[30]

Whereas writers on *amor hereos* picked up the language of *species* in the late thirteenth century, it was not until the fourteenth century that the debates on imagination and magic were perceived as relevant to the medical doctrines on lovesickness. The crucial step of linking visual *species* and the imagination to magic in the particular context of lovesickness is well illustrated in Gentile da Foligno's mid-fourteenth century commentary on Avicenna's *Canon.*[31] In the chapter on *ilisci* or lovesickness, Gentile's interest in natural magic prompts him to ask whether incantations and suspensions are of any use in curing the lover's malady. He advances two arguments that involve visual *species*. First, incantations generate a *species* in the mind, and this causes, according to a dictum of Aristotle, a change that can affect the body. Second, since a *species* in the mind is the cause of health, according to Avicenna, and since an incantation can call forth such a *species*, incantations can cure. Gentile concludes, however, with a skepticism typical of natural philosophy (and hence of medicine as its subspecies) in the fourteenth century, that "neither man nor God achieves anything through incantations."[32]

To recapitulate: Physicians writing on the causes of lovesickness followed the lead of natural philosophers in gradually adopting the terminology of visual *species* and an interest in connecting *species*, imagination, and magic. The subject of imagination and magic now requires us to trace a parallel development in demonology. While the physicians were integrating visual *species* into the panoply of causes of lovesickness, natural philosphers were combatting the tendency to explain optical illusions and mental delusions by recourse to magical or diabolical agency. Demonological controversies that pitted natural philosophers against theologians contributed much to the new fifteenth- and sixteenth-century synthesis of medical views on lovesickness.

Theologians generally held that the devil or his agents could delude man by manipulating images in his imagination, and that man was especially vulnerable in sexual matters to this interference.[33] The scientists, however, were concerned to make this the explanation of last recourse; only after ordinary causes had been excluded might there be talk of magical or diabolical agency.

The Silesian perspectivist Witelo, best known for his optical work *Perspectiva*, also composed an *Epistula de causa primaria poenitentiae in hominibus et substantia et natura daemonum* while a student in canon law in 1268.[34] In this treatise, Witelo is concerned among other things to debunk current ideas about the apparition of demons, clarifying such visions as the result of disease, emotional stress, or other natural causes.[35] He explains that the optical illusions in *amor hereos*—as when a lover thinks he sees his beloved standing before him when in fact she is not present—are not the works of the devil, but rather the effects of a strong impression in the imagination.[36]

Witelo's thesis on *amor hereos* was corroborated by his contemporary, the Catalan physician Arnald of Villanova. Foreshadowing sixteenth-century debates over witchcraft and melancholy, Arnald declares in his *De improbatione maleficiorum* (ca. 1276–1288) that those who are convinced that they are the victims of demonic activity are, in fact, suffering from melancholic diseases. These diseases cause disturbances of sense perception and of bodily functioning. As an example of such a disease, and for further information on melancholia, Arnald refers the reader to his treatise on lovesickness, the *Liber de amore heroico*.[37]

However, as Jean Céard and others have shown, the attraction between melancholy and the demonic was also construed in ways other than Witelo and Arnald had proposed. Melancholy is, as Ferrand says, "le baing du diable." Black, cold, and terrestrial, the devil and melancholy have a natural affinity for each other.[38] As Pertelote the hen explains to her husband Chauntecleer in Chaucer's *Nun's Priest's Tale*, "the humour of malencolie / Causeth ful many a man in sleep to crie / For feere of blake beres, or boles blake, / Or elles blake develes wol hem take" (VII 2933–36). Hamlet fears an even more direct link between melancholy and the devil:

> . . . The spirit that I have seen
> May be a devil, and the devil hath power
> T'assume a pleasing shape, yea, and perhaps
> Out of my weakness and my melancholy,
> As he is very potent with such spirits,
> Abuses me to damn me.
> (II.ii.594-99).[39]

Because lovesickness was classified as a subspecies of melancholy, it could hardly resist the taint of the demonic, despite the disclaimers of scientists such as Witelo and Arnald.

Beliefs in demonically inspired illusions associated with lovesickness must have had some currency in order to call forth Witelo's and Arnald's polemics. While they are not reflected in contemporary (i.e. 13th century) medical treatises, in the fourteenth and fifteenth centuries, the nexus between lovesickness and demonic magic does grow tighter as simple amatory magic is drawn into the sphere of diabolic witchcraft.[40]

A key figure in the more general process of the demonization of medicine is Jean Gerson, rector of the University of Paris.[41] An oration addressed to medical students in 1398 reveals not only that by that time folk magic and demonology had claimed the attention of intellectuals, but also that the subject was of pressing concern for physicians, precisely because the powers of the imagination could be manipulated for health or disease. Entitled "De erroribus circa artem magicam," Gerson condemns the "pestiferous superstitions of magicians and the stupidities of old witches (*sortilegarum*) by which they promise to heal patients through certain condemned rites."[42]

These "rites" include ligatures, characters, figures, and "verbis peregrinis et incognitis," whose efficacy is attested not only by ancient medical writings, but also by the poets and "vox publica." Though Gerson argues that a philosophic or medical view should in no way admit superstitious traditions, he insists on the reality of demonic interference. Nonetheless, the physician need not manipulate the imagination through magic or demons, even when such manipulation might correspond to the beliefs and expectations of the patient.

Gerson's polemic against magic is, on the surface, theologically motivated; the theme of his talk is "Physician, heal thyself." We may, nonetheless, suspect a partial displacement of another issue—the struggle for professional control of medicine.[43] As Gerson's oration shows, charges of sorcery were a powerful weapon in that battle. A generation later, professional rivalries are not only overt in a discussion of lovesickness, but have also been coupled to diabolical witchcraft. In his commentary on Avicenna's *Canon*, written around 1440–1444, the learned physician Jacques Despars feels compelled to reject the magical origin of insane love by the external agency of witches or demons. In the chapter on *ilisci* or *amor hereos* he enjoins his readers not to accept the opinion of the *stolidum vulgus* that insane love is caused by the sortilege of old women practicing diabolical arts, who have the power to bind men with such love or loose them from it. He then recounts the case of a woman in his city who indulges in such practices and has amassed great wealth from the simple, credulous people of the area.[44] Despars' caution to his colleagues suggests that some of them might indeed have been tempted—given the lucrative possibilities—to follow the opinion of the *stolidum vulgus* in granting efficacy to *veneficiis et incantationibus* to provoke love or lovesickness.[45] Economic envy as much as superior *scientia* seems to imbue Despars' remarks.

Our subject takes a more sinister turn in the fifteenth century, when the type of empiric medicine *cum* folk magic Despars inveighed against was subsumed into the heresy of demonic witchcraft. The Inquisitorial trial in Arras in 1460 illustrates how amatory magic was identified with diabolical witchcraft. Among the crimes of the "Valdenses ydolatrae," in addition to consorting with demons, infanticide, and desecration of the Host, are various *maleficia*, including "fascinaciones per pulveres amatorios aut pocula vel houppellos amatorios sibi datos a demone."[46]

The most insidious result of this trend to amalgamate popular magic and demonic witchcraft in the realm of the erotic was the enormously influential *Malleus maleficarum*. In this treatise natural philosophical explanations of illusion like Witelo's or Arnald's are swept aside in favor of all-pervasive diabolical activity. The *Hammer of Witches*, published by two German Dominicans in 1486 as a professional manual for witch hunters, declares that *amor hereos* results from the "maleficiis demonum et maleficarum" and that it is a widespread form of witchcraft.[47] In order to satisfy their filthy lusts, women turn the minds of "seculi potentes" and others to *amor hereos* or philocaption. Exactly how the mind can be turned by an outside agency entails a long explanation of the devil's activity that hinges on visible species and the imagination (Part I, quest. 7). Demons "can stir up and excite spirits and species retained in repositories [i.e., the memory] are drawn out from their treasuries [and made apparent] to the *principia sensitiva*, namely to the imaginative and fantastic faculties, so that these things are imagined to be true." If *amor hereos* or philocaption is not due to witchcraft, the authors recommend the cures for lovesickness from Avicenna's *Canon.*[48] And, finally, lest their scholastic explanations be too complicated for the common man, they offer a method of "proposing the foregoing concerning *amor hereos* in sermons to the people."[49]

The relations of lovesickness and magic were configured somewhat differently among writers with Neoplatonic inclinations. The late medieval concern with visual *species* was a perfect point of congruence between theories of lovesickness and Neoplatonic ideas of the power of sight not only in the generation of love—*eros quasi 'orasis'*—but as a conduit of occult powers in general. Moreover, the "vis imaginativa" was just as important for Neoplatonists' analysis of the occult workings of natural magic as for the theologians' explanations of demonic magic. But instead of demonic magic, we find fascination or "infection" through visual rays as a cause of lovesickness among writers like Ficino, Paracelsus, and François Valleriola.[50] Following Ficino, Valleriola explains in his *Observationum medicinalium libri VI* (before 1576) how insane love is a type of fascination, by which the lover is infected by the subtle darts of extromitted visual rays.[51]

In addition to the foregoing intellectual and social developments, the general revival of classical learning also enhanced the acceptability of magical topics in medical treatises. Classical texts, with even greater *auctoritas* than before, abounded with examples of love magic, and learned magic itself enjoyed a renaissance. Physicians eager to show off their humanistic achievements dotted their discourses with references to the magic and philters of Circe, Medea, and a host of other classical figures. The authority of classical literature thus seemed to confirm the reality of popular superstitions, a point Gerson made in his speech at the University of Paris.[52]

The incorporation of magic into medicine was accelerated by the invention of printing, which made available the works of ancient authors, of demonologists, of physicians and natural scientists. Moreover, printing enabled learned authors to address a wider public than manuscript culture had allowed. It also allowed "le menu peuple," as Natalie Davis calls them, the opportunity to air their ideas. In response, some intellectuals wrote in order to combat what they perceived as popular errors infesting their subjects.[53] Ferrand, for example, quotes Joubert's *Popular Errors* (concerning health and medicine) as to popular customs and superstitions about love. Women in some places command the midwives attending the birth of a daughter to save the "vedille" or "nombril" (navel cord), so that in later years they can make a powder of it to give to the man whom they would like to fall instantly in love with their daughters.[54] In a more general attack on popular superstition, Ferrand denies that a philtre can be found "qui face que Iean aime Ieanne plutost que Jacquette"; nonetheless, "le vulgaire en mette supersticieusement plusieurs en usage, qui ressentent le paganisme" (pp. 227–29).

Ferrand's relation to popular culture differs from Peter of Spain's, and in that difference we can summarize some of the changes between the high Middle Ages and the early modern period. Ferrand is, like Peter, bi-cultural; however, those cultures are both closer and farther apart for him than for Peter. Closer, in that popular ideas are directly articulated in a learned treatise, and not funnelled into a separate work; farther apart, in that the purpose of voicing those ideas is not to minister to the people by working within their system of beliefs, but to eradicate those beliefs in favor of learned theorizing.

Two literary works, one from roughly 1385, the other from 1499, offer another angle of vision on the web of changes I have traced—synchronic counterpoints to the diachronic analysis above. The hero of Chaucer's late fourteenth-century masterpiece, *Troilus and Criseyde*, suffers from a classic case of lovesickness caused by a glimpse of the beautiful widow Criseyde. His friend Pandarus, a respected member of the Trojan nobility, undertakes to heal him, as I have argued elsewhere, playing the *doctor amoris* not once, but twice in the course of the poem.[55] The causes of love, its symptoms, and proposed remedies are consonant with those a contemporary physician might have found in the standard medical authorities. In other words, Chaucer's representations in the courtly, conservative poem *Troilus* are in keeping with the best learned medicine of his time, but steer clear of the controversies about imagination, witchcraft, and diabolical activity that were growing more frequent and more heated among theologians and natural philosophers.[56]

La Celestina, written over a century later by Fernando de Rojas, begins with the same situation: the nobleman Calisto is striken with lovesickness for the lovely Melibea, who is immured in her parents' house. To assuage his malady, he enlists the aid of a go-between, Celestina.[57] She is a professional procuress, a repairer of prematurely ruptured hymens (thus a health professional of sorts), and boasts of her skills in witchcraft.[58] In order to effect the union between Calisto and Melibea, at the end of Act 3 she conjures Pluto with blood, names, characters, and a viperous unguent to come without delay and obey her will. She anoints a thread with the oil and conjures "Old Evil" into the thread, which she later sells to Melibea in order to entangle her in love with Calisto. When Melibea later falls ill with the usual symptoms of lovesickness, we can see that at the level of surface narrative, at least, her illness has been "caused" by diabolical witchcraft. Fernando de Rojas' depiction of Celestina not only links lovesickness with amatory magic, but also ties magic to demonic witchcraft. The Spanish author thus gives literary form to notions prevalent among theologians and demonologues, but that were only gradually gaining currency among medical writers on the lover's malady.

In summary, then, in the realm of lovesickness the interchanges among medicine, theology, natural philosophy, popular culture, and literature were not symmetrical or reciprocal. Medical writing on lovesickness initially held itself aloof both from popular notions about amatory magic and from theological views of demonic illusions. Theology, in contrast, continuously grappled with magic and demonology in both learned and popular forms. The first clash between theological and scientific views of lovesickness occurred in natural philosophical rather than medical treatises (Witelo et al.). However, medical and theological views increasingly accommodated each other from the late fourteenth century onwards, interestingly enough, through common reliance on natural philosophic views of perception and imagination. In the fifteenth century, then, the *Malleus maleficarum* appropriated the medical discourse of *amor hereos* in order to elaborate its demonology, and medical writers parried threats to professional hegemony over lovesickness with charges of witchcraft against popular healers. Other social and technical developments further increased the respectability of magical topics within medical discourse on lovesickness. Finally, when we turn to literature, we find that, untrammeled by the conventions and controversies of academic discourse, it could embody any level of the changing debate on the occulted causes of the lover's malady.

Stanford University

NOTES

1 *The Riverside Chaucer*, ed. Larry Benson et al. (Boston: Houghton Mifflin, 1987), III (D) 563–76. All quotations of Chaucer will be from this edition.

2 On the medical books available at Oxford in the late fourteenth century, see J.A.W. Bennett, *Chaucer at Oxford and at Cambridge* (Toronto: Toronto UP, 1974).

3 Noted by Urs Benno Birchler, *Der Liebeszauber (Philtrum) und sein Zusammenhang mit der Liebeskrankheit in der Medizin besonders des 16.–18. Jahrhunderts*, Züricher Medizingeschichtliche Abhandlungen, n.R. 110 (Zürich: Juris, 1975), 11. General histories of lovesickness include Hjalmar Chrohns, "Zur Geschichte der Liebe als 'Krankheit'," *Archiv für Kulturgeschichte* 3 (1905), pp. 66–86; John L. Lowes, "The Loveres Maladye of Hereos," *Modern Philology* 11 (1913/14), pp. 491–546; Massimo Ciavolella, *La 'malattia d'amore' dall'antichità al medioevo* (Rome: Bulzoni, 1976); and Adalheid Giedke, "Liebe als Krankheit in der Geschichte der Medizin" (Ph.D. diss., University of Düsseldorf, 1983).

4 *L'Antidote de l'amour avec un ample discours contenant la nature et les causes d'iceluy, ensemble les remèdes les plus singuliers pour le preserver et guérir des passions amoureuses* (Paris: Claude Chappelet, 1599).

5 Daniel Sennert, *Institutiones medicae* in *Opera omnia* (Lyons, 1676) vol. 3, lib. 2, pars 3, sect. 2, cap. 4, "de amore insano"; Jacques Ferrand, *De la maladie d'amour ou melancholie érotique* (Paris: Denis Moreau, 1623; rpt. Liechtenstein: Kraus, 1978). See also Robert Burton, *The Anatomy of Melancholy*, ed. Holbrook Jackson (New York: Random House, 1977), "Love Melancholy," pp. 85 ff. On the generally anti-occult stance of these three authors, see Brian Vickers, "Analogy versus Identity: The Rejection of Occult Symbolism, 1580–1680," in *Occult and Scientific Mentalities in the Renaissance*, ed. Brian Vickers (Cambridge: Cambridge UP, 1984), pp. 95–164.

6 The diachronic analysis offered here could be refined by further study of the origin of the treatises (geographical area, university milieu), of sex roles in lovesickness and witchcraft, and of other types of source materials (e.g., Sentences, commentaries, sermons). Birchler (n. 3 above) suggests three reasons for the appearance of magic in Renaissance medical writing on lovesickness: "Der Hexenwahn, die Sympathielehre und das starke allgemeine Interesse an den Giften" (p. 29). However, our analyses only minimally overlap.

7 On Eros *pharmakeus*, see Jacques Derrida, "Plato's Pharmacy" in *Disseminations*, trans. Barbara Herrnstein Smith (Chicago: University of Chicago Press,

1981). At this writing a widely advertised French perfume is called, appropriately enough, "Poison." Arnold van Gennep, *Manuel de folklore français contemporain* (Paris: Auguste Picard, 1943; rpt. 1972) 1.238–46, documents twentieth-century amatory magic in France; see also E. Hoffmann-Krayer and Hans Bächtold-Stäubli, *Handwörterbuch des deutschen Aberglaubens* (Berlin and Leipzig: Walter de Gruyter, 1932–33) 5.1279–97: "Liebeszauber."

8 Pliny, *Natural History* 28.27.101, 106. On the association of love madness and magic in antiquity and the Middle Ages, see the brief resumé by Urs Benno Birchler, "Die Rolle der Frau bei der Liebeskrankheit und den Liebestränken," *Sudhoffs Archiv* 59 (1975), pp. 311–20. On love magic in antiquity, see Georg Luck, *Arcana Mundi: Magic and the Occult in the Greek and Roman Worlds* (Baltimore: Johns Hopkins University Press, 1985).

9 On magic in canon law, see Henry C. Lea, *Materials Toward a History of Witchcraft* (Philadelphia: University of Pennsylvania Press, 1939) vol. 1, and Edward Peters, *The Magician The Witch and the Law* (Philadelphia: University of Pennsylvania Press, 1978). On magical use of the sacrament, see Peter Brouwe, S.J., "Die Eucharistie als Zaubermittel im Mittelalter," *Archiv für Kulturageschichte* 20 (1930), pp. 134–54.

10 Irmgard Müller, "Liebestränke, Liebeszauber, und Schlafmittel in der mittelalterlichen Literatur," in *Liebe—Ehe—Ehebruch in der Literatur des Mittelalters*, ed. Xenja von Ertzdorff and Marianne Wynn, Beiträge zur deutschen Philologie, 58 (Giessen: Wilhelm Schmitz, 1984), pp. 71–87; Lea, *Materials*, 1:211, 245, 247; Keith Thomas, *Religion and the Decline of Magic* (New York: Charles Scribner's Sons, 1971), pp. 233–4; Richard Kieckhefer, *European Witch Trials: Their Foundations In Popular and Learned Culture 1300–1500* (Berkeley and Los Angeles: University of California Press, 1976), pp. 56–61. The *Life of Christina of Markyate, a Twelfth-Century Recluse*, ed. and trans. C.H. Talbot (Oxford: Clarendon, 1959), pp. 72–75, contains a notable episode involving love potions.

11 See, for example, the enormously popular *Summa confessorum* of Thomas of Chobham (early 13th c.), ed. F. Broomfield, Analecta Mediaevalia Namurcensia, 25 (Louvain and Paris: Nauwelaerts, 1968), p. 473; Jeffrey Burton Russell, *Witchcraft In the Middle Ages* (Ithaca: Cornell University Press, 1972), pp. 75–84 and 291–3; George Lyman Kittredge, *Witchcraft in Old and New England* (Cambridge, Mass.: Harvard University Press, 1929), pp. 30 and 382–3; Joseph Hansen, *Zauberwahn Inquisition und Hexenprozess im Mittelalter* (Munich: Oldenbourg, 1900), pp. 43-9.

12 Gillis Kristensson, *John Mirk's Instructions for Parish Priests*, Lund Studies in English, 49 (Lund: Gleerup, 1974), p. 118, ll. 860–61. Cf. Chaucer's *Friar's Tale*, in which the archdeacon "boldely did execucioun / In punysshynge of fornicacioun, / Of wicchecraft, and eek of bawderye" as well as the *Parson's Tale*, 340 and 975. John Bromyard's manual for preachers, *Summa praedicantium* (Venice: Dominicus Nicolinus, 1586), 368v–373v, part 1, cap. 11

"sortilegium," includes amatory magic among the other forms of sortilege to be condemned, calling them all superstitious, illicit, and "tanquam idolatria."

13 Derek Pearsall, ed., *Piers Plowman by William Langland: An Edition of the C-Text* (Berkeley and Los Angeles: University of California, 1979), Passus 6:189–91. Cf. E. William Monter, *Witchcraft in France and Switzerland* (Ithaca: Cornell UP, 1976), 189–90 for love magic recipes in early modern popular books ("grimoires" of the "bibliothèque bleue").

14 Peters, *Magician*, pp. 22–8.

15 *Magician*, pp. 121–23. On the circumstances of the charges against Alice Perrers, see F. George Kay, *Lady of the Sun: The Life and Times of Alice Perrers* (New York: Barnes and Noble, 1966), pp. 7–8 (for the biased source) and 138–41. See also Henry A. Kelly, "English Kings and the Fear of Sorcery," *Mediaeval Studies* 39 (1977), pp. 206–38. For instances of trials of commoners involving allegations of love magic or "love powders," see Alan Macfarlane, *Witchcraft in Tudor and Stuart England: A Regional and Comparative Study* (London: Routledge and Kegan Paul, 1970), pp. 77, 288, 292, 303. Froissart's *Chronicles* story is conveniently available in the translation of Geoffrey Brereton (Harmondsworth: Penguin, 1978), pp. 266–74.

16 An exception seems to prove the rule. In his commentary on the *Tabulas Salerni*, Bernardus Provincialis (s. 122) does mention what is obviously a folk remedy for lovesickness (drinking water in which incandescent iron has been extinguished with hands tied behind the back), but takes pains to explain that it is a "phisicum et empiricum et rationale remedium." In Salvatore de Renzi, *Collectio salernitana* (Naples, 1859), vol. 5, pp. 299–300.

17 Jole Agrimi and Chiara Crisciani, "Medici e 'Vetulae' dal Duecento al Quattrocento: Problemi di Una Ricerca," in *Cultura Popolare e Cultura Dotta nel Seicento*, Atti del Convegno di Studio di Genova, 23–25 novembre 1982 (Milan: Franco Angeli, 1983), pp. 144–59 use the term "integrazione controllata" in their analysis of the relations between learned and unlearned healers.

18 For references to bibliography on Peter of Spain and for a study of his questions on lovesickness, see Mary F. Wack, "The Measure of Pleasure: Peter of Spain on Men, Women, and Lovesickness," *Viator* 17 (1986), pp. 173–96 and "New Medieval Medical Texts on amor hereos," in *Zusammenhänge Einflüsse Wirkungen*, Kongressakten zum ersten Symposium des Mediävistenverbandes in Tübingen, 1984, ed. Joerg Fichte, Karl Heinz Göller, and Bernhard Schimmelpfennig (Berlin: De Gruyter, 1986), pp. 288–98.

19 Maria Helena da Rocha Pereira, ed., *Thesaurus pauperum* in *Obras Médicas de Pedro Hispano* (Coimbra: University, 1973), pp. 237–39, ch. 37. See also Lynn Thorndike, *A History of Magic and Experimental Science* (London: Macmillan, 1923), vol. 2, pp. 490–98. The question of Peter's authorship of the *Thesaurus pauperum* has not been definitively settled. Even if he is not the author, another learned physician probably is, and thus my larger argument about the bifurcation of discourse in terms of audience would still hold. On "Experi-

mentator" see J.O. Liebowitz and S. Marcus, *"Sefer Hanisyonot": The Book of Medical Experiences Attributed to Abraham Ibn Ezra* (Jerusalem: The Magnes Press, The Hebrew University, 1984), p. 36. They are inclined to identify "Experimentator" with Abraham Ibn Ezra (1092–1167). Though I have not been able to locate this particular recipe in their edition, there is a chapter entitled "On What Increases Love" (pp. 254–57) that contains similar kinds of procedures. This particular recipe seems to have circulated rather widely, appearing in pseudo-Arnald of Villanova's *Remedia contra maleficium* and in works by Peter of Angelata and Savonarola. See Gerda Hoffmann, "Beiträge zur Lehre von der durch Zauber Verursachten Krankheit und ihrer Behandlung in der Medizin des Mittelalters," *Janus* 37 (1933), pp. 129–44, 179–92, 211–20.

20 Agrimi and Crisciani, "Medici," pp. 152–53.

21 The *Dialogus de nobilitate et rusticitate*, composed by Felix Hemmerlin ca. 1444–50, can be found in Joseph Hansen, *Quellen und Untersuchungen zur Geschichte des Hexenwahns und der Hexenverfolgung im Mittelalter* (Bonn: Carl Georgi, 1901), pp. 109–12.

22 Peter Burke, *Popular Culture in Early Modern Europe* (New York: Harper and Row, 1978), pp. 28-29.

23 On the intellectual challenges posed by the unusual, see Stuart Clark, "The Scientific Status of Demonology" in *Occult*, ed. Vickers, pp. 351–74. On the imagination, see Ioan Peter Couliano, *Eros et magie à la Renaissance: 1484* (Paris: Flammarion, 1984). I would like to thank Massimo Ciavolella for bringing this work to my attention.

24 Katherine Tachau, "The Problem of the Species in Medio at Oxford in the Generation after Ockham," *Mediaeval Studies* 44 (1982), pp. 349–443 and "The Response to Ockham's and Aureol's Epistemology (1320–1340)," in *English Logic In Italy in the 14th and 15th Centuries*, ed. Alfonso Maierù (Naples: Bibliopolis, 1982). For a general survey of optical theory, see David C. Lindberg, *Theories of Vision from Al-Kindi to Kepler* (Chicago: Chicago UP, 1976). For the term species, see Pierre Michaud-Quantin, "Les champs sémantiques de *species*: tradition latine et traduction du grec," in *Études sur le vocabulaire philosophique du Moyen-Age* (Rome: Edizioni dell'Ateneo, 1970), pp. 113–50.

25 *Practica* (Venice, 1508), f. 23v: "Dico quod causa primitiva est aspectus rei habentis figuram mulieris decorem. Per aspectum enim cor accenditur sicut stupa a sole mediante cristallo vel vitro."

26 G. Favati, "La glossa latina di Dino Del Garbo a 'Donna me prega' del Cavalcanti," *Annali della r. scuola normale superiore di Pisa*, Lettere, storia, e filosofia, Serie 2, v. 21 (1952), pp. 70–103: "impressio speciei rei, ex qua creatur amor, conseruatur in memoria" (p. 90); "Alia res concurrit ad causandam aliquam passionem, que est res extrinseca que suam ymaginem uel speciem causat in virtute sensitiua, ad quam cognitionem uel apprehensionem consequitur appetitus talis uel talis" (p. 91); and p. 92, the interpretation of "Vien da veduta forma." See also Maria Corti, *La felicità mentale* (Turin: Einaudi,

1983), pp. 3–37, "Guido Cavalcanti e una diagnosi dell'amore" and Marie-Madeleine Fontaine, "La ligné des commentaires à la chanson de Guido Cavalcanti, *Donna me prega*: Évolution des relations entre philosophie, médecine et littérature dans le débat sur la nature d'Amour (de la fin du XIIIe siécle à celle du XVIe)," in *La folie et le corps*, ed. Jean Céard (Paris: Ecole Normale Supérieure, 1985), pp. 179–97.

27 *Commentum super nono almansoris cum textu* (Venice, 1505), f. 34: "[Causa] principalis est obiectum delectabile imprimens suam speciem in virtute ymaginativa et estimativa, et virtus estimativa mediante specie impressa."

28 Among the many works on imagination in the Middle Ages, the following are helpful in this context in addition to Couliano, *Eros*: Murray Wright Bundy, *Theory of the Imagination in Classical and Mediaeval Thought*, University of Illinois Studies in Language and Literature, 12 (Urbana: Urbana UP, 1927); Lynn Thorndike, "Imagination and Magic: The Force of Imagination on the Human Body and of Magic on the Human Mind," *Mélanges Eugéne Tisserant*, Studi e Testi, 237 (Città del Vaticano: Biblioteca Apostolica, 1964), vol. 7, pp. 353–58; L.J. Rather, "Thomas Fienus' (1567–1631) Dialectical Investigation of the Imagination as Cause and Cure of Bodily Disease," *Bulletin of the History of Medicine* 41 (1961), pp. 349–67.

29 See, for example, Urso of Calabria, Glosula 39 on incantation and imagination in Rudolph Creutz, "Die medizinisch-naturphilosophischen Aphorismen und Kommentare des Magister Urso Salernitanus," *Quellen und Studien zur Geschichte der Naturwissenschaften und der Medizin* 5 (1936), pp. 13–14 and 69–73. See also Pietro d'Abano in *Conciliator*, Differentia 156, "an precantatio in cura confert?" on which see Per-Gunnar Ottosson, *Scholastic Medicine and Philosophy* (Naples: Bibliopolis, 1984), pp. 264–70.

30 Marshall Clagett, *Nicole Oresme and the Medieval Geometry of Qualities and Motions* (Madison: University of Wisconsin Press, 1968), pp. 342–45: "Ad quedam namque maleficia magica peragenda sunt apte vetule quedam quarum virtus ymaginativa ex malicia complexionis cerebri viciata est et corrupta et aliquibus rebus nimis affixa. Ideoque ymaginatione sua possunt multa miranda facere, sicut deducit Algazel in 5º phisice sue, qui omnes huiusmodi effectus artis magice et fascinationis et talia reducit ad causam predictam. Non igitur fiunt a demone sed ut plurimum ymaginatione." See also Bert Hansen, ed., *Nicole Oresme and the Marvels of Nature*, Studies and Texts, 68 (Toronto: Pontifical Institute of Medieval Studies, 1985), pp. 156-7, 262–5, 312–5 and Thorndike, *History*, vol. 3, pp. 432–5. Cf. Gentile da Cingoli's question, "Utrum species sensibilis vel intelligibilis habeat virtutem alterandi corpus ad caliditatem vel frigiditatem," in which he takes up the problem of fascination, in Martin Grabmann, "Gentile da Cingoli, ein italienischer Aristoteleserklärer aus der Zeit Dantes," *Sitzungsberichte der Bayerischen Akademie der Wissenschaften*, Philosophischehistorische Abteilung (1940), pp. 68–88.

31 *Expositio super tertium canonis Avicennae.* Printed editions of this work are

rare; I am indebted to Joseph Gwara for a transcription of the chapter on lovesickness from a copy in Madrid, Biblioteca Nacional. See also Thorndike, *History*, vol. 3, pp. 233–52.

32 "Item ratione non minoris est entitatis incantatio et similia quam species in anima. Sed tales species alterant, ut Aristoteles in libro de causa motus animalium ubi dicit alterant autem sensus et fantasie, ergo et c. Amplius illud potest curare quod potest vehementiam speciei sanitatis inducere. Sed incantatio et similia hec possunt ut est notum. Maior probatur, quia species de sanitate aliquando plus facit quam medicus cum instrumentis, ut Avicenna 6° de naturalibus, particula 4a, penultimo capitulo. Et ideo ille plures sanat de quo plures confidunt. . . . In contrarium est Galienus. . . . Ergo incantationibus nec homo nec deus aliquid agunt."

33 E.g., Thomas Aquinas, *In quattuor libros Sententiarum*, lib. 2, dist. 8, q. 1, art. 5; Aegidius Romanus, *In secundum librum sententiarum*, dist. 8, q. 2, art. 5; and cf. A. Lecoy de la Marche, *Anecdotes historiques: légendes et apologues tirés du receuil inédit d'Étienne de Bourbon dominicain du xiiie siécle* (Paris: Renouard, 1877), p. 200. Jacques Despars' (n. 44 below) contemporary, John of Turrecremata, affirms in his commentary on *Canon Episcopi* (on sorcery and witchcraft) that although the devil cannot create visual species, he can manipulate what lies in the *fantasia* so that the victim believes he sees an exterior object (Hansen, Quellen, pp. 113–5). For the devil's penchant for interfering in man's passions, see *The malleus maleficarum* of Heinrich Kramer and James Sprenger, trans. and introd. by Montague Summers (1948; rpt. New York: Dover, 1971), pp. 26–28 and 48–54. On the role of imagination in medical theories of sexuality, see Mary F. Wack, "Imagination, Medicine, and Rhetoric in Andreas Capellanus' *De amore*," in *Magister Regis: Studies in Honor of Robert Earl Kaske*, ed. Arthur Groos (New York: Fordham UP, 1986), pp. 101–15.

34 Jerzy Burchardt, *Witelo filosofo della natura del XIII secolo: una biografia*, Accademia Polacca della Scienze, Biblioteca e Centro di Studi a Roma, Conferenze 87 (Wrocław: Ossolinski, 1984).

35 The text may be found in Jerzy Burchardt, *List Witelona do Ludwika we Lwówku Slaskim: Problematyka Teoriopoznawcza Kosmologiczna i Medyczna*, Studia Copernicana 19 (Wrocław: Ossolinski, 1979), pp. 161–208 at p. 170, l. 420: "Hominibus etiam vigilantibus saepe videntur mirabilia. Et hoc fit per fortem imaginationem, formam suam sensui communi imprimentem, ut patet in<a>moratis amore hereos, qui formam sensibilem amati primo debiliter phantasiae impresserunt, quam cum saepe replicaverunt apud illam, conservaverunt diutius. Ut sic accidit hanc formam ex multis motibus spirituum, aliquando formas deferentium, sensui communi incidere, in quo fit iudicium omnis sensatae visionis, quia non fit visio in oculo, nisi ut in speculo habente reflexionem, sed in sensu communi, ut in iudicante, completur visio. . . . Tunc itaque tales inamorati se credunt amata praesentialiter videre. Et cum apprehendere putant,

surgunt aliqualiter propter motus spiritus in capite ipsorum, et tandem, cum spiritus redeunt ad posterius capitis, formae visae evanescunt. Et dicunt se illi per daemones illusos." The text has also been recently edited by Eugenia Paschetto, *Demoni e prodigi: note su alcuni scritti di Witelo e di Oresme* (Torino: Giappichelli, 1978), pp. 83–132. In addition, see Jerzy Burchardt, *La psicopatologia nei concetti di Witelo filosofo della natura del XIII secolo*, Accademia Polacca della Scienze, Biblioteca e Centro di Studi a Roma, Conferenze 94 (Wrocław: Polskiej Akademii Nauk, 1986).

36 A number of writers on optics, from Nicole Oresme in the fourteenth century to others in the sixteenth, adopted Witelo's remarks about the visual illusions in *amor hereos* caused by strong impressions in the imagination. See Aleksander Birkenmajer, "Deux écrits inconnus de Witelo," in *Études d'Histoire des Sciences en Pologne*, Studia Copernicana, IV (Warsaw: Ossoliński, 1972), p. 166, for Oresme's *Quaestiones meteorum*, lib. 3, q. 19: "Dico, quod uerisimilius est, ut puto, quod propter infirmitatem et propter fortem imaginationem, quam habuit super illo, quod uideret imaginem suam ante se, hoc sibi apparuit, sicut in somniis apparet hominibus, quod aliquid uideant, licet tamen nihil uideant—sicut etiam accidit uigilantibus phreneticis et aliis habentibus amorem hereos, qui fortiter imaginantur de amica sua et credunt se eam uidere, quando tamen non uident." See also pp. 145–6 for the same explanation by an anonymous 14th or 15th c. author. Themo Judei, who taught 1349–60, repeated Oresme's explanation in his own *Quaestiones meteorum* (Birkenmajer, 208) and Claudius Caelestinus (*De mirabilibus* [Paris, 1542]) repeated Witelo: "Laborans amore heroico amicam se amplecti ex sola phantasia suspicatur" (Birkenmajer, pp. 244–5).

37 Paul Diepgen, "Arnaldus de Villanova De improbatione maleficiorum," *Archiv für Kulturgeschichte* 9 (1911), pp. 385–403. For a discussion of Arnald's theorizing on lovesickness, see Michael R. McVaugh, ed., *Liber de amore heroico, Opera medica omnia Arnaldi de Villanova* III (Barcelona: Seminarium Historiae Medicinae Granatensis, 1985) and also Danielle Jacquart and Claude Thomasset, "L'Amour 'heroïque' à travers le traité d'Arnaud de Villeneuve," in *La folie*, ed. Céard, pp. 143–58.

38 Jean Céard, "Folie et demonologie au XVIe siécle," in *Folie et Déraison à la Renaissance*, Travaux de l'Institut pour l'étude de la Renaissance et de l'Humanisme, Université Libre de Bruxelles, 5 (Bruxelles: Editions de l'Université, 1976), pp. 129–47; Sydney Anglo, "Melancholia and Witchcraft: The Debate between Wier, Bodin, and Scot," ibid., pp. 209–22; and Maxime Preaud, "La mélancholie diabolique," *La sorcellerie*, Les Cahiers de Fontenay, 11–12 (1978), pp. 123–38.

39 Ed. Harold Jenkins (London: Methuen, 1982).

40 One symptom of these developments is Oldradus da Ponte's discussion (1323–27) whether "dare pocula amatoria" is heretical (Hansen, *Quellen*, pp. 55–59 and Zauberwahn, pp. 263–67). See also Peters, pp. 132–34 and 165, and

Kieckhefer, *Trials*, pp. 78–88.

41 On Gerson in the history of science, see Thorndike, *History*, vol. 4, pp. 114–31, esp. pp. 125–8; Peters, pp. 143–6.

42 Jean Gerson, *L'Oeuvre polémique*, *Oeuvres complétes*, ed. P. Glorieux (Paris: Desclée, 1973), vol. 10, pp. 77–90.

43 Agrimi and Crisciani, "Medici," pp. 156–9. Cf. Pearl Kibre, "The Faculty of Medicine at Paris, Charlatanism and Unlicensed Medical Practices in the Later Middle Ages," *Bulletin of the History of Medicine* 27 (1953), pp. 1–20; Vern Bullough, "Status and Medieval Medicine," *Journal of Health and Human Behavior* 2 (1961), pp. 204–10.

44 Avicenna, *Canon (liber III) cum Jacobus de Partibus* (Lyons: Trechsel, 1498), f. Niii^{r}ff.: "Attende secundo quod stolidum vulgus insanos amores sortilegijs imputat ad vetulas recurrens diabolicas astutas quas scire existimat et ligare homines suis sortilegijs hoc insano amore et absolvere eos quando placet eis. Intra quas est una dolosissima anus in hac civitate que se per urinas cognoscere iactat sortilegiatos et sortilegia quibus illigati sunt. Et plurimos ponit recurrentes ad eos in tantis fantasijs et melancolijs quod timore arescunt et ethicantur et finaliter obeunt. Et alijs porrigit medicinas fortes magne violentie quibus ipsa deijcit eorum virtutes et languidos efficiuntur. [She also induces abortions]. Et his mendatijs dolis et astucijs plusquam .xx. annis emunxit argentum et aurum non modicum a simplici gente regionis huius. Attende tertio quod in veneficijs et incantationibus nulla est in hoc casu fides adhibenda." Biographical information may be found in Danielle Jacquart, "Le regard d'un médecin sur son temps: Jacques Despars (1380?–1458)," *Bibliothéque de l'école des Chartes* 138 (1980), pp. 35–86.

45 Such professional tensions are evident in the marginal notes of Stanford's copy of Despars' commentary. Next to the passage quoted in n. 43 above, the annotator notes that when he was a student in 1500 there was a certain "antiqua vetula (que vulgo nominatur Die toufft Iudin auff sant petrisfriedhoff)"—thus doubly marginal by sex and religion of birth—who had a great practice inspecting urines "cum vulgo et presertim cum mulieribus," who were so attached to this "muliercula" that "verba ipsius evangelium putarent." Another note records that in 1510 in a village called Dagezshaim near Stuttgart, "quidam faber qui et urine inspectione nomen, artem, egritudines longo tempore preteritos et varia mirabilia alia dixit. Credo demonum habuisse."

46 Hansen, *Quellen*, pp. 149–83, esp. p. 167.

47 *Malleus maleficarum* (Nuremberg, 1494), part 1, questions 6 and 7, fols. XXIr-XXIVr, and part 2, q. 2, cap. 3, fols. LXXIIIIr-v: "De tercio quod amor hereos proveniet ex maleficiis demonum et maleficarum possibilitas huius maleficii supra in questionibus prime partis, an demones per maleficas mentes hominum ad amorem vel odium immutare et incitare valeant, ad longum deducitur, per varia etiam gesta et acta a nobis reperta comprobatur, immo inter omnia maleficia minimum propter sui generalitatem reputatur." For a critical evaluation of

the *Malleus*, see Sydney Anglo, "Evident Authority and Authoritative Evidence: The *Malleus Maleficarum*," in *The Damned Art: Essays in the Literature of Witchcraft*, ed. Sydney Anglo (London: Routledge and Kegan Paul, 1977), pp. 1–31.

48 Fol. XXIIv. As Jean Céard points out in his essay in this volume, the authors of the *Malleus* borrowed heavily from Johannes Nider's *Formicarius* for their analysis of demonically caused love. In the edition of *Formicarius* that I consulted (Lyons, 1669), pp. 326–7 Nider equates *amor illicitus* with *philocaptio* and *Hissithi ut Avicenna loquitur* (i.e., *ilischi* or *al-'ishq*).

49 Fol. XXIIIr: "Methodus proponendi premissa de amore hereos in sermonibus ad populum."

50 D.P. Walker, *Spiritual and Demonic Magic From Ficino to Campanella* (Notre Dame: University of Notre Dame Press, 1969); Thomas, *Religion*, p. 437. On Ficino, Valleriola, and the idiosyncratic Paracelsus, see Giedke, "Liebeskrankheit," pp. 55–63.

51 *Observationum medicinalium libri vi* (Lyons: Antonius Candidus, 1588), observatio vii, pp. 184–219. See also Couliano, *Eros*, esp. pp. 162–77.

52 On medicine and humanism, see Gerhard Baader, "Die Antikerezeption in der Entwicklung der medizinischen Wissenschaft während der Renaissance," in *Humanismus und Medizin*, ed. Rudolf Schmitz and Gundolf Keil, Mitteilung XI der Kommission für Humanismusforschung (Weinheim: Acta Humaniora, 1984), pp. 51–66, and Wolf-Dieter Müller-Jahncke, "Zum Magie-Begriff in der Renaissance-Medizin und -Pharmazie," in *Humanismus*, pp. 99–116, as well as Elizabeth Eisenstein, *The Printing Press as an Agent of Change* (Cambridge: Cambridge UP, 1979), vol. 1, pp. 272–90.

53 Natalie Zemon Davis, *Society and Culture in Early Modern France* (Stanford: Stanford UP, 1975), pp. 224 ff., and ch. 8; Burke, *Popular Culture*, p. 273; and Eisenstein, *Press*, vol. 1, pp. 71–80.

54 *Maladie*, pp. 223–4.

55 Mary F. Wack, "Lovesickness in Troilus," *Pacific Coast Philology* 19 (1984), pp. 55–61, and "Pandarus, Poetry, and Healing," *Studies in the Age of Chaucer, Proceedings*, 2 (1987).

56 Several characters do voice in passing a more popular view of healing (charms and herbs), but these comments are meant to contrast with the "real" healing of lovesickness undertaken by Pandarus and Criseyde, namely therapeutic intercourse in the best tradition of academic medicine.

57 *Celestina*, trans. Mack Hendricks Singleton (Madison: University of Wisconsin Press, 1958). For the influence of medical writing on lovesickness in the play, see Michael J. Ruggerio, *The Evolution of the Go-Between In Spanish Literature Through the Sixteenth Century*, University of California Publications in Modern Philology, 78 (Berkeley and Los Angeles: University of California Press, 1966), pp. 22–23 and Dennis P. Seniff, "Bernardo Gordonio's Lilio de Medicina: A Possible Source of Celestina?" *Celestinesca* 10 (1986), pp. 13–18.

58 On witchcraft as Celestina's distinctive characteristic, see Ruggerio, *Evolution*, pp. 4–16, as well as Julius Berzunza, "Miscellaneous Notes on Witchcraft and *Alcahuetería*," *Romanic Review* 19 (1928), pp. 141–50, and P.E. Russell, "La Magia como Tema Integral de la Tragicomedia de Calisto y Melibea," in *Studia Philologica: Homenaje ofrecido a Dámaso Alonso* (Madrid: Editorial Gredos, 1963), vol. 3, pp. 337–54.

Jean Céard

The Devil and Lovesickness: Views of 16th Century Physicians and Demonologists

The dialogue between demonology and medicine has a history of its own, and one which deserves to be written.[1] Much has been made and justifiably so, of the debate between Bodin and Wier,[2] but this was only a particularly intense moment, albeit one of essential import, in a much longer, and not always conflictual, encounter. There is no doubt that demonologists long reproached physicians for giving undue weight to the humours. Michael Psellos had already observed that it is men who "know nothing but what they perceive with their senses, and who pay attention only to the body"[3] who negate the role of demons in affections such as lethargy and frenzy. Conversely, physicians well before Wier objected that demonologists neglected nature too much, citing as authority, for example, Hippocrates' *De sacro morbo*. But it appears that in the sixteenth century at least, positions were never taken to such an extreme that one side completely contested the competence of the other. It is in this sense that the debate between Wier and Bodin marks an epoch: when he sent Wier packing to examine "the colour and state of urines and other such things" and forbade him to "touch sacred things,"[4] Bodin challenged the very legitimacy of those exchanges which, though not always peaceful, had up until then been concerned to determine the conditions under which two models of explanation might co-exist. The result had been that medicine and demonology, each for its own ends, asked the other discipline for information and for theses which it would then attempt to link up with its own. For example, C. Peucer, in his celebrated *De praecipuis divinationum generibus*, published in 1553, conceded to the physicians that "there are very few cases of ecstacy without melancholy," and that lycanthropy can be placed "amongst the ranks of the melancholic passions."[5] Again, Johann Nider holds along with Albertus Magnus, Avicenna and Galen that under certain circumstances a man may, without demons being involved, contract a disease called mania, which inclines him to see apparitions whose reality is merely "fantastic."[6]

These encounters between the two disciplines had certain privileged terrains, some of which have just been cited. In fact, according to the demonologists, even if the Devil can inflict all manner of illnesses—and we shall see later how he does this—he nonetheless has a predilection for two kinds of affections: on the one hand, those which attack the brain and nerves,[7] and on the other, those which have to do with sexuality. In the former instances, he attacks the use of reason, that is, man's supreme dignity. As for the latter, those concerned with sexuality, the *Malleus maleficarum* for its part takes up the argument of St. Thomas which "gives the reasons for which God permitted the Devil greater malefic power over the sexual acts of man than over the others. . . . In fact, he says that the primordial corruption of the sin by which man became a slave of the Devil reaches us by way of the genital act. Whence God permitted the Devil to exercise a stronger malefic power over this act than over the others."[8] In the same manner, Thomas adds, sorcerers have more power over serpents than over any of the other animals; the serpent was, indeed, the means by which the Devil tempted the woman. Nider already calls upon this authority.[9] The *Malleus* even adds that although the nutritive power is less noble than the sensitive, and the Devil can therefore more readily disturb it (for example, by slowing or accelerating the movement of some matter towards the bones or the flesh), he nonetheless does not do so, because "it is more advantageous for him to labour at the deception of the senses and at the working of illusion upon the intelligence."[10]

It is in this context that the demonologists examine the *aegritudo amoris*. The *Malleus*, summarizing the bull *Summis desiderantes* of Pope Innocent VIII (1485), posits that there are seven means by which the sexual act and the fruits of conception may be infected by evil spells; and, before mentioning the inhibition of potency, the removal of the sexual organs, the metamorphosis of men into beasts, the interruption of the woman's fertility, abortion, and the sacrifice of children to demons, the *Malleus* cites what it calls inordinate love, "inordinatus amor."[11] A little later, it designates this love by another name, *philocaptio*, a hybrid term, both Greek and Latin, used frequently in this literature, and which Johann Nider explicitly identifies with lovesickness: "illicit love, or *philocaptio*, or *Hislithi* as Avicenna says, the disease which one contracts from love."[12] In the term *Hislithi*, one can easily recognize the word *ilisci*, a transliteration used by Gerard of Cremona in his translation of the *Canon* of Avicenna. Nider's editors in turn gloss it with the aid of the classical expression *amor qui dicitur hereos*; in the margin of the passage cited above they write: "Quid sit philocaptio, seu Hislithi Avicennae seu amor hereos." Besides, they knew its origin, for in the margin of the *Malleus* they note: "Amor haereos. . . . Per Haereos graecum vocabulum Ερως intelligunt, quod amorem designat."[13] One might, moreover, ask whether the transliteration *haereos* does not show the traces of other etymological attempts which would be interesting to seek out.

Concerning the causes of *philocaptio*, let us listen first to what Nider has to say, for on this point, as on many others, he is the source of the *Malleus*.[14] According to Nider,[15] *philocaptio*, or "the inordinate love of one sex for the other," has three possible causes: imprudence of the eyes alone, temptation by demons alone, or the combination of the evil spells of necromancers and demons. Then he explains and illustrates these three causes. The first, imprudence of the eyes alone, is mentioned in the *Epistle of James*: "But every man is tempted, when he is drawn away of his own lust, and enticed. Then when lust hath conceived, it bringeth forth sin: and sin, when it is finished, bringeth forth death."[16] For example, the love of Shechem for Dinah: "And Dinah . . . went out to see the daughters of the land. And when Shechem . . . saw her, he took her, and lay with her, and defiled her. And his soul clave unto Dinah. . . ."[17] The second *philocaptio* comes principally from the temptation of demons. For example, Ammon and Tamar: "And it came to pass after this, that Absalom the son of David had a fair sister, whose name was Tamar; and Ammon the son of David loved her. And Ammon was so vexed, that he fell sick for his sister Tamar . . . "[18] —a demonic temptation, for, Nider observes, he would not have been corrupted to the point of plunging into such a crime "had he not been sorely tempted by the Devil." Examples abound of this type of love: the *Lives of the Fathers* are full of them, and report that "in the desert, some of these men avoided all the carnal temptations, but were nonetheless sometimes possessed to an incredible degree by the love of women."[19] It is of this sort of temptation that Paul speaks when he says that a thorn had been put in his flesh, an angel of Satan to buffet him.[20] The final species of *philocaptio*, that which comes from the spells of demons and their henchmen, is the one which obviously captures most of the attention of our demonologist.

But he only proposed this division into three types in order to better answer a question which had been put to him. The Theologian's interlocutor, who is called *Piger*, "lazy," had indeed noted: "We have heard tell of many people in our day who, by the agency of sorcerers, have been so enflamed with love for women other than their wives, and even women who were so enamoured with men who were not their husbands, that one could not bring them to put a stop to it either by shaming them, beating them, or by words or deeds." By the same token, there can be a hatred between married people which nothing can appease. But since hatred and love have their seat in the soul, how can one ascribe them to the Devil, who, according to the theologians, cannot penetrate into souls? The Theologian replies that this remark is correct, but that the Devil, without being able to operate directly upon intelligence and will, can act upon the body and the powers connected with the body, whether these be the external senses—our five senses—or the internal senses, that is to say common sense, imagination or fantasy, estimation, and memory. Is there a way to secure oneself against such attacks? The Theologian replies with the words of Cassian: the Devil can do nothing unless he first succeeds in stripping the soul of every holy thought and draining it of spiritual contemplation. As for *philocaptio* without evil spells—it is at this point that Nider refers to *Hislithi*—the remedies set forth are the seven remedies of Avicenna,[21] which he summarizes, or rather bowdlerizes, as follows: "First, find out with whom the patient is in love, either by his own admission, or by examining the variation of his pulse when one names the beloved, for she is the root of the illness. . . . Secondly, marriage, if the law permits, for one heals by obeying nature. Thirdly, administration of the medicines which he discusses in that place. Fourthly, let the sick man, by licit remedies, turn his love for the beloved towards another object which he will begin to prefer to the first, and thus he will escape from the power of the beloved, for it is by this means that the mind is distracted. Fifthly, if the patient is reasonable, correct him, exhort him, torment him, and show him what a misery love is. Sixthly, refer to him women, preferably old ones, who as much as they are able, saving God and the truth, will speak ill of the body, aptitudes and character of the beloved. . . . Seventh, occupy him with difficult tasks and distracting activities." Nider has no objection to these seven remedies, but he points out that one should make no less use of the "theological" remedies used to care for the bewitched: pilgrimage, prayer, confession, etc.

This is the material to which the *Malleus* fell heir. It uses it in two chapters, one in the first part which deals with the question of "whether sorcerers can modify the inclinations of minds towards love or hate," the other in the second section of the second part which studies "remedies to be used in the case of people who, through witchcraft, feel inordinate love or hatred." While approving Nider's positions to the point of reproducing them, the *Malleus* places them in a context or accompanies them by commentaries which deflect their meaning or significance. The scholastic method of exposition used by the writers of the *Malleus* permits one readily to grasp what is at stake in the question, for they first present contradictory positions, then set out the proposition which they maintain, then prove it by authority and reason, and finally offer a dialectical refutation of the opposing arguments. In the question which concerns us,[22] the contrary thesis consists in denying that the Devil can alter the mind towards love or towards hatred because he cannot know the inner thoughts of the soul, and moreover, love and hate depend upon the will. The answer of the *Malleus* consists in maintaining that the Devil, without being able to force the will, can nonetheless act by way of persuasion or by way of inclination. "He persuades when he proposes to the cognitive power something as a good"; he acts by way of inclination when, for example, he stirs up the mind and the humour in such a manner as to incline to concupiscence, and thus renders man more prone to consent.

Let us leave aside the complex question—but one which greatly preoccupied the compilers of the *Malleus* in view of their goal of pursuing witches—of how one can know whether such operations are the work of the devil, of a witch, or of both together, and in what circumstances. In any case, an attempt to unravel such questions does not suffer for lack of facts: "How many adulterous men have abandoned very beautiful wives and are consumed with passion for repulsive women!" Here is even a precise piece of evidence: "I knew an old woman who, as a rumour circulating amongst the brothers of the monastery still attests, not only bewitched three abbots, but drove a fourth mad by the same means. And she admitted it openly, and did not fear to say: I did it then and I do it now, and they cannot tear themselves away from my love, for they have eaten my turds, as big as this (and she indicated the size on her outstretched arm)." Reading this account, one might ask oneself whether the compilers of the *Malleus* have arrived at the notion that the more inordinate the love, the greater the role the witch played in it. They see nothing but diabolical temptation in the story of Ammon and the fair Tamar, which they relate here. On the other hand, in order to ascertain if sorcery is at work, they ask that one investigate the following questions: does the man who is tempted have a beautiful and virtuous wife, or if it is a woman, does she have such a husband? Is the judgement of the reason so entirely fettered that neither blows, nor words, nor deeds, nor even shame can bring them to recant? And particularly, is the person incapable of preventing himself from suddenly covering long distances, day and night, despite the difficulties of the route?

The second chapter devoted to this question concerns remedies.[23] The authors, who do not blush to repeat themselves, reiterate in detail that there are three types of *philocaptio*. It is here that they reproduce Nider verbatim, with some significant additions. Of course it is the third type, that produced by witchcraft, which inspires the longest addition because, they stress, "of all forms of witchcraft, this is the worst because the most widespread"; and they add: "Princes, prelates and other rich people are frequently enveloped in its miseries. And certainly this age is the age of woman (*tempus muliebre*) which Hildegard of Bingen predicted would not endure as long as it has persisted hitherto, because the world is already full of adulterers, particularly amongst princes."[24] Cold comfort to know that one day this age will come to an end; for the present, one must live in it, in the feverish, aggressive and suspicious vigilance of our Inquisitors. For they had the means to see which of the three *philocaptiones* was the most frequently at work, and lest anyone forget it, they remind us of how we can recognize witchcraft: "when someone is so caught in the toils of fleshly, concupiscent love, and enflamed by it, that neither shame, nor words, nor blows, nor deeds can make him recant; when someone abandons a beautiful wife in order to attach himself, as often happens, to a hag; when he cannot sleep at night, and raves to the point of wandering far afield." Amongst the great of this world, examples abound today. Hence the downcast question of our Inquisitors: "Is there any need for remedies for those who abhor remedies?" It is only to satisfy the reader that they reproduce Avicenna's list of seven remedies: in fact, the authors write, "even as man's animal nature is healed by remedies of this sort, just so, with regard to man's spiritual nature, these remedies, taken one by one, will edify the inner being anew"; "Let him obey the law of the mind instead of that of nature, let him turn his love towards delights which are sure, let him recall how ephemeral is that which gives pleasure and how everlasting that which torments, let him seek for delights in the life where they begin and never end," etc. For the rest, if there is witchcraft, one must have recourse to what Nider calls theological remedies.

The first of these remedies is, of course, to live in charity. The *Malleus* tells the story of a beautiful and virtuous young lady of Lindau in the diocese of Constance, who refused the advances of a wicked priest. Faced with her refusal, he made certain that she would be compelled to love him: he was suspected of incantations and witchcraft. Shortly thereafter, in fact, she began to conceive amourous imaginations concerning him. She appealed to the Virgin, prayed and went to confession. And she was delivered. "One must conclude that such remedies are very certain against this type of malady." In short, only those who wish to do so succumb to *philocaptio*.

While we cannot examine the whole corpus of demonological literature, let us present here the various problems which caught the attention of subsequent demonologists, and by means of a few examples see how the physicians echoed them or retorted.

To begin with, there was no doubt on the part of the demonologists that the devil could provoke all types of illness, lovesickness being only a single case of this general power. If Nider and the *Malleus* did not bother to define the manner in which the devil operates, a certain number of physicians occupied themselves with the matter, and particularly from the middle of the sixteenth century onwards, which already suggests an evolution. Already in Jason Pratz's *De cerebri morbis* (1549) one can read these words: "Without doubt it happens that the demons, being subtle and elusive creatures, insinuate themselves into human bodies and, hidden away in the bowels, they ruin health, provoke illness, send terrifying dreams, stir up the spirits by making them furious, so much so that it is by no means out of the question that maniacs are agitated in this manner by a spirit."[25] But one of the most precise is the famous Francisco Vallès, who in his *De sacra philosophia* studies problems of natural history raised by Scripture. He places the accent on melancholy. The demon, he says, "is not born secretly in the body itself, but penetrates it from without to bring illness upon it; and hence he does not bring upon it those diseases which are dependent upon matter in any other way than do other procatarctic causes, for example by exciting within us the illness of melancholy, by augmenting the melancholic fluid, by troubling that which was already there, by transporting black vapours to the brain and to the seats of the inner senses. He can augment natural melancholy by preventing it from being evacuated or by exciting diverse causes of adustion . . . and by accumulating thick fluids in the ventricles of the brain and at the very roots of the nerves."[26]

To be sure, these physicians were only developing an ancient idea. If we are to believe Wier, St. Jerome had already said that "melancholy is the devil's bath."[27] And Wier himself held that "the devil changes himself at will into this substance, as being the most apt to his illusions."[28] As for the *Malleus*, it already said that the devil, in order to inflict lovesickness, can operate "by means of disposition." It is this thesis which the physicians refined and medicalized after a fashion—thus deflecting what the demonologists were saying. This is quite clearly seen in the chapter which Del Rio devotes to the question.[29] He begins by juxtaposing those physicians who attribute all illnesses to strictly natural causes—he names here Avicenna, Galen and perhaps Hippocrates, and amongst the moderns, Pomponazzi and Lemnius—and those who think the contrary, notably Codronchi, Cesalpino, Fernel and Vallès. The latter denounce the fallacious argument of their adversaries; listen to Vallès: "this reasoning is worthless: it can happen that melancholy and epilepsy, like any other malady, can be produced without the demon because of fluids which are disturbed or vitiated for one reason or another; therefore they cannot be produced by the action of the demon."[30] This denunciation is found everywhere. But it seems that under the influence of "naturalist" physicians, those who acknowledged the demon's capacity to provoke illness came more and more to admit that he could not do so save by acting after the manner of a natural agent. It is striking to observe that it is Vallès who cites these words of Avicenna: "Certain physicians have thought that melancholy happens by the demon's action, but when we treat of physical matters, it makes no difference to us to know whether it happens by his action or not, since if it happens by his action, then it happens in such a manner as to change his complexion and render it melancholic; thus the immediate cause of the evil is the melancholy, and it matters little whether the cause of the melancholy be the demon or no."[31] Act upon the immediate cause and you will cure the disease. Solving the problem of the ultimate origin of the evil may be left to the demonologist; such a doubtful matter does not stop the physician from taking action.

This is perhaps why the demonologists seem increasingly to divert the question and to focus attention upon the love-spell (*amatorium maleficium*). According to Del Rio[32] Grillando gives the best and most accurate account of the matter. This Italian is the author of a *Tractatus de sortilegiis*,[33] wherein he distinguishes three principal types of spells: divination, love-spells and spells of poisoning. The second type is called *amatoria* because it refers to libidinous love, and because it seeks to incline chaste souls toward such a love. It acts within the body by means of philtres, and by compounds which act upon the body when placed in proximity to it. Del Rio reproduces this analysis, but here again—under the influence of the physicians, perhaps—he is much less prone than Grillando to deny any inherent power to these evil spells. For Grillando, no one can sin against his will, and since love depends upon free will, these evil spells are only powerful to the extent that the demon persuades his victims that they are.[34] For Del Rio, doubtless "one can not, by means of these philtres, force one to love someone one does not want to, but it could very well be that by their means the imagination is troubled, the humours excited, and the entire body, as it were, set aflame within to such a pitch that when the devil suggests the seductions of various temptations, one is tormented by the goad of sensual delight, and thus violently driven to desire carnal copulation."[35] The will remains free, but people do not know how to distinguish the actions of the will from the movements of fleshly desire, and so they say that they are forced to love.

Such analyses reoriented the examination of what Wier's translator called "drogues amatoires" (amatory drugs). They no longer have any real specificity, but only create a certain bodily disposition favourable to diabolical temptation, that is, to *philocaptio* of the second type. Wier states it explicitly: "Moreover, certain distinguished persons are of the opinion that love potions, Hippomanes and other such things are of little virtue, indeed of no worth whatsoever to really move someone to love; rather, they make people mad."[36] It is in this chapter that Wier recounts the story of the old woman and the three abbots, and he has this to say about the coprophagy of which she was so proud: "As for me, I am of the opinion that the droppings which she said she gave them to eat were nothing other than the filthy sensuous delights which these monks, like swine wallowing in the mire, had frequently enjoyed with this old bawd. . . . This is the amorous beverage, this the old whore's excrement, as big as her arm, which the monks ate."[37] Since, according to Bodin, Wier is an unbeliever, let us hear from another physician. In his commentary on Fernel's *De abditis rerum causis*, Jean Riolan devotes a short chapter to philtres.[38] He examines them only from the point of view of their intrinsic efficacy. These philtres can excite, but nothing more, because—and here he recalls all that the demonologists have said—love is a free act; the will is free and cannot be coerced. By means of a drug one can fill a woman with love, but not for a particular person: "by means of a philtre a sorcerer or even a physician can cause you to love . . . but he cannot contrive that you will love in a predetermined manner this or that woman." The only efficacious philtres, he adds, are money, amiability, compatibility of minds and manners, and ready speech.

Here we can see a transformation in the division of labour established between the physicians and the demonologists. If the lovesickness which the demonologists are considering is instigated by the devil, then one must certainly combat it by spiritual means, but they admit that one can have recourse to medical remedies because the devil uses nature. For their part, the physicians, by dint of looking at nothing but the person's condition and attacking nothing but the immediate causes of the ailment, were inclined to deny any other cause, and found themselves energetically reproved by the demonologists. From this point of view Del Rio's position is significant because of the place it devotes to medical considerations. He does not repudiate the use of "antidotes," but always with the proviso that these be strictly natural drugs to purge melancholy and calm the ardour of amorous desire, and that they do not injure health. After these, he gives his highest recommendation to "Christian remedies," and notably the "moral remedies," penance, fasting, scourging and so forth, as well as serious occupations, meditation upon death and hell, the reading of good books, and prayer to God, the saints, the angels, and especially to the Virgin, to whom chastity is particularly dear. And it is here that he mentions obliquely, following Nider's modified version, Avicenna's seven remedies, which he classifies with these moral remedies. Thus at the same time as the physicians were tending to medicalize lovesickness completely, the demonologists were coming to see it as first and foremost a moral disease; even if they obviously did not reject the possibility of enchantment, they were inclined to attenuate its mysterious character.

Another very interesting example is provided by Pierre Le Loyer, who in 1586 published a voluminous treatise *Des spectres.* He devotes an entire chapter to establishing that "contrary to the natural philosophers, the devil often invades corrupted senses and afflicted fantasy."[39] His particular targets were Pomponazzi and Lemnius. Against them he proved that devils use the dispositions of nature, that they "operate according to the natural virtues and faculties, and take the aptitude of the body into account in their works and effects."[40] Hence it happens that by the local movement of the humours they can impose upon the mind the illusion of spectres and phantoms which have no reality. That does not hinder him from also stating that they lend efficacy to charms and enchantments, amongst which he frequently cites those connected with love.[41] But on this issue Le Loyer makes no allusion whatsoever to lovesickness. It is not that he is ignorant of it; on the contrary, he devotes several rather curious pages to it, but at the point in his discussion where he is attempting to define "what persons are voluntarily subjected to receiving false imaginings and phantasms and have a troubled and distracted brain."[42] These persons are of two kinds: on the one hand there are fearful people, amongst whom he ranges the superstitious, children, old people and women, but also people guilty of some crime, tyrants and so forth; on the other hand there are those who "for the affection and passion which dominate them are so estranged from their natural condition that they fall into mania, and therein imagine things both absurd and abhorrent."[43] It is here that he speaks of lovers: "lovers belong to the first rank of those concerning whom Aristotle writes that their desires and passions are so great that they alter the body, and provoke furors in some of them." Why? Because "love comes from the sensual and brutish part."[44] Moreover, the Greeks call it Ἔρως, a term which does not derive from any of the etymologies proposed by Plato, "but rather ἀπὸ τῆς ἔρας, from the earth, which is likewise called *Erets* in Hebrew." In fact, continues Le Loyer, "the most furious love which physicians know is Heroic love which is wont to overtake heroes and men of valour in whom the sensual element abounds because they have a greater share of earthly spirits and a body filled only with hot and wicked blood." Amorous heroes are dominated by the irascible and the concupiscible: consider Hercules, Marc Antony, or Ariosto's Orlando. And here is a tale which, with a little more development, might well be made into a novel. Le Loyer had it from president Jacques Minut, who was of Italian origin. A gentleman of Toulouse visited Venice and fell in love with a lady, who rejected him. This drove him mad, and in the Church of San Marco he tried to pick a quarrel with the Doge, who was present at the time. He was arrested and examined by Fracastoro, who offered to take care of him. "Then Fracastoro, having him in his power, brought to him a courtesan; he bade her give pleasure to the gentleman and let him stay with her until he was exhausted, and afterwards she was to cover him up well with clothing so that he would sweat."[45] The remedy was a well-known one, and Le Loyer knew it: "I do not dispute Fracastoro's cure, knowing that there have been other physicians of his own day and earlier who, attempting a similar cure to this one, have emerged with honour. The books of our modern physicians are full of this cure so there is no reason to put it forward here, as it is not to our purpose to treat of lovesickness."[46] In any case, these words suffice to assure us that the demonologist Le Loyer was well-informed. Moreover, he adds: "And it suffices for me to say that this is a type of melancholy for whose cure many learned and experienced physicians teach that the remedy is carnal copulation with a woman, for by this means, they say, one is rid of the smoky vapours of semen which trouble and corrupt the brain and principally afflict amorous persons, so that the longer it stays in the body, the more it engenders and accumulates the thoughts and cares that transform themselves into raving." The time had not yet come when people would be scandalized at the use of such a remedy.

Le Loyer says nothing more about these "lovers seized by Heroic and furious love." When a little further on he comes to speak of the manner in which the Devil invades corrupted senses and afflicted fantasy, he does not think to examine the case of lovers afresh. Thus it all unfolds as if from this time forth the demonologists had abandoned the lovers to the physicians, while reserving the right to contest the physicians' absolute competence in other cases such as nightmare, lycanthropy, or ecstasy. Del Rio, who followed Le loyer in time, and who had also read his treatise carefully,[47] ought to have known Nider and the *Malleus* as well. Nonetheless, he behaves like Le Loyer, and lovesickness is not explicitly named amongst the maladies in which the devil has a role, even though he maintains the theoretical position that no disease is barred to him; and as we have seen, he only discusses love from the point of view of philtres. If he admits that love can be inordinate, he does not really envisage it as other than a moral evil, and restricts the possibility of medical treatment to the physical disorders which can be associated with it. Amongst the moral remedies, as we said, he places Avicenna's seven remedies, but this is almost a concession, because for his part he gives stronger recommendation to other remedies which are efficacious in other ways, for example, meditating on the sullying and corruption of the flesh; he reports that the renowned Hypatia, incessantly importuned by the demands of a lover, showed him her linens soiled with menstrual blood. For the rest, Del Rio does not fail to note that, as those who support Avicenna themselves admit, the sixth remedy—disparaging remarks by old women on the physical charms of the beloved—is not always efficacious![48] But there is a comparable process in Ferrand who, all the while repeating advice about the means of diverting the patient's mind, gives all of his attention to the pharmaceutical cures.[49] The moral remedies, which were the place where demonologists and physicians might have encountered one another, lost their importance, and competence in the matter of lovesickness had been relinquished to the physicians.

This is fresh evidence that at the turn of the seventeenth century physicians and demonolgists were tending to rupture an alliance which, although not always peaceable, had for a long time seemed normal: now each claimed full mastery over what he deemed relevant to his competence.[50] In this period it is a very clear plea on the part of the physicians to admit that when the devil intervenes, he does not confine himself to simulating nature, and that consequently, as the physician Marescot said in the case of Marthe Brossier, "nothing should be ascribed to the demon which does not have something extraordinary about it that goes beyond the laws of nature." The demonologists response was henceforward to forbid them access to certain questions; in 1599 one sees the future Cardinal Bérulle, in his *Traicté des Energumènes*, attack Marescot for daring to pronounce "on a properly ecclesiastical subject." But this vexation was not without concession, for the physicians saw their competence recognized in the area of what Nider would call inordinate love. Indeed, it is very striking to notice that the space devoted to this subject in the demonological literature continually shrinks while Nider and the *Malleus* treat it at length, a Le Loyer or a Del Rio only speaks of it indirectly, and Bodin, though he loves to remonstrate with the physicians, says nothing about it at all.

Université de Paris XII

NOTES

1 Preliminary reflections on this question are presented by Jean Céard, "Folie et démonologie au XVIe s.," in *Folie et déraison à la Renaissance* (Paris: P.U.F.; Bruxelles: P.U.B., 1976), pp. 129–147; see also the same author's contribution to the *Nouvelle histoire de la psychiatrie* (Toulouse: Privat, 1983).

2 The latest in this line is Sidney Anglo's "Melancholia and Witchcraft: the Debate Between Wier, Bodin and Scott," in *Folie et déraison*, pp. 209–27.

3 M. Psellos, *De daemonum operatione*, XIV (PG CXXII, col. 852–3). Ficino translates this text as follows: "Nihil mirum est haec medicos dicere, qui nihil noverunt praeter sensum, sed corporibus tantum imbuerint cognoscendis."

4 Jean Bodin, *De la démonomanie des sorciers* (1580), p. 236 (1587 ed., p. 257).

5 Cited by Jean Céard, "Folie et démonologie . . . , " p. 130.

6 Johann Nider, *De maleficis et eorum deceptionibus*, in *Malleus maleficarum ex plurimis auctoribus coaceruatus* (Lyon: P. Landry, 1615), 1.470.

7 See Del Rio, *Disquisitiones magicae*, III, I, q. IV, s. V, "De morbis variis a daemone illatis," who finds in Scripture, besides Job's boils, an epileptic, a lycanthropic maniac, a woman afflicted with convulsion of the spine, etc.

8 *Malleus maleficarum* I, vi (1.71); see also II, II, ii (p. 276). These two passages quote St. Thomas' *Commentary on the Sentences*, I, 34, 1, 3. The same thesis, with different proofs, is found in *Malleus* I, iii (1.33).

9 Nider, p. 495: "Plus autem permittit Deus super hunc actum, per quem primum peccatum diffunditur, quam super alios actus humanos, sicut et super serpentes qui magis incantationibus deseruiunt quam alia animalia."

10 *Malleus*, I, vii (1.83).

11 *Malleus* I, vi (1.70).

12 Nider, p. 501: "De amore illicito seu philocaptione vel Hislithi, ut Avicenna loquitur, quae est aegritudo, quam aliquis incurrit propter amorem." Du Cange lists only the adjective *philocaptus*.

13 *Malleus*, II, II, iii (1.281).

14 This is a point noted by Le Loyer, *IV Livres des Spectres* (Angers, 1586), 1.270–71. Historians are not always aware of this.

15 Nider, pp. 494 ff.

16 *James* 1:14–15.

17 *Genesis* 34:1–3.
18 *II Samuel* 13:1–2.
19 See the example reported by Nider, pp. 503–4, of the monk Elias, from the *Paradise* of St. Heraclides (PL LXXIV, col. 293–94).
20 *II Corinthians* 12:7, a text copiously discussed by the exegetes. Cornelius a Lapide gives a useful inventory.
21 See M. Ciavolella, *La malattia d'amore dall'antichità al medioevo* (Rome: Bulzoni, 1976): 58 ff.
22 *Malleus*, I, vii.
23 *Malleus*, II, II, iii.
24 *Malleus*, II, II, iii, p. 281. This information comes from Vincent of Beauvais, *Speculum maius* iv, 31, 94. This final section of the *Speculum* dates from the fifteenth century.
25 Jason Pratz, *De cerebri morbis* (Basel, 1549), pp. 213–14: "Accidit profecto daemones, ut sunt tenues, et incompraehensibiles spiritus, sese insinuare corporibus hominum, qui occulte in visceribus operti valetudinem vitiant, morbos citant, somniis animos exterrent, mentes furoribus quatiunt, ut omnino alienum non fuerit de mania correptis ambigere, huiusmodo ne spiritu pulsentur."
26 F. Vallesius, *De iis quae scripta sunt physice in libris sacris, siue de sacra philosophia* (Lyon: Fr. Le Fevre, 1587), pp. 226–27.
27 Wier, *Histoires, disputes et discours des illusions et impostures des diables . . .*, IV, 25. (Paris: Progrès mèdical, A. Delahaye et Lecrosnier, 1885), vol. I, p. 603.
28 Wier, III, 8 (vol. I, p. 312).
29 Del Rio, III, I, q. IV, s. V.
30 Vallesius, p. 223.
31 Vallesius, pp. 220–1. This text is also cited by Cesalpino, *Daemonum inuestigatio peripatetica* (Florence: apud Juntas, 1580), p. 86. See also Thomas à Viega, *Tomus primus comment. in Cl. Galeni opera* (Antwerp: Chr. Plantin, 1564), vol. 2 (*In libris seu de locis affectis*, 1566), p. 160.
32 Del Rio, III, I, q. III (p. 395 in the ed. Cologne: P. Henning, 1657).
33 The text is included in the *Malleus maleficarum ex plurimis auctoribus coacervatus* (Lyon: P. Landry, 1620), vol. 2, pp. 344 fl.
34 *Malleus maleficarum*, p. 364.
35 Del Rio, III, I, q. III, s. II (*ed. cit.*, p. 397).
36 Wier, III, 40 (vol. I, p. 476).
37 Wier, III, 40 (vol. I, p. 480).
38 Jean Riolan, *Ad libros Fernelii de abditis rerum causis* (Parisiis: apud H. Parier, in officina Plantiniana, 1598), pp. 112–13.
39 Le Loyer, I, 11 (vol. 1, p. 252).
40 Le Loyer, vol. 1, pp. 285–86.
41 Le Loyer, pp. 290, 293, 295 fl.
42 Le Loyer, p. 225.

43 Le Loyer, p. 243.
44 Le Loyer, p. 244.
45 Le Loyer, p. 247: "Doncques Fracastor l'ayant entre ses mains attiltra une Courtisane à laquelle il commanda faire le plaisir du gentilhomme et le laisser habiter avecques elle jusques à lassitude, et puis apres qu'elle le couvrist bien d'habillemens tant qu'il suast."
46 Le Loyer, p. 248: "Je ne disputeray point de la cure de Fracastor comme sçachant qu il y a eu d'autres medecins de son temps et devant, qui tentans une pareille cure à ceste cy en sont venuz à leur honneur. Les livres en sont plains de noz modernes qu'il n'est besoin d'alleguer icy comme n'estant nostre subject de traicter de la maladie d amour."
47 He refers precisely (*Disquisitiones magicae*, III, I, q. IV, s.V) to the chapter where Le Loyer establishes that the demon sometimes invades corrupted senses and afflicted fantasy.
48 Del Rio, III, I, q. III *in fine*: "His remediis continentur, quae ex Auicenna Niderius posuit excepto sexto, quod ipsemet fatetur saepe non proficere."
49 See D.A. Beecher, "Des médicaments pour soigner la mélancholie: Jacques Ferrand et la maladie de l'amour." *Nouvelle revue du XVIe siècle*, 4 (1986), p. 88.
50 See Jean Céard, "Folie et dèmonologie . . . " (*vide supra*, n. 1).

(*Article translated by Faith Wallis*)

Donald A. Beecher

Quattrocento Views on the Eroticization of the Imagination

The nature of erotic love—how it was generated and how it might be controlled—was a topic in the vanguard of intellectual thought toward the end of the fifteenth century, not only as a subject of philosophical speculation, but as a matter of social urgency. Thinkers continued to strive after a more pragmatic correlation between philosophical definitions and the various manifestations of erotic excesses in society. That debate took a number of significant turns in the second half of the century, developments that created not only the terms of philosophical discussion that would preoccupy later thinkers, but that sought to carry theory into practice for the management of venereal longings, whether in the context of the ecclesiastical courts, the poetic culture of the Petrarchans, or the medical clinic. Those three spheres of influence shared a common vocabulary of analysis, yet differed in radical ways concerning the nature of eroticism, its relation to the soul, its effects upon the body, and the means for controlling the appetites. Within the tradition of the Italian *trattati* on love, that eclectic integration of vocabularies drawn from divergent sources—medical, theological, poetic, mythological and philosophical—compounded the nature of their discourse, camouflaged principles of order, perhaps with an intentional degree of esotericism. But positions became increasingly clear and intransigent when more pragmatic questions were asked, such as who would assume the care of those whose venereal obsessions and manias intruded upon domestic tranquillity or collective morality. As theory became socialized, positions were radicalized, particularly between those who identified with the mandate of the Church, and those who identified with the prerogatives of the medical profession. Add to this confrontation the values and attitudes of Petrarchan court culture and the neoplatonic vocabulary of Ficino that cut across the medico-scholastic world, and the elements are established in a debate not easily characterized—a debate that may be seen in retrospect as a crisis at the end of the Middle Ages in the definition and management of Eros.

Among the common denominators in the general discourse on love was the phantasm as the necessary object of every lover's imagination. It was widely accepted by the physicians and philosophers that love was generated by a lack, an overwhelming desire, that must be focused upon an image of a beloved object held in the memory. Whether Eros itself was perceived to be a spiritual state or merely a natural one, as Couliano points out, "those two traditions have one point in common: the recognition, if not of the nature of Eros, at least of its phantasmic techniques."[1] They were agreed that such an image must enter through the eyes, that it must be transformed from substance to species, and that the copy must be passed from ventricle to ventricle of the brain until it lodged in the imagination and memory. The received ideas concerning the physiology of sight and the processes of faculty psychology conspired, with the weight of their scholastic authority, to dictate a mechanism whereby it was understood that those who suffered from *amor hereos*, philocaption or "folles amours" suffered from a tyrannous preoccupation with an image of a desired object variously falsified by the passions of desire, the temperaments of the body, astral influences, even preconscious aesthetic and spiritual ideas, and by the processes of the mental faculties themselves. Mental devotion to such an object could lead to an obsession that, in accordance with the interpretation of the contributing causes, could be perceived variously as a state of sinful temptation and lust after a depraved and degenerate phantasm, as evidence of a mental derangement produced by the adustion of the humours and an overeroticized psyche, and as a necessary process in the quest for divine beauty through the cultivation of the senses. There was, in fact, no general agreement among the theoreticians of Eros in Italian aristocratic circles of the Quattrocento and after as to whether the phantasms evoked, described, and celebrated in the works of the Petrarchan poets were not dangerous indulgences of the fancy, rather than admirable reflections of a state of sensuous spirituality. That debate would polarize a new generation of authors of *trattati* on love following the publication in 1484 of Ficino's *Commentary on Plato's Symposium on Love.* The only perceptible norm in that unfolding debate was the agreement that the quality and meaning of Eros must be demonstrated through definitions that deal with the origin and nature of the lover's phantasms.

In order to place that essentially Italian and elitist debate into its broadest intellectual context, it is best to begin with a document far removed in spirit from the love *trattati*, and yet one which shares in the general vocabulary of the age concerning amorous phantasms and the need to channel or control the erotic impulses of the individual. Just as the humanist philosophers borrowed from the mechanisms of scholastic psychology to account for the formation of images, so the two Dominican monks who wrote the *Malleus maleficarum* turned to scholastic authority in search of the scientific justification for assuming judicial control over amatory irregularities associated with supernatural causes. Kramer and Sprenger presented their rationale for pursuing all manner of witchcraft and sorcery throughout their Rhineland and Northern German jurisdiction in the *Hammer of Witches*, published between 1487 and 1489—hence three to five years after the publication of Ficino's Commentary—in order to persuade such authorities as the Dean of the University of Cologne and Maximilian, King of Rome that their mandate from Pope Urban VIII was a sacred and legitimate charge. Their scholarly instincts, motivated by self-justification, inspired them to literalize and mechanize a number of disperately received notions about witchcraft and the role of demons in the process of temptation and sin by linking them causally to the received notions of faculty psychology. There was nothing new in theory, but the result was a consolidation of ideas that brought theory to practice through the medium of the Inquisition. As Zilboorg points out, "the thesis of the *Malleus* is as simple as it seems horrible to us," namely, to prove the existence of witches and of witchcraft, and to maintain that all who doubted should be convicted of heresy; to show through a number of case studies how witches function; to demand that witches be prosecuted through legal procedures; and show how the devils that haunt them may be exorcised.[2]

In the process of their collection of data from the scriptures, from writers of the Church, and from contemporary accounts, they assumed all the more forcefully the premise—so fundamental to Christian thought—that the world is inhabited by supernatural creatures, products of the hierarchy of the spiritual world, arranged of necessity according to moral polarities, and that these forces seek expression through involvement in human affairs. In such a thesis there was no novelty whatsoever. But in the comprehensive scope of their survey of behaviors deemed subject to such demonic influences, these writers produced a frighteningly novel view of the social world both as an inner psychological battleground where malign creatures could insidiously alter and control the contents of the mind and the health of the body, and as a collectivity redefined in terms of the spirit world that surrounds it. Among those many forms of aberrant conduct was philocaption or inordinate love of one person for another, appearing under the heading "Remedies prescribed for those who are Bewitched by being Influenced with Inordinate love or Extraordinary Hatred."[3] They raise the subject precisely in those terms agreed upon by the age, namely that erotic love was a matter of the imagination held captive by degenerate phantasms, overshadowed only by the assumption that among the causes of such phantasms was "the temptation of devils" or "the spells of necromancers and witches with the help of devils."[4] The force of their assertion depended upon the belief that devils had the power to tempt the individual to sin through the creation and manipulation of mental images, for how otherwise should the mind be brought to the fall than by working upon the fancy in a way that created inordinate desire? Assuming as doctrine that the devils "can act upon the body, or upon the faculties belonging to or allied to the body, whether they be the inner or outter perceptions," such creatures can easily "affect the inner fancy and darken the understanding" through the medium of phantasms without directly compromising the freedom of the soul.[5] Since nothing can he loved unless it is known, and nothing known except through phantasms, the course was set whereby all the medical tradition concerning the psychopathology of phantasms could be effectively incorporated into their theories of demonopathy. Any number of texts could have served their ends, such as the statement by Bernard of Gordon in the *Lilium medicinae*, that

> amor, qui hereos dicitur, est solicitudo melancholica propter mulieris amorem. Causa huius passionis est corruptio aestimativae, propter formam et figuram fortiter affixam; unde, cum aliquis philocaptus est in amore alicuius mulieris, ita fortiter concipit formam et figuram et modum, quoniam credit et opinatur hanc esse meliorem, pulchriorem et magis venerabilem, magis speciosam et melius dotatam in naturalibis et moralibus quam aliquam aliarum.[6]

Hence, just as devils could seek intercourse with humans through incubi and succubi, or cause sterility through the invocation of witches, they could, without such agents, raise violent amorous passions in the body or generate enticing phantasms in the mind in order to lure the individual to sin. In this way these two theologians made the condition known as *amor hereos* described by Avicenna and his followers, including Bernard of Gordon in the passage cited above, synonymous with philocaption provoked by demons or witches. Kramer and Sprenger, in deference to that tradition, allowed that inordinate love could be sometimes due "to a lack of control over the eyes"[7] and that when physical illness follows from this condition that Avicenna's seven remedies may be consulted. These they listed in accurate résumé, indicating a close familiarity with the main texts of the medical tradition. Nevertheless, the section is prefaced by the comment that such cures "are hardly relevant to our inquiry except in so far as they may be of service to the sickness of the soul"[8] —an ambiguous qualifier insofar as Kramer and Sprenger do not endorse such cures for the sinsick soul, but rather exorcism, prayer and penance. Hence, the effect of their treatise was to bring all manner of erotic obsession, characterized by a diseased imagination, within the causal realm of supernatural agents, placing erotic melancholy among the "sacred" diseases that cannot respond to natural remedies.

In this process, all the characterizing qualities pertaining to mental illness, hysteria or mania are forfeited in clinical terms. The flights of erotic fancy primed by youth, warm blood, and high living now fall within the range of willful sin, if not of demonic abuse, since where there is a preoccupation with the image of an erotic object there is, *ipso facto*, an absence of spiritual integrity. Even a state of depression over the loss or inaccessibility of the beloved becomes barely distinguishable from a form of possession and hence of heresy. It was an extraordinary concatenation of assertions that, carried to logical conclusions, provided the Church with a remarkable intellectual position *vis-à-vis* the entire Petrarchan cult of poeticized phantasms and willful suffering over a potentially corrupt or corruptible image of the beloved.

This innovative and judicially assertive doctrine of demonopathy was a profound set back for the medical tradition concerned with love as a clinical phenomenon. Avicenna had contributed to the Latin West a rich legacy of medical theory that included a description of *amor hereos* as a disease of melancholy in which the phantasm of the lover was generated not only by the physiology of thought, but by the adustion of bile in the hypochondries, the vapors of which polluted the imagination. That vocabulary of analysis remained largely unchallenged for several hundred years and furnished practitioners with the definitions and diagnostics necessary to treat patients afflicted by such erotic disorders in at least a quasi-clinical way. But the logic of the *Malleus* was to reinterpret nearly every psychopathological condition in terms of supernatural causes, whereby such conditions as erotic melancholy or mania were wrested from medical hands. Their influence was sufficiently strong that many physicians themselves capitulated to ecclesiastical reasoning by including demonic agents in their analyses of the causes of psychopathic states down to the end of the sixteenth century.[9] Gregory Zilboorg summarized the age as one in which "the divorcement of medical science from psychopathology was so definite that the latter was almost totally relegated to the domain of theology and ecclesiastical and civil law—two fields which naturally became further and further removed from medicine."[10] By reason of the enormous influence of the Inquisition throughout the sixteenth century, the *Malleus* must represent for that age a kind of normative position with regard to the question of philocaption. One result was that in the matter of inordinate erotic passion and its pathological states, the authority of medical philosophers had been largely preempted so that the development of a more clinical orientation would be retarded for nearly a century.

Perhaps no intellectual environment could seem more removed from that of the *Malleus maleficarum* than the Florence of Ficino in the 1470s and 80s. It was there that the celebrated commentary on Plato's *Symposium on Love* was written, perhaps as early as 1469, and published in 1484. Ficino had clearly steeped himself in the writings of Plato, Proclus, Plotinus and the commentaries on Cavalcanti, but equally so in the writings of Aquinas, Lucretius and the medical philosophers who wrote on the diseases of love. His treatise was a new departure, a break from Aristotelian thought and scientific style, a treatise that, within a short time, became one of the most consulted of the *trattati* on love in the elite circles of Europe. Whereas Kramer and Sprenger spoke in general terms about phantasmic perception, Ficino elaborated at length upon a complex theory of causation derived from his interest in the spirits and the blood vapors—those quasi-spiritual, quasi-physiological elements that inhabit a space between medicine and mysticism. Whereas the inquisitors directed their definition toward an analysis of sin and demon possession, Ficino concerned himself with love as the desire to enjoy a form of beauty innate to the human soul whose counterpart in the world of extension served merely to quicken the process of spiritual pleasure. Fundamentally, however, these works dipped into a common repertory of discourse: they shared an interest in the production of phantasms and in the principles of magic that characterized the fixations of the imagination. These treatises were separated only by their moral and philosophical orientations.

Ficino, too, was interested in the influence of demons, being persuaded that the hierarchy of the universe was inhabited by a parallel hierarchy of supernatural creatures capable of influencing human conduct. Ficino, however, asserted the benign influence of such creatures. His premise was that love alone magnified and purified the soul, despite its many pains and sorrows. To this end, "the instinct of love . . . we have received from the supreme God, and from Venus, who is called a goddess, and from Venerean daemons."[11] Such intermediary creatures, in provoking erotic phantasms, can only contribute to the good of the soul. It was a curious invention: just as Kramer and Sprenger had transposed amorous desire into a fully demonic medium, so Ficino now welcomed his Venerean demons into the spiritual realm. Demons "involve themselves very closely and zealously in taking care of the affairs of lower creatures, especially human beings. Because of this service, all daemons seem good. Some Platonists and Christian theologians have said that there are some other daemons which are evil, but for the present we shall not argue about the evil daemons."[12] And, indeed, he does not argue about them, though it is a telling concession that in speaking of such creatures he assures the reader he is making no special distinction in kind from those referred to by the theologians. It is perhaps a figurative vocabulary for asserting the remarkable coalescence of divine love and venereal attractions that make up his eroticized world order, and yet that range of reference, in its own terms, asserts an incontestable literalness that helps Ficino to maintain that creative play between erotic instincts and aesthetic mysticism that characterizes his philosophy of love.

At the same time, Ficino turns back to the medical tradition, fully willing in chapter 3 of the Seventh Oration to speak of that vulgar love which is a form of insanity brought on by black bile or burned blood. Such erotic alienation can be cured only by traditional medical means if at all. In the final analysis, however, Ficino is no more adept than his contemporaries in distinguishing between the mad phantasms of the melancholy lovers and the sweet imaginings of the contemplative who risks all the commotions of the body in seeking a vision of true beauty. This crux must remain among the imponderables of his work and one of its most contested points among the antiplatonists.

It was in his innovations concerning the physiology of sight that Ficino was to extend the analysis of love's genesis. He developed a vocabulary of material causation that, with its overtones of coersive magic and enchantment, likewise trailed into the spirit world: for what is the invasion through the eyes of an alien blood vapor capable of inciting love involuntarily in the beholder but a form of spell that is no less witch-like in its means for having been cast by a beautiful person? Ficino reasoned in considerable detail either that lovers are victims of such a transference of spirits that exit and enter through the eyes, or that lovers mutually exchange images of themselves through these same vapors—an exchange tantamount to a mutual estrangement of souls. By the same means, lovers are subject to a dangerous depletion of those spirits lost in the act of gazing, as well as to diseases of the blood brought about through the poisoning properties of foreign vapors deposited in the veins. Challenged by the Platonic philosophy that the eyes were the agents of love, and versed in the theories relating to the production of spirits through the rarefication of blood, Ficino reasoned that love was a kind of enchantment or *fascinatio*, a transaction related to occult causes enjoining spiritual ends with a physiological system hovering between received theory and symbolic application. Ficino's influence was widespread among medical writers during the following century and a half.[13] Even the purest of all the Galenists writing on love in the following century, André Dulaurens, in his short but comprehensive treatise on melancholy diseases, mentions the blood vapors that enter by the eye as agents in the combustion of biles in the liver, while Burton, in the *Anatomy of Melancholy*, accepts the entire pathological sequence as a form of bewitchment.[14] Jacques Ferrand, though more skeptical about the *fascinatio*, given the possibility of falling in love without actually seeing the desired object, or of falling in love with a statue which, by definition, emits no blood vapors, nevertheless provides the following account: "François Valleriola . . . and Marsilio Ficino, in his commentary on Plato's *Symposium*, claim that love is caused by means of an enchantment or charm, seeing that according to them, the animal spirits radiate from the lover toward the beloved and are returned again where, because of their great thinness and subtlety, they enter the lover's entrails and spread throughout the body by means of the veins and arteries, troubling the blood and thereby bringing on the disease. This state, for them, is nothing but a perturbation of the blood and especially of the melancholy."[15] That is to say, major medical theorists with an eye to clinical applications were willing to endorse this pathological program as one of the material causes of love in the body, linking the shock of amorous gazing with the formation both of the phantasms in the imagination and with the adustion of biles, thereby integrating the role of the blood humors into more comprehensive pathological systems. Such were the syncretist habits of the age.

Nevertheless, Ficino remained at the edge of the medical tradition concerning the diseases of love insofar as he concentrated upon supernatural causation and treated the ends of love as a mystical vision. Those merely carnal appetites devoid of a capacity to produce true love he looked upon as aberrancies of nature in need of the ministrations of physicians. Such love as they produced he described as bestial, a form of insanity brought on by defects of the brain and by the combustion of black bile. This love, too, was a form of enchantment, he declared, and the "anxious care by which vulgar lovers are vexed day and night is a certain species of madness."[16] Such a bewitchment could only be cured by drainng off the poisoned blood through phlebotomy, by purging of the black biles, or by coitus to draw off the offending surfeit of sperm. Included in his regimen of cures were recommendations for exercise, sweating, and intoxication. Finally, there was therapeutic marriage, or at least the physical joining of the lovers that automatically cures the disease. Nevertheless, the orientation of Ficino's treatise is philosophical, not clinical. "True love is nothing other than a certain flying up to divine beauty, aroused by the sight of corporeal beauty. But adulterous love is a falling down from sight to touch."[17] Paradoxically, the same madness is operative in both forms of love, the same processes of enchantment occur through the simultaneous reception and loss of blood vapors, and the same formation of phantasms materialize whereby the contemplative lover possesses divine beauty and the vulgar lover falls into a state of chronic disease. Nowhere does Ficino indicate how those processes may be differentiated other than by the crasis of the individual and a kind of mystical intentionality. In the final analysis there is perhaps no retreat from this systemic confusion, though apologists have been resourceful in explaining the Ficinian method as an intended departure from Aristotelian systematization. Sears Jayne takes his cue from Agostino Nifo in stating that this work is to be read first as a vast "compilation of ideas about love."[18] Ficino may well have been a syncretist, but the methods of such an argument are not clear. Jayne's theory concerning a stratified style designed to appeal simultaneously to esoteric and to exoteric interests has considerable merit.[19] But Ficino's account of love in general could not satisfy those who saw the inducement of eroticized phantasms, even in the cause of aesthetic mysticism, as a threat to health, and probably more centrally as a menace to social well being and to the interests of the collectivity.

In effect, Ficino's work had come to the rescue, philosophically, of an elite poetic culture inspired by the model of Petrarch, by furnishing a spiritual rationale for the phantasms and attendant sufferings of the poetic spirit, and in recommending Eros, with its foundation in sensual meditation, as a high social good. Cardinal Bembo carried that vision outside of the Florentine circles in the *Asolani*. In Ficino's neoplatonic theories Bembo saw a theoretical foundation for the sonnets of Petrarch and his imitators, thereby building up a complete vision of love as it was revealed through the themes and modes of individual poems. It was in the name of Bembo that Castiglione placed the conduct and values of the Petrarchan lover-courtier into the context of court life in his celebrated *The Book of the Courtier*. There followed a spate of treatises in which contemporary poetry became the center of the discussion of love as the highest good in human conduct. That is to say, Ficino's philosophy of love was seen to have its counterpart in social behavior, so that a treatise which began descriptively and speculatively, soon after assumed a prescriptive role. There were those who understood from the outset of the inquiry into love that the praises of a spiritualized Eros were nevertheless an invitation to dangerous and counterproductive behavior. Love was to be cautioned against, not merely as a sinful enticement, but as a threat to health. Those were, in fact, the only ready-to-hand terms for preaching against the personal and social risks of this cult of self-induced amorous phantasms.

It was in reaction to this cult of spiritualized Eros that writers of a more pragmatic bias would simultaneously restore the language of psychopathology of the medical tradition. Arguably, the greater importance of those "contramour" treatises in the long term was not so much their direct opposition to the Petrarchan cult, but the quality of their discourse based on natural causation, and their more critical examination of the diversity of erotic phantasms now restored and expanded. There can be little doubt that these works passed as counter-statements to Ficino's *Commentary*, and that hence they belonged to the corpus of elite and esoteric aristocratic treatises on love. But they contained a more pragmatic approach to love as a social malaise, and they provided important models of discourse for those physicians a century later who sought to oppose the legacy of Sprenger and Kramer with a more clinical approach to the diseases of the soul and imagination. It was in fact under cover of a medical assault upon the abuses of the Petrarchan culture that physicians could rebuild their arguments favoring a medical regimen for the treatment of erotic melancholy.

That polemical operation began soon after the publication of Ficino's *Commentary* with the publication, in 1496, of Battista Fregoso's *Anteros, sive tractatus contra amorem.* So conventional is the format of this work that its significance has been overlooked. No notice has been given to it by the principal modern scholars of the *topos.* It does not figure among the list of *trattati* in Jayne's introduction to Ficino's *Commentary*, nor is it mentioned by Nelson in *Renaissance Theory of Love*, nor by Couliano in *Eros and Magic in the Renaissance.* To be sure, critical interests have grouped themselves around Ficino and his followers, not around his opponents. Yet for that reason, we have underweighted the polemics of that age which dealt with the question of love. Ficino has come to represent the philosophical norm concerning love in the Renaissance, when in fact the Church and the medical tradition offered opposing voices to the Petrarchan cult of love.

The *Anteros* bears many of the characteristics of works of its age. It is an expansive treatise calling upon the most heterodox lore on love in order to embellish the arguments of the three interlocutors in the dialogue. It would, hence, appear in its way to be yet another compendium on love, blending in Aristotelian and medical views with ancient fable and poetry, and by illustration, legends of good and bad lovers. But it is in the rhetorical design of the dialogue itself that the book discloses an otherwise unsuspected cogency, for by the end, two of the participants are entirely convinced by the arguments of the third, and as they submit to correction and edification, the arguments they had espoused in the definition of love must also be seen to be either under correction or entirely denied. These interlocutors are Fregoso himself, Claude de Savoie and Platina (Piattino Piatti). What is certain, is that the *contra amorem* tradition was an established position in intellectual circles and one as much to be absorbed by polemicists on the side of Ficino, as the new neoplatonic views were to be absorbed by the physicians. Important for our purposes is that we are dealing with a tradition that may make claims for a normative status throughout the last half of the fifteenth century.

Between the demonopathy of the inquisitors, whereby those suffering from erotic fixations or mental delusions were subject to torture and exorcism, and the idealized celebration of love of the neoplatonists, was the voice of the medical tradition cautioning against the excesses of eroticism and offering practical counsel for the victims of such obsessions. In the dialogue that constitutes the *Anteros*, Fregoso and Claude appear as courtiers who have known the afflictions of love. It is Fregoso, as a participant in the dialogue, who makes all the arguments in defense of Petrarchan love and the good which derives from love's sorrows. He advances theories concerning love as a form of enchantment, and at the same time speaks for the Hippocratic school on the role of sperm and the erotic instincts and appetites that incite carnal love. Claude advances the theory of demons and supernatural agents. But the long and final word is given to Platina, who convinces his well-intending friends of the fallacies of their positions, offering instead a well-reasoned therapeutic approach to the treatment of lovesickness. Platina took up his case against Petrarchan court culture in the only terms available to him, namely a reassessment of the production of erotic phantasms, but now in relation to the humors and the diseases of melancholy. The rhetorical advantages of the dialogue is its *discordia concors* design whereby all the major intellectual traditions concerning love receive a hearing, but by which their conflicting elements are resolved through argumentation, concession and capitulation.

There is nothing covert about the attack on Petrarchan values. The poet is cited against himself on numerous occasions where the speaker wishes to demonstrate the dangerous excesses of love. In effect, the poetic facts, without the values of love, reveal abnormal states of behavior: weeping, sleeplessness, obsession, feelings of inadequacy or defeat. In these terms Fregoso the writer sets out to examine the neurosis of a culture that values foreordained failures in love as means to quickening sorrow and the poetic muse. It is a form of self-induced despair that flirts with madness and chronic affliction when desire generates pathological responses. Only through the careful attention of a physician could such patients hope to return to normal and productive lives. The point is made early in the treatise that the victims of Cupid's triumph become so either because the ardor of their desire itself has been allowed to exceed all measure, or because they could not enjoy the object of the devotion.[20] This is a vital new distinction that seeks to classify the nature of the obsession, whether as a phantasmic indulgence, or as asocial calamity. But either way, such patients are the victims of hyperbolical phantasms and of inordinate desire. Once again we find ourselves back to the fundamental vocabulary that forms the point of departure for the analysis of love during the age.

Fregoso sets out to write a treatise that preaches the dangers of love according to the examples provided by Plato in the *Phaedra*, by Diogenes, Epicurus, Chrysippus, and Lucretius. This is to be carried out through an exercise in definition that leads all the interlocutors to their best efforts in describing love in terms of its causes and essences by which alone its nature could be known. After many starts and detours, the prevailing voice holds that love is an unreasonable appetite, ravished by beauty, that in turn conquers the course of virtue.[21] It is driven by sensual desires, leading to a corruption of the reason. The moral overtones are clear, and yet never merely Christian, insofar as this corruption of the reason is always understood as an accident of the combustion of humors and of the tyranny of the phantasms, together with a peccant weakness of the will. There was a delicate balance always to be maintained.

As a contramour, the treatise had to set out, as fully as possible, the ways in which Eros is a cruel and destructive appetite that must be restrained in the name of health and the rational life. By degrees, Platina draws upon the medical sources for a vocabulary that allows him to demonstrate the inherent pathological capabilities latent in all the practices and accidents of love and at the same time rebutt those theories that lead away from the clinical management of those stricken by the disease. Such a treatise could only be a long sermon against the neoplatonists and the Petrarchan cult. Fregoso's treatise, therefore, must take its place in a continuum that has its final outburst perhaps in Giordano Bruno's dedication to Philip Sidney of his *Heroici furori* where he accuses Petrarch of being that "poet who sighed for a girl of Valchiusa . . . lacking the intelligence to apply himself to better things, cultivated by his melancholy assiduously, thereby yielding to the tyranny of base, idiotic and filthy bestiality."[22] Bruno was coming at Petrarch from the opposite side of the debate, casting him with Ficino's vulgar lovers in opposition to true love. But insofar as Bembo had seen the relationship otherwise, this wedge driven between Petrarch and the neoplatonists reveals in its way the ambiguity that had always been perceived in the Petrarchan discourse; that poets in the tradition had either exercised their own indulgent narcissism in nurturing their poetic phantasms, or had covertly used the language of suffering and renunciation to cast a coercive spell of words around the unwilling object to force her into submission. For Bruno, Petrarch's poems revealed an "obsessional contemplation of an unworthy object, as the wasted suffering of a sick imagination, against whose pernicious influence Bruno fights with all his might."[23]

In the second part of the treatise, each speaker in turn offers his explanation of the origins of love in the body. Fregoso speaks first, claiming that love is above all the desire for carnal conjunction, and that such cravings are caused by sperm, with its tickling sensations and "ventosity" which in turn stimulate an urgent desire to cast this excremental humor out of the body through coitus.[24] He explains both how sperm is generated, and how a surfeit of sperm has pathological powers that can afflict the heart and brain and bring on a state of disease. To this theory he adds the eye beams as a material cause of the venerean, explaining how the pestilent vapors can both corrupt the blood and at the same time develop a fervent desire in the recipient to seek union with the person initiating the infection.

Claude follows with his assertion that love is a carnal concupiscence caused by the temptations of evil spirits. His evidence is drawn from the same passages from St. Paul employed by Kramer and Sprenger, proving that Satan himself is the author of those longings of the flesh. He defends out of Lactantius the means whereby such subtle spirits can secretly enter the body, alter the organs to incite lust, corrupt the mind with dreams and phantasms, destroy health and drive men to fury.[25] The list of authorities is long who show how the devil can inflame the imagination in order to produce both ardent desire and madness, conditions to be averted only through prayer and the pious life. At this juncture he takes up from Ficino the hierarchical order of demons and spirits, finally offsetting them with the Christian order of angels and devils with their moral polarities. We have in summary the received ideas both of the inquisition and of the neoplatonists concerning the origins of erotic desire, both resorting to the logic of magic or to supernatural agents.

Platina then engages them with the arguments of the natural philosopher who dismantles both systems through a series of questions based on the necessity of universal results in the wake of common causes. That is, if sperm is the cause of carnal desire, how is it that some men seek and wait for one woman only, when any woman would serve to relieve the surfeit? Conversely if men engage in coitus, how is it that the expenditure of seed heightens rather than assuages the appetites, since pleasure seeks rather to repeat itself than to be refused? Likewise, he reasons that the eye beams may not be the material cause of love since by such logic all men would be afflicted equally by the glance of a beautiful woman, or if the affectionate glance alone has the power to poison, then no man would love who was not also loved by the enchantress, which we know often not to be the case. With similar questions challenging the general effects implicit in general material causes, Platina shows that the individualization of love must come from sources other than those material causes. Likewise, he challenges the validity of devils as primary causes citing Origen, Isidore, St. Augustine, and St. Ambrose as worthy authorities who relegate such influence to secondary roles or less in their defenses of the freedom of the soul and the responsibility of the moral will. Valid or false, these arguments were taken for gospel by all participants in the dialogue, giving a clear rhetorical field to a definition of love in terms of a natural causation that begins with the soul itself and with the thoughts of the individual as framed and conditioned by a wide variety of natural and spiritual influences.

This solution would seem to take us back where we began, with all the arguments remaining more or less where they were. But for Platina this is the occasion to turn to a more closely observed analysis of the thought processes as they build their own enclosures, nets, and labyrinths, thereby giving a specific content to the more generalized pattern of disease that ensues from the vortex created by the passions, the melancholy temperament, and all the other contributing causes. The source of this approach is none other than the section on *amor hereos* in Avicenna's *Canon*, the founding scripture of the physicians concerning amorous melancholy. The condition is there described as a passion of the soul capable of producing fear and sorrow and uncontrollable phantasms that in turn burn the biles and discharge noxious vapors.[26] This leads Platina back to a study of the phantasms of the desired object, falsified by the processes of the imagination and the deceptions produced by intense desire. The quality of this process can only be differentiated by the quality and conjunction of the humors, or by the stars that preside over the occasion. Once the proper order of causes has been demonstrated, Platina can move on to a carefully reasoned set of remedies that correspond to the diverse states of the disease.

Platina makes a distinction between those phases of the condition that are by-products of a perverse will, and those that are pathological. By clearing away the predominance of seed, blood vapors, and demons, he not only banishes the relevance of their defenders, but clears the way to practical care. Neither exorcism nor sublimation were reasonahle answers to those suffering from a natural disease brought on by excess thought and aggravated by physiological conditions. The only sensible way to rehabilitate distracted lovers was to deliver them from the tyranny of their phantasms. Speaking for Fregoso the author, Platina outlines a complex program of social therapy whereby the false judgments of the lover are submitted to reason, altered through an assault upon the worthiness of the object, or displaced by more immediate matters of business or pleasure. If the patient's health continues to deteriorate he suggests driving out the old love with new, or even to satiate the lover with other women. The chronic stages of this dementia, he urges, can only be handled by a trained physician, again underscoring the medical bias of his treatise and of its sources. He joins with Erasistratus and Avicenna in recommending coitus, and more particularly union with the specific beloved, as the only means for rescuing the patient from death. Fregoso is unable to anticipate the importance, merely hinted at by Avicenna, that will be given to the pharmaceutical cures in treatises expanding upon this clinical approach a century later.

Fregoso's list of methodical cures does not in any way go beyond a selection of recommendations from his sources. Nevertheless, his treatise is of great importance in bringing the medical analysis of love, with its clinical and empirical biases, into the circle of discourse that had been polarized between theologians and neoplatonists. Fregoso draws from both vocabularies of analysis, yet renders order through the rhetorical and reasoned priority assigned to the logic of medical analysis through the strategies of the humanist dialogue. In an age during which psychopathology had been entirely usurped by the ecclesiastical courts in the north and allegorized in the love *trattati* of Italy, the anti-Petrarchan crusade was perhaps the only context in which the more sympathetic approach of the clinic could be urged as the means most suited to the care of erotic mania and depression.

The *contramour* argument was not merely a counter argument on philosophical grounds, but the foundation for a program of care administered by physicians and necessitated by the personal casualties created by the Petrarchan culture. Uniting all these treatises was a common understanding that Eros was potentially dangerous because of its tendency to create tyrannous phantasms that resulted in obsessive desire, withdrawal, and even death. Fregoso's treatise represents a norm based on the traditional analysis of melancholy diseases. Possibly that approach had become less visible in late fifteenth-century Italy, and by all indications entirely invisible in northern Europe. But the clinical perception of love was to stage a dynamic return in the late sixteenth century, culminating in the *Traicté de la maladie d'amour ou melancholie erotique* of Jacques Ferrand, and in the literary extension of those concepts in the *Anatomy of Melancholy* of Robert Burton.

Carleton University

NOTES

1 Ioan P. Couliano, *Eros and Magic in the Renaissance* (Chicago and London: The University of Chicago Press, 1987), p. 39.
2 Gregory Zilboorg, *The Medical Man and the Witch During the Renaissance* (New York: Cooper Square Publishing, 1935 , 1969), pp. 6–7.
3 *Malleus maleficarum*, trans. Rev. Montague Summers (London: The Pushkin Press, 1928, 1951), p. 170.
4 *Malleus maleficarum*, p. 170.
5 *Malleus maleficarum*, pp. 50–51.
6 Bernard of Gordon, *Opus lilium medicinae inscriptum* (Lugduni: apud G. Rovillium, 1574), p. 216.
7 *Malleus maleficarum*, p. 170.
8 *Malleus maleficarum*, p. 171.
9 Jacques Ferrand, *A Treatise on Lovesickness*, eds. Donald Beecher and Massimo Ciavolella (Syracuse: Syracuse UP, 1990), pp. 87–89.
10 *The Medical Man and the Witch During the Renaissance*, p. 3.
11 Marsilio Ficino, *Commentary on Plato's Symposium on Love*, trans. Sears Jayne (Dallas: Spring Publications Inc., 1985), p. 112.
12 *Commentary on Plato's Symposium on Love*, p. 112.
13 One of those physicians was François Valleriola in his *Observationum medicinalium libri sex* (Lugduni: apud Antonium Candidum, 1588), p. 197.
14 Robert Burton, *The Anatomy of Melancholy*, eds. Floyd Dell and Paul Jordan-Smith (New York: Tudor Publishing, 1927), p. 681.
15 *A Treatise on Lovesickness*, pp. 252–53.

16 *Commentary on Plato's Symposium on Love*, p. 168.
17 *Commentary on Plato's Symposium on Love*, p. 172.
18 *Commentary on Plato's Symposium on Love*, p. 4.
19 *Commentary on Plato's Symposium on Love*, pp. 16–17.
20 Giovan Battista Fregoso, *L'anteros ou contramour*, trans. Thomas Sibilet (Paris: chez Martin le Jeune, 1581), p. 11.
21 *L'anteros ou contramour*, p. 8.
22 *Eros and Magic in the Renaissance*, p. 68.
23 *Eros and Magic in the Renaissance*, p. 68.
24 *L'anteros ou contramour*, p. 140.
25 *L'anteros ou contramour*, p. 161.
26 *L'anteros ou contramour*, p. 190.

Maristella Lorch

A Defense of the Senses in Lorenzo Valla's Theory of Pleasure

A defense of the senses constitutes the very basis upon which Lorenzo Valla (Rome 1406–1456) built what I define as his *theory of pleasure*.[1] He articulated it while in his early twenties in the Rome of Pope Martin V (an intellectual desert), and was probably stimulated by the presence there of the Florentines Leonardo Bruni and N. Niccoli, and by the *grand viveur*, author of the elegant and obscene *Hermaphroditus*, Antonio Beccadelli, called Panormita.[2] He enlarged the dialogue and reinforced his thesis later, first as a *magister* at the Studium of Pavia (in Piacenza in 1431, and in Milan in 1433), and again while in Naples in the service of King Alfonso V of Aragon, in 1444. There is proof, moreover, of at least one further revision, that of 1449.[3]

The defense of nature with which the epicurean interlocutor responds to the attack, by the stoic who preceeds him, upon nature as a malignant stepmother to humanity is based on a defense of the word *voluptas*, which appears in the prologue of the first version of the dialogue, *De voluptate* (1431). There the author strives to discover a new meaning in an old word.[4] Although the defense of the word *voluptas* is eliminated from the later versions, the thesis remains unchanged: *voluptas* is not a *summum bonum* (as it is in Cicero's *De finibus bonorum et malorum*) but the *unicum bonum*. It is the very act of life as it is being lived, life in its mercurial quality, always varied, different, unexpected, new. *Libertas*, understood as full freedom in the "interpretation of texts," and *risus*, the expression of *voluptas*' generosity (not mockery and scorn but a means to penetrate into the secrets of human nature and at the same time to upturn a given situation), are essential elements of the new method (*nova ratio*) that the *rhetor* Valla adopts for the purpose of discovering life's essence.[5] To discover life's deepest motivation as a *rhetor* instead of as a *philosophus* signifies to work first and foremost with language, common everyday language, the direct expression of man as he lives his life. Accordingly, the written text must be interpreted as the reflection of one particular moment in man's history, unique and unrepeatable. In this sense *philologia*, the art of interpreting texts, becomes the true *philosophia*, the art of living life. How does the rehabilitation of the senses fit into this "rhetorical" context?

Valla was well aware of the rehabilitation of Epicurus taking place around him. He probably held in hand the manuscript of Lucretius' *De rerum natura*, which was discovered in 1418 by Poggio Bracciolini, an interlocutor of the *De voluptatae*. Yet, he works with the *De rerum*, as with all the texts available to him, in a way quite different from his contemporaries. Hence the results obtained are quite unique and original. His theory of pleasure is, more than any other humanistic work, an expression of the tremendous vitality of the Italy of the first half of the fifteenth century. An enthusiastic awareness of the exceptional blooming of the arts, his *voluptas*, as it is derived from the Epicurean-Lucretian *temeritas atomorum*, or atomic theory, is based on natural providence. It comes to light in a dialectical process with the *ratio vivendi* of the ancients accepted by most contemporary humanists as gospel: a neostatic, ciceronian *honestas*, or virtue. Thus the dialogue *On Pleasure* is a celebration of the victory of *voluptas* over *honestas*. *Voluptas* implies the superiority of the world of the senses, understood as the world of passions, desire, and imagination over the world of intellectual abstractions. Life, experienced through the senses, hence becomes the field of study of our *rhetor/philologus*, the kingdom within which the phenomenon *voluptas*/life emerges first and foremost. Life, Quintilian tells us, is the true field of rhetoric. According to Valla's theory of pleasure, man is a creature made of senses, superior to the other animals because of the intensity of his perception through these senses. This is confirmed at the very conclusion of the Epicurean oratio (end of Book II) after the hymn to the serenity of Epicurus' death, and in the articulation of Valla's theory of "contemplation," that is, knowledge. Initial knowledge comes to us through the senses, *videre oculis*.

Health and especially beauty are essential to our understanding of what is *good* (Books I, XVI–XXVI). As I said above, the antithesis of *voluptas-honestas* materializes in the form of two contrasting ways of life: one inspired by *voluptas*, congenial to life; the other informed by *honestas*, harmful to it. *Voluptas* is identified with *utilitas*, or "what is advantageous," because it is strictly dependent on the senses that tell us what is useful to life. *Utilitas* signals what is useful and joyful to the senses, what satisfies a sensual need. With the definitions of the two words *voluptas* and *honestas* representing the ideas of the two contending parties, the fight is on. (*De vero falsoque bono* I.XVI). Cicero provides the definitions from the *de Finibus* (II.I.3 *On Pleasure* XV.1). Yet, what is at stake is not a simple definition of what is *bonum*, but *life* itself. The focus is therefore on those goods of body and fortune that are traditionally considered to be of secondary importance. *Utilitas*, or the expedient, is at the root of *jocundas*, or joy. *Voluptas* is the realization in life of *utilitas*.

Health and beauty are considered essential elements for the realization of man's pleasure and well-being.[6] In dealing with beauty Valla has unavoidably moved into the world of the senses. Are the senses good? Beauty, health, and strength are traditionally considered *goods* of the body, *bona corporis*. They have been shown to be such by the virtue of their *utilitas*. It is obvious that their usefulness to man depends on the perception of the senses. So far, the senses in question have been sight and touch: "Hec de aspectu quidem et tactu dixi, idque tantum de uno genere" (XX.3). These senses relate to one particular experience—beauty. With the focus constantly on *voluptas* as enjoyment, the field is now open to all of Nature around us and to all the senses. Nature and man are brought together by the human senses to create man's *bonum*. The desire comes at the right moment when man experiences the availability of a benevolent Nature. All of Nature's gifts serve for the adornment of man.

The focus is strongly kept, not on what is good *per se*, but on *what makes a good*: a human experience involving the gift of a benevolent Nature and the senses, and first of all the sense of sight. Thus the treatment of *pulchritudo* serves as a model for the discovery of many other goods that involve senses other than sight and touch. And with the emergence of other "combinations" of objects and senses we penetrate deeper into the secrets of the world of pleasure/*voluptas*.

The sense of hearing (XXII) calls for speech, sweet speech, song pleasant to hear, and pleasant sounds. The cultivation of music is attributed by common sense to the attraction of our senses to pleasant sounds and to the "use" of them with enjoyment (*frui*). Yet the topic is informed by *voluptas-utilitas*, since music is considered the most ancient of all arts and hence proof that the pursuit of pleasure was the most ancient study. Music and musical instruments that are also common among illiterate people prove what an instinctive element *voluptas* is. Poetry is seen as a sister to music, purely as an object created for pleasure. "Et poete, qui se deorum vates appellant, semper *canunt*, sive diis sive hominibus sive utrique *gratum facientes*." This pleasurable quality of music and poetry was considered *wisdom* in ancient times. "Illis antiquis temporibus iidem et *musici* et *vates* et *sapientes* iudicabantur." Yet, why does one study music or poetry or oratorial art if not because they are *res suavissima*, that is, they cause pleasure? Never for a moment is the sense of hearing conceived of by itself, but always strictly in connection with the object that attracts it, this connection being pleasurable. Not for a moment is an art (music or poetry) conceived of by itself, but exclusively as what produces satisfaction for the senses: a fusion of *usus* and *fruitio*.

The natural goods that come to light as *goods*, because of their usefulness to man through the sense of taste, are foods (cookbooks!) in which human ingenuity has labored hard to attract man's enjoyment with infinite variety—like women's beauty. Hence, a praiser of food is a praiser of life; and consequently, the *philosophi* who preach abstinence are praisers of death. "Plus hic videntur mortem laudare quam vitam" (XXIII.1).

With the use of food another aspect of Valla's *voluptas* surfaces: its concreteness, the stress on the individual and the fusion of senses and object. Apart from the fact that most of the *philosophi* preach abstinence without practising it, are their admonitions to be followed indiscriminately? Certainly not. One should carefully examine the *individual* situations and decide accordingly, remembering the fact that the food is there to be used. Also, in this case the *tempus*, or circumstance, must be taken into serious consideration: we must not consider who it is that does something, but for what purpose and how rightly (*qua causa et quam recte faciat*). Thus the abstinence of an Epicurus or the excesses which caused the Trojan war cannot be taken automatically as examples, respectively, to follow or to avoid. There are no "goods" in themselves but purely in relation to a situation.

Finally, the wish to have "a neck like a crane so as to savor at greater length the pleasure of taste" is a colorful illustration of the fact that our senses have been given to us so that we might use and enjoy them. The wish with which the issue closes is the natural conclusion of the argument, oratorically and poetically: "Utinam non quinque sed quinquaginta aut quingenti sensus in homine essent!"—especially so when *natura* and *artificium*, natural goods in themselves, and what men can do with them, collaborate to excite man, as it happens sometimes, in women's adornments.

Is not wine the most eloquent example of such a pleasure-generating combination: a gift of Nature further "elaborated" by man? The example is in itself so powerful as to be alotted a whole chapter (XXIV). The topic of wine (*De vino*) is presented as a challenge and realized in the form of a contest. It is a challenge for the orator because *wine* and *words* (together with laughter) are discovered to be, in the reality of life and in the poetry of Homer and Horace, the only two *gifts* which Nature has conferred to man alone and not to any other creature. The contest will therefore be between the *oratio* itself, the words of the Epicurean, and *wine*.

The long additions to the original chapter on "Taste and Wine," by stressing the added enjoyment brought together by refinement and civilization, and mostly by revealing in the enjoyment of the sense of taste the quintessence of *voluptas* as sensual tension towards the object and perfect fusion with it, indicate that Valla intended to exploit the topic of *wine* in particular as the paradigmatic revelation of *voluptas* insofar as it brings about the fusion of the object with the senses.

What, finally, is the purpose of the relation of wine to the gift of speaking? First we discover through this relation that speaking implies enjoyment but not always the same enjoyment. Then the relation suggested by the *res*, *voluptas*, in its aspect of *utilitas*, challenges Valla to a contest that, while implicit in the case of the other senses, realizes itself now within the sense of taste as if the words of the eulogy were flying free, liberated by the powerful influence of wine. Valla expresses this challenge through the special use of his sources, the poets Tibullus, Juvenal, and especially Horace.

The two chapters XXIII and XXIV were conceived by Valla as a unity with corresponding parts, with the intent of conveying the reality of life. Chapter XXV reflects on the results they have produced: the audience wants to experience immediately what the *oratio* has suggested. The conversation suggests that the audience is one step further than the speaker on the road to the discovery of the *res*.

In dealing with the sense of smell, our humanist distinguishes between things that belong to nature, such as the smells of flowers, and smells that are discovered by the skill of man, such as banquets and ointments. This is a distinction he had previously made in the case of food, suggesting a refinement of the natural objects in consequence of the refinement of the senses. Thus the more advanced a civilization is, the greater its *voluptas*. In an analagous manner, as for the previous senses, the focus is here on the social element: wives who smell badly can be repudiated; men should not appear in public smelling badly.

Finally, as in the case of speech and wine, the word (*oratio, verbum*) and the sense of smell are related, since "what discourse avoids is almost exclusively matters related to this sense" (par. 3). Jokingly, what the Stoics consider natural—"indulging in bad odors and obscene speeches"—is said to be most unnatural. We conclude that the greater the enjoyment, the greater the *utilitas* that ensues from the human experience. The enjoyment feeds the *usus*. The power of *fruitio* as well as of *usus* is a human power.

All the way through, the *usus* of speech is kept parallel to the *usus* that may come from each of the senses. The answer to the problem is then given by the fact that *cognitio* and *fruitio*, knowledge and enjoyment of what is *good*, among all the possible *goods* that Nature displays, are exclusive posessions of man and are innate to him. Man has no knowledge of Nature *per se* but rather a knowledge of what in Nature can be good for him. Life's eternal source is man's knowledge of what can be enjoyable and thus useful, and also the power to enjoy it.

It should be observed that in the analysis of the senses in describing the object, an *externum bonum* (be it a flower, a poem, a song, a man-made perfume, a beautiful face, or wine), Valla laid constant stress on its capacity of arousing *fruitio* as well as *usus*. Consequently, those objects that are given greater emphases can arouse greater enjoyment (beauty of women, special food, wine). Moreover, most of the emendations of the later version of the *De voluptate* confirm the author's intention to stress the privileged state of mankind versus animals, not in the *use* of the external *bona*, but in a greater refinement of such use so as to produce enjoyment: in *fruitio* not in *usus*. Progress in enjoyment is hailed as the progress of civilization itself. This also explains why health and strength *per se* are easily dismissed in favor of beauty.

Is it not the purpose of this section of the dialogue to celebrate man's unique position in the world? "*Hominem voluptati natum magis quam cetera animalia*" reads the title of Chapter XXVII in the third version of the dialogue. The aim is to discover what *voluptas* is, and in the process to discover man's privileged condition. The dialogue itself, and this first book in particular, is a kind of exploratory voyage into the kingdom of pleasure from which some facts about pleasure itself emerge. The most evident is that man's *excellentia* and hence his *nobilitas* do not consist in his *intellectual* capacities.

What then is a *bonum* in the light of this analysis of the senses at work? The definition will not surprise us. The senses themselves make us aware that *bonum* implies equally *usus* and *fruitio*. *Bonum* is the point of concurrence of the two elements: one, the senses that receive; the other, the object of desire that is received. Which among the examples presented earlier are those that reflect best this truth? The eyes and the palate, in union respectively with the light (or beauty) and the pomegranate. Sight and taste are mentioned here as the two senses in which the elements of fusion, the *utrunque concurrit*, is most evident. Splendor and food are noted as the two objects which facilitate the best fusion. *Pulchritudo* in its miraculous essence is like light. The pomegranate reflects in its combination of attractions the best food. "Quare," the text continues, "voluptatem recte bonum appellamus que ex his ambobus *quasi utroque parente perficitur*. Porro *animus* et *corpus* recipiunt *externa*, recipuntur." Body and soul are one in the process of receiving. The particle *quare* indicates that logically there is no escape. There is one *bonum* for sure, a *something* we can call rightly a *bonum* because it reflects the fusion of eyes and light. And this *something* is the human experience of pleasure, *voluptas*. How does *voluptas* emerge now in relation to the ciceronian definition that served as a point of departure in the argument? As a *bonum* that finds its completion (*perficitur*) in the result of a marriage, the *fructus* of a marriage, *ex his ambobus quasi utroque parente*. Instantly we are reminded of the Stoic's attack on Nature, of his desperate appeal to Nature to act as *mater* to man and not as *noverca*, and also of the long distance the Epicurean has covered in his answer to the Stoic in order to reveal, or rather to *un-veil*, Nature's benevolent quality. Instantly we see what unifies Valla's argument: his effort to detect in the traditionally much-vituperated human senses the potential openness to discover the immense richness of the world of which man is an intimate part.

Barnard College and Columbia University

NOTES

1 M. de P. Lorch, *A Defense of Life*, "Humanistische Bibliothek" (Munich, 1986), ch. IV in particular.
2 Valla, *On Pleasure*, trans. A.K. Hieatt and M. Lorch; Intro. and Appendices by M. Lorch (New York: Abaris, 1977), pp. 16–26.
3 Valla, *De vero falsoque bone*, ed. M. de P. Lorch (Bari: Adriatica editrice, 1970), Introduction. See also *A Defense* . . . , ch. II, pt. I, no. 2.
4 *A Defense* . . . , ch. II, "Voluptas: Introducing a New Meaning and Function in an Old Word," pp. 27–43.
5 *A Defense* . . . , ch. III, pt. II, no. 2, "The function of laughter and freedom (*libertas*)," pp. 58–61.
6 *A Defense* . . . , ch. IV, "In the world of Voluptas," pt. I, no. 6: "Health, Strength and Beauty," pp. 84–87.

Massimo Ciavolella

Eros and the Phantasms of *Hereos*

When in 1838 Jean Etienne Dominique Esquirol defined erotomania (or, as he calls it, *monomanie erotique*) "une affection cérébrale, chronique, caractérisée par un amour excessif, tantôt pour un object connu, tantôt pour un object imaginaire" and insisted on the fact that it is a true disease characterized by the fixation of the image of the object of desire upon the imagination and memory of the lover: "dans cette maladie, l'imagination seule est lésée: il y a erreur de l'entendement. C'est une affection mentale, dans laquelle les idées amoureuses sont fixes et dominantes . . . "[1] he did little more than follow faithfully the salient points of a theory of erotic obsession of Greek origin, codified in a scientific/philosophical system universally accepted from the first century A.D. Even the "case histories" which the French physician documents are taken from models already proposed by a long literary and medical tradition. Just as traditional are the literary examples he offers—Amnon and Tamara, Sappho, Antiochus and Stratonice, Justina and Pilades, the poet Lucretius, Torquato Tasso, Cervantes—and the diagnostic and therapeutic methods he describes.[2]

If we go back to the beginning of this tradition and we examine a text such as Plutarch's *Amatorius*—a text to which was attributed, for centuries, the merit of having "invented" the term "erotomania," a text constantly cited by writers on love and on love-as-disease—and if we also examine the pages which focus on the passion of love, we detect immediately the insistence on the role of the imagination and on the concept of polarization of the object of desire:

> Whereas the fury of love, wherever in seizes either man or woman, sets them in a flame; no music, no appeasing incantations, no changes of place are able to quench or put a stop to it; but being in presence, they abandon themselves to their passion; being absent, they desire; by day they prosecute their importunate visits; by night they stand awake at their windows; sober, they are continually calling upon their love; and when they are inebriated, they are always teasing the company with their love songs. Neither, as one was pleased to say, are poetical fancies, by reason of their lively expressions, rightly called waking dreams; but the dialogues of

persons enamoured, discoursing with their absent loves, and dallying, embracing, and expostulating with them as if they were present, much rather deserve this name. For the sight seems to delineate other fancies in the water, that quickly glide away and slip out of the mind; whereas the imaginations of lovers, being as it were impressed upon the memory of the lover in fiery characters, just like encaustum paintings, remain forever moving, living, speaking.[3]

Quite evident is the emphasis on the power of imagination, which can move the passions, create illusions but also new realities, can be a *pharmakos* but also the cause of fatal diseases. Let us read a paragraph taken from the "esposizione" that the illustrious Neapolitan physician Marco Aurelio Severino—who died of the plague which in 1656 decimated the population of Naples—affixed to the sonnet of Monsignor della Casa "Sì cocente pensier":

Ma per discutere del principal sentimento del Sonetto, stimo, che fia bene discorrer prima, che cosa sia Amore: e lasciando al presente la via de' Platonici, e d'altri Filosofi, seguirò quella de' Medici, che è più sensata. *Amor*, dicono costoro, *est corruptio virtutis Imaginativae, falsa rapraesentantis Ratiocinativae*. Il perché riferiscono tutto l'esser d'Amor all'Imaginativa, e in quella il ripongono. E di vero nell'Imaginativa è tutta la possanza, e tutta la forza d'amore; anzi il vero suo seggio, ove è fondato e radicato, è l'Imaginativa. Per l'Imaginativa è sempre presente agli amanti l'amato oggetto. Per l'Immaginativa un tronco, un sasso, uno sterpo, un albero par loro l'amata Donna. Per l'Imaginativa parlano e non parlano, par loro stringere e non stringono, par loro camminare e nulla si muovono. Per l'Imaginativa non gustano del mangiare, né del bere, né dell'altre cose che piacciono. Per l'Imaginativa vegghiano le notti intiere. Per l'Imaginativa soffrono quel che per verun'altro conto non soffrirebbono. E in somma tutte cose buone ree si sentono dagli amanti per cagion della lor imaginazione.[4]

[But in order to discuss the main sentiment of the sonnet, I believe it proper to discuss first of all what love is: and leaving aside for the time being the ways of the Platonists, and of other philosophers, I will follow the physicians, who are more sensible. *Amor*, they say, *est corruptio virtutis Imaginativae, falsa rapraesentantis Ratiocinativae*. The reason is because they relate the entire existence of love to the faculty of imagination, and they place it within imagination. And indeed all the power, all the force of love rests in the imagination; in fact its true seat, the place where it is founded and rooted, is the faculty of imagination. Through the imagination the loved object is always present to the lovers. Through the imagination a tree-trunk, a stone, a dry twig, a tree seems to them the woman they love. Through the imagination they speak while silent, they believe they are embracing [their love] but they are not, they think they are walking and yet they are still. Through the imagination they do not enjoy their food, their drinks, nor the other things that people like. Through the imagination they remain awake all night long. Through the imagination they suffer what they would never suffer for any other reason. In other words, all of the good and evil things that befall lovers are caused by their imagination.]

The similarities between Severino's and Plutarch's texts are quite remarkable; just as noteworthy is their insistence on the role of imagination upon the erotic process. However, what distinguishes Severino from Plutarch, is his attempt to offer a more "clinical" chart of love, to organize his definition of erotic passion within a precise frame validated by a millenary medical and philosophical tradition, and to express himself in a scientifically "correct" language. Hence the reference to the *virtus imaginativa* of the lover, and contextually to that doctrine of the internal senses and of perception, of Aristotelian and Galenic origin, which has shaped the western concept of man for over two thousand years.

A final example: the most complete and most interesting study on erotomania written before the dawn of modernity is the treatise *De la maladie d'amour ou melancholie erotique* published in 1623 by the French physician Jacques Ferrand, a text which Esquirol still considers of fundamental importance for the study of erotic monomania. In his discussion "Si en la Melancholie Erotique le coeur est le siege de la maladie, ou le cerveau," Ferrand appropriates a comment taken from Mario Equicola's *Libro de natura de amore* in order to confirm the essential role that imagination and memory play in the erotic process:

Guydo Cavalcanti en une sienne chanson, que Dine Corbo [sic] Medecin Italien a commenté, prouve que le cerveau est le siege de l'Amour, aussi bien que de la memoire, car in iceluy gist l'impression de la chose aimee, d'où vient que les amans sur toutes choses desirent estre en la souvenance de la chose aimee.[5]

[Guido Cavalcanti, in one of his canzoni commented upon by the Italian physician Dino del Garbo, demonstrates that the brain is the seat of love as well as the memory, for in the memory is lodged the image and imprint of the cherished object. So it is that lovers above all else enjoy reflecting upon their memories of the beloved.]

Together with other perhaps better known treatises—for example the treatise on melancholy by André du Laurens, or the *Anatomy of Melancholy* by Robert Burton, the texts cited above mark the outer limits of a culture of eros of Greek medical extraction founded on the following fundamental axiom: it is inside the brain that love takes its seat, inasmuch as the image of the object of desire remains *pathologically* fixed upon the organ of memory. The truth of this axiom is clearly demonstrated by classical literature, and, therefore, refractory to whatever type of diagnostic test, of collation of case histories. Love, once it becomes the object of study, is analyzed exclusively on the basis of other texts: on those offered by the literary tradition in order to demonstrate that its pathological conditions are universally recognized and recognizable; on the treatises of the great masters of medicine of the past and present in order to study its etiology, its prognosis, and the therapies required to cure it.

We must, therefore, rely mainly on medieval and Renaissance medical treatises in order to discuss those mechanisms which were thought to control the birth and growth of love and of erotic passion, and to define the role played by melancholy in this pathological process. Starting from the axiom I presented above, I shall concentrate on love as obsession, as *immoderata cogitatio*—that *assidua cogitatione* of which Marsilio Ficino speaks in an exemplary manner in the ninth chapter of the sixth speech of his *Book on Love*:

> Chi è quello che non sappia quelle cose essere aride e secche, alle quali manca l'umore? E chi negherà la squalidezza e giallura venire da difeto di caldo sanguigno? Ancora per lungo Amore gli huomini pallidi e magri divengono perché la forza della natura non può bene due opere diverse insieme fare. La intentione dello amante tutta si rivolta nella assidua cogitatione della persona amata e quivi tutta la forza e la naturale complessione è attenta, e però el cibo nello stomaco male si cuoce.[6]

> [who does not know that arid and dry things are those which moisture forsakes? Likewise, who would say that pallor and squalor [the yellow-green colour of lovers, or "green sickness," as it will be later called] come from anything else than a lack of sanguine heat? Moreover, in a long-lasting love mortals become pale and thin. Certainly the power of nature does not usually suffice for two tasks at once. The entire attention of a lover's soul is devoted to continuous thought [assidua cogitatione] about the beloved. And to this all the force of the natural complexion is directed. For this reason the food in the stomach is not digested prefectly.]

The expression *assidua cogitatione* derives from the current medical tradition. Even the name Ficino uses to denote this passion, "heroes," is traditionally associated with the more technical "hereos" by the *physici* because—to quote the commentary of Gerard of Berry on the *Viaticum* (a very popular medical vade-mecum written around the year 1000 by the Arabic physician Abu Jafar Aḥmed Ibn Ibrāhīm Ibn 'Alī Khālid, but attributed in the Latin West to its translator, Constantinus Africanus)—

"vires nobiles [sunt] qui propter divitias et vite molliciem atque delicias tali potius laborant passione" (it is the noble persons who, because of their wealth and the easiness of their life are more often troubled by this passion).[7] Ficino continues:

> Aggiugnesi che dove l'assidua intentione dell'Animo ci trasporta quivi volano anche gli spiriti che sono carro e istrumento dell'anima. Questi spiriti si generano dal caldo del cuore della sottilissima parte del sangue. L'animo dello amante è rapito inverso la imagine dello amato che è nella fantasia scolpita. . . .[8]
>
> [Moreover, wherever the continuous attention of the soul is carried, there also fly the spirits, which are the chariots, or instruments of the soul. The spirits are produced in the heart from the thinnest part of the blood. The lover's soul is carried towards the image of the beloved planted in the imagination, and thence towards the beloved himself.]

In a very concise manner, yet undoubtedly clear to contemporary readers, Ficino—not unlike the authors mentioned above—refers to a doctrine of the passions derived from Aristotle that reappears in Galen and in Arabic and scholastic medicine and natural philosophy.

According to this doctrine, the birth of desire is strictly bound to an alteration of the vital heat of the body. With the growth of desire and of the heat that desire creates, the malignant humours of the body also increase, and especially black bile. When the image of an object of desire reaches the internal faculties of the soul the vital spirits, because of the sudden pleasure, multiply. This growth of the spirits generates heat, and the heat generates a motion upwards.[9] As a consequence, from the left ventricle of the heart the vital spirits propagate throughout the body, overheating the natural and animal spirits. The receptacle of the faculty of estimation, that is to say the dorsal part of the middle ventricle of the brain, being in contact with the burning spirits coming from the heart, also becomes inflamed. It is from this state of inflammation that the permanence of the phantasms of perception occurs.

The faculty of estimation controls the *imaginativa*, and the permanency of the images of perception, of the *phantasmata* in the faculty of imagination, depends upon its degree of dryness. The heating of the *aestimativa* through an overheating of the encephalic area of the *imaginativa* causes a state of excessive dryness. This process of physiological disruption causes the growth of the melancholic humour—dry and cold—which, once it overflows into the cavities of the brain, fixes the image of the object of desire in the organ of imagination and of memory, polarizing the attention of thought itself.[10] Thus the image perceived by the senses remains the only datum present to the consciousness of the lover. This condition is named *complexio venerea.*

The *phantasia* assumes an essential role in the process of knowing. The fundamental axiom of Aristotle's psychophysiology, that the soul cannot know if not by means of the phantasm, is at the very basis of the system of the passions developed by ancient and medieval medicine. The image is a potential intelligible which is actualized by the active intellect: that is to say that the image contains the form of the external object, a form which is extracted and abstracted (Avicenna speaks of *denudatio* of the image) from its materiality by means of the active intellect through a process of illumination. When the image enters in relation with the active intellect, the form within the image finds once again its intrinsic, dinamogenic power. This dinamogenic power which is communicated to the possible intellect through the image and under the guide of the active intellect is that *species intelligibilis* which is located within memory and which completes the process of cogitation. Having thus become aware of the external object, imagination presents it as a desirable or non desirable end, as an object to pursue or to avoid by means of the practical intellect.

In optimal conditions, so to speak, eros is in the faculty of memory as *species intelligibilis* of the object of desire, and in the sensitive appetites as a *phantasma* of the imagination. But if the desire of the senses grows unchecked and the phantasm "fixes itself" upon the organ of the imagination and of memory, it remains the only "Good" that is present to the consciousness of the lover, a perverse image of a form which can no longer become an object of knowledge.

The fundamental contradiction of passionate love consists in this: the *complexio venerea* fixes the image upon the sensitive memory of the soul; however, being the only datum present to the consciousness of the lover because of the perversion of the process of intellection, the *phantasma* is identified as the only true Good. In other words the Good, which should be the only true object of man's desires, is identified with the *phantasma*, with the image of an object of sensual desire. The melancholy delirium which springs from this perversion of the internal senses, drags the lover into an insane quest for an image forever reflected within his own memory, into a vain, obsessive attempt to possess an object of desire that can never be reached nor seized.

Inevitably, therefore, the war against the perverted eros, against erotomania, must be fought on the front of the internal senses, especially that of the faculties of estimation and of memory. First of all, one must try to distract the erotomaniac from his fixation by forcing him to spend time in conversation with a few close friends. Walking in green meadows and listening to music can also constitute a valid palliative against the anguish of love. Just as important, the physician must impose the proper diet (food produces blood which produces semen), and also prescribe tepid baths, humidifying, purgative, and narcotic drugs. These therapies, acting upon the memory and upon the rest of the organism, may create a state of forgetfulness. In addition, acting upon the movement of the spirits, upon inner heat, and upon digestion, they help to re-establish a certain equilibrium between the humours and the radical qualities of the organism.

If this psychological treatment does not produce a resolution of the obsession, it will be necessary to move to more drastic methods of cure.

In the category of physiological cures, the lover, where it is possible, is allowed to have sexual relations with the object of desire. In this manner the malignant humours are evacuated, and there exists the possibility that the *phantasma*, fixed in the memory of the lover, may be eradicated by the living object of desire.

If the erotomaniac is a male, and if it is not possible to convince the woman he loves to go to bed with him, she must be replaced by one or more young women, in the hope that intercourse may evacuate part of the malignant humours in the excessive semen, thus constituting a valid therapy.

But if the one who suffers from erotomania is a woman, and if it is not possible to join her in marriage with the man she craves, it may be necessary to commit her to an asylum, or even to a *carneficina*, a place of torture, where terrible diets, continuous bloodletting, tortures of various kinds, and more often forced coitus imposed as a therapy by physicians and male attendants, should act as a palliative against her obsession.

Since inordinate desire is caused by an "orgasm of blood and animal spirits," bloodletting, even if applied in an excessive manner, must always be part of the therapy against excessive erotic desire. An example of its indiscriminate use is recounted by M. Lochner in his medical dissertation defended at the end of the seventeenth century, and repeatedly quoted until the nineteenth century:

> A French girl, both noble and marriageable, was leading an idle life and following a warm diet. After she had a clandestine love affair with someone below her station, to whom her parents refused to give the nod, she began to be worn out by insomnia. For several days she began to call out loudly, to exhibit the part of her body that distinguishes the sexes, to sing lascivious songs, to look ferociously, and when someone tried to resist the woman in her sexual fury her excitement

increased. In fact, if she were not bound with strong chains and held in bed by two or three men, she would conceive a fire in her joints and leap naked from the bed, and if she should encounter some man she would rush fiercely at him and lustfully beg him to perform the rites of Venus with her. She was constantly awake, her eyes glowed, her intentions were bad, her speech was coaxing. Her face was wholly inflamed and swollen. A pungent, sticky mucous humour that almost rotted the bed linen flowed at irregular intervals through the portal of modesty. "And foul breath pouring from black jaws strikes the nostrils with its odour." The pulse was strong, the tongue dried out and there was wasting of the whole body. When a doctor was called, he had the girl confined in a French Medical Torture house [carneficina] where after bloodletting, repeated 30 times in six days, he drew from the girl along with her blood at the same time her insane mind, mad love, dear life.[11]

At the level of the *virtus estimativa*, the doctor must try to denigrate, as much as possible, the object of desire, often by securing the help of an old woman. Old women, as the *auctoritas* of the *physici* and of the great authors of the past clearly demonstrates, are expert in this "art." This process of denigration should uncover the "true" nature of the object of desire, thus jolting the lover from his obsession.[12]

At the level of the *virtus memorativa*, the doctor must experiment with those therapies which act directly upon the phantasm fixed upon the organ of memory. If the narcotic drugs and the other therapies cannot erase the object of desire, the lover must be surgically "shocked," and the organic substance of the encephalic area in which the power of imagination resides, and which imprisons the image of the object of desire, must be forcefully liquified. And since the fixation of the image of the phantasm is caused by the excessive cooling of the black bile created by the sudden overheating of the brain cavities due to erotic desire, the method adopted to "shock" and at the same time "liquefy" the receptacle of memory—a kind of hardened wax, according to a tradition that dates back to Plato[13]—is to overheat artificially the cranium of the erotomaniac. A classical example of the misuse of this method is related by Petrus Forestus in a chapter dedicated to erotic folly in his *Observationum et curationum medicinalium ac chirirgicarum opera omnia*:

But another young man of Delph also driven insane by love was lying bound to his bed where he lay neglected and wretched. After six weeks, when he was consumed by his insanity as by a wasting illness, I was summoned. We found him not only insane but so ill treated from the various remedies of attending simple-minded women that I had never seen anything comparable or anything so horrible to describe. They had placed on his bare head a bronze device ordinarily used to warm the bed, so hot when lit that they burned the whole crown of his head.

In the wound that followed the whole pericranium and skin were removed right down to the skull, so that the skull and cranium were stripped bare in an area the size of a crown. They treated the young maniac so wretchedly that for many days altogether he stayed wide awake, and leapt out of his bed so that he had to be confined there by a strong man. We prescribed sedatives for sleep but they scarcely did any good.

When we saw the man altogether neglected, and when we saw that the women were taking such care of his bare head, we ordered rather that a learned and skilled surgeon should be called in to care for the wound since the women had been all along treating him so poorly. We scolded those who were there but accomplished little that was good, and were left grieving that the art of medicine, so excellent and necessary, was held in such disregard by so many, since the sick slip into the hands of the empirics.[14]

The proof that not only the uneducated women mentioned by Forestus used this method to cure erotic melancholy, but that on the contrary, if properly applied, it was part of common medical practice against epilepsy, melancholy, and erotomania, can be found in Jacques Ferrand's treatise on erotomania:

Me contenant de vous dire, que si ceste maladie empiroit de telle façon, qu'on doutast que le Melancholique Erotique devint loup garrou, alors il le fault seigner des veins du bras jusques au syncope ou defaillement de coeur exclusivement, et neantmoins on luy appliquera un cautere actuel, ou en son refus, ou defaut, un potentiel sur le devant de la teste, ainsi que nous ont enseigné de faire Paul Aeginette, Oribase, Avicenne, et autres autheurs classiques. . . .[15]

[I will simply add here that if the condition grows worse in a way suggesting that the erotic melancholy could turn into lycanthropy, then the veins in the arms must be bled until the patient faints or until there is a total failure of the heart, and in spite of this, one must continue by cauterizing the front of the head with a searing iron [actual cautery], or if he refuses or cannot bear it, with a caustic compound [potential cautery], applied to the same place, as we have been taught to do by Paul of Aegina, Oribasius, Avicenna, and other classical authors. . . .]

The women described by Forestus quite obviously knew that erotomania can be cured by applying a burning object to the pericranium. However, since they did not have the medical training necessary in order to carry out properly such an operation, and since they did not possess the proper surgical instruments, they used a household object which can easily be heated in a fireplace, an iron used to warm the bed. Ferrand prescribes the proper instrument, the searing iron which must be applied to the forehead of the lover, just as it is done to cure madmen and epileptics. This therapy would have been used only as a last resort to save the insane lover, an *ars oblivionalis* which, should it not manage to remove surgically the obsessive memory of the object of desire, it had the merit—according to our physicians—of removing the wretched lover from this world, and thus from his incurable obsession and insanity.

University of Toronto

NOTES

1 J.E.D. Esquirol, *Des maladies mentales* (Paris: Chez J.-B.-Bailliére, 1838), vol. 2, p. 32.
2 For the chapter on erotic monomania see pp. 32–49.
3 Plutarch, *Of Love*, in *Plutarch's Morals*, vol. 4 (Boston: Little, Brown, and Company, 1874), trans. W.W. Goodwin, p. 280. For the original Greek see *Moralia*, vol. 4, ed. C. Hubert (Leipzig: Teubner, 1971), pp. 362–63.
4 *Opere di Monsignor Giovanni della Casa* (Venice: appresso Angiolo Pasinello, 1728), vol. II, p. 14. The translation is mine.
5 Jacques Ferrand, *De la maladie d'amour ou melancholie erotique* (Paris: Chez Denis Moreau, 1623; rpr. Liechtenstein: Kraus, 1978), p. 63 ; translated into English as *A Treatise on Lovesickness*, ed. D.A. Beecher and M. Ciavolella (Syracuse: Syracuse UP, 1990), p. 257.
6 Marsilio Ficino, *El libro dell'Amore*, ed. S. Niccoli (Firenze: Olschki, 1987), p. 135; translated into English as *Commentary on Plato's Symposium on Love*, ed. Sears Jayne (Dallas: Spring Publications, 1985), p. 121.
7 [Ibn Edjazzar], *Breviarium Constantini dictum Viaticum* (Lugduni, 1510), I, xx, fl. 12-r-v. However, this concept is repeated by all the medical texts on love.
8 *El libro dell'Amore*, p. 136; *Commentary on Plato's Symposium on Love*, p. 121.
9 For a detailed explanation of the psycho-physiological process engendered by excessive love see the introduction to Jacques Ferrand, *A Treatise on Lovesickness*, esp. pp. 70–82.
10 Arnald of Villanova, *Tractatus de amore heroico*, in *Opera medica omnia*, vol. 3, ed. M.R. McVaugh (Barcelona: Universitat de Barcelona, 1985), p. 50: "Ex predictis iterum elicere convenit propter quod imaginativa fixa sic permanet circa rem, unde talem gratum anima preconcepit; oportet enim similiter ex organi vitio seu aliqua malitia. Cum itaque firma retentio formarum in multis quibuslibet nequaquam effici valeat sine sicco, necessario sequitur cerebellarem partem imaginative virtutis aliqualiter exsiccari. Hoc vero ex pretactis sic ostenditur: cum et fortis et frequens sit transitus calidorum spirituum ad cellam estimative fluentium ad iudicium celebrandum, pars anterior in qua virtus imaginativa residet propter humidi consumptionem a calore spirituum derelicta remanet necessario siccior seu minus humida quam fuerit per naturam. Hac igitur introducta qualitate, sequitur—maxime si aliqua frigiditas coniungatur—

quod forma imaginationis in organo firmius retinetur necnon multa sollicitudo validius excitatur."

11 M.F. Lochner, *De nymphomania historiam medicam*, quoted in O. Diethelm, *Medical Dissertations of Psychiatric Interest* (Basel: S. Karger, 1971), p. 66.

12 For the use of this topos in Dante Alighieri's *Divine Comedy* see P. Cherchi, "Per la 'femmina balba'," *Quaderni d'italianistica*, VI, 2 (1985), pp. 228–32.

13 See Plato, *Theaetetus* 191*d-e*, and also Aristotle, *De anima* 424*a* and *De memoria* 450*a*.

14 Quoted in Diethelm, p. 63.

15 *De la maladie d'amour ou melancholie erotique*, pp. 250-51; *A Treatise on Lovesickness*, p. 357.

Enrico Musacchio

The Role of the Senses in Mario Equicola's Philosophy of Love

For the historians of Italian literature, keen organizers of handy classifications, the case of Mario Equicola seems to have presented no problem. Essays on the philosophy of love from that era seem to form a homogenous Renaissance genre, platonic in inspiration, all of them tracing their origins to Ficino's *De Amore*, itself being no more than a commentary on Plato's *Symposium.* Hence, historians of Italian literature have generally assumed that Equicola, author of another of the early Renaissance treatises on love (the *De natura de amore* of 1525), must also be a platonist.[1] The claim has been universal and, as far as I know, undisputed.[2] Equicola's period of study in Florence has suggested to biographers that he must have been a student of Ficino's, and that possibility, and the presumed similarity of their works, has turned possibility into fact. But the documentary evidence is slight. Rather, these biographical hypotheses have been built merely to explain why and how Equicola's treatise is so dependent on Ficino's platonism.[3] Is Equicola's treatise in fact so platonic? Is it at least dependent on basic platonic or neo-platonic concepts? A careful reading of the text suggests otherwise. Equicola certainly quotes Plato, but he also refers to Aristotle, to Cicero, and to a host of other classical authors. What filters through the maze of innumerable quotations, digressions, and excursus in the more than 480 pages of this very large, very tediously written, thoroughly pedantic treatise is a "philosophy of love" that is quite original, remarkably different from other platonic dialogues of the Renaissance, and pointedly different from its supposed model, Ficino's *De Amore.* Equicola is neither an extraordinarily original thinker nor a very lucid philospher. But the pragmatic logic of his approach to the problem of love and the cavalier fashion with which he treats preconceived neo-platonic ideas are in themselves quite fascinating.

The originality of Equicola's philosophy of love is evident in his phenomenological discussion of the role of the five senses. The measure of his originality can best be made by contrasting his treatment of the *topos* with that of his putative teacher, Ficino. Ficino's discourse on love is, in reality, a cosmological discourse. The manifestations of love are dealt with as testimony to a certain order of the universe, as symptoms of the cohesiveness of the world, rather than being analyzed for their own sake. This does not mean that Ficino writes of love in an abstract way. His treatise is full of surprisingly acute remarks on the phenomenology of love, as well as of equally surprising poetical flights.[4] These parts, however, are clearly subservient to a general description of the creation of the universe and of the workings of the "machine" of the world. Ficino posits that God created the world by infusing life into an inert pre-existing chaos. The created world, at first confusingly, but with increasing consciousness, strives to rediscover the creator until it finally burns with the desire to return to its origins. This movement back from the created to the creator is love. Love, then, is the converging desire of the universe to return to God.

Let us note, in passing, that this notion describes more fittingly the love of the created for the creator than it does the opposite—the more traditional concept of a love of the creator for the creature. This approach is in keeping with the classical notion that the imperfect being can love the perfect one, not vice versa. But Ficino uses the same term, "amor," for the two movements, rather than the term "amor" in connection with the love of the creature for the creator and the term "benivolentia" for the reverse case.[5] But indeed, if, schematically, the universe consists of an irradiating life-giving force, Goodness itself, which transforms the shapeless cloud of chaos outside itself into a world, and which is loved in return by that created world, the two roles—of the creator and of the created—are, in fact, not so drastically distinguished. On the contrary, the soul is described as having a not inherently or passive role. It has a natural, inborn desire to receive the light of God. It turns, of its own accord, so as to be enlightened.[6] Perhaps Ficino, who explains the act of creation with visual images, was influenced in this by the theory propounded in the *Republic*, and even more clearly in the *Timaeus* (and traces of it can be discovered in medieval literature, such as the poetry of the "Scuola Siciliana"), according to which, in the act of vision the eye participates not only passively but actively by sending its force to catch the image to be impressed upon the retina.[7] We would be, therefore, quite wrong if we stopped at a strictly centrifugally conceived image of the cosmos, because the universe, as Ficino sees it, is not a static mechanism in which the roles are fixed forever, but an organism pulsating with life, each part of it with its role to play.[8]

There is even an actual interchange of roles. Ficino explicitly mentions the presence of God in all parts of the universe, centre and periphery equally, and inversely the co-presence of the periphery at the centre. This he explains with the metaphor of the circle and the centre: "Such is the nature of the centre, that although it is one, indivisible and fixed, it is found nevertheless in every part of many, nay of all the moving and divisible lines, because the point is in each part of each line,"[9] and "God, which is the centre of all things, who is simple unity and pure act, puts himself in all things. . . . And it is necessary that created things . . . approach their creator."[10]

Ficino thus establishes the nature of the universe and the role of love in it as the striving of all things toward the perfection that is God through the natural attraction of beauty, which itself is the outward face of Goodness. He then discusses the six instruments by which man perceives or discovers beauty. These are the mind and the five senses. Beauty (that is Goodness or God) is essentially harmony, which can be perceived by the mind and also by sight and hearing. We might expect at this juncture the same task to be assigned to the remaining senses of smell, taste, and touch. However, having just identified all five senses as instrumental in the discovery of beauty, Ficino, surprisingly, marks a very sharp distinction between sight and hearing on one side, and the other three senses on the other, for smell, taste, and touch are not quite capable, for Ficino, of truly apprehending harmony.[11]

In the phenomenology of love in Ficino, very much depends on this distinction which differentiates sharply between two categories of senses as qualitatively different and as instinctively ordered, whether explicitly or implicitly, from the "highest" (sight) to the "lowest" (touch). But I am unable to find, in Ficino, a proper philosophical basis for the distinction. What has been said about the instruments for the apprehension of beauty and harmony does not, in itself, justify distinguishing the two higher senses from the other three, and one cannot but suspect that Ficino was theorizing under other presuppositions at this point. Two illustrations, it is true, are given for this fundamental dichotomy. One concerns the distance of the object to which the several senses address themselves. Touch apprehends its objects by contiguity; taste requires the thin, but material, connective of saliva; and smell can act on objects that are very near. But sight and hearing can perceive objects over great distances (even though not quite so far away as the mind).[12] However, the proximity of an object to the organ of sense, cannot by itself, justify a method for qualitatively differentiating the value of the several senses. Or at least, Ficino does not argue for it. The second illustration seems to hint at a hierarchical structuring of the four basic elements, but only by implication can it be used to support a vertical ordering of the five senses. The relationship between the senses and the four elements is derived from ancient science: sight, connected with fire, is the highest; hearing, connected with air, is just below; smell, a mixture of air and water, is next; then taste, associated with water; and finally touch, always the lowest in all classifications, belongs with earth.[13]

Rather than deducing the distinction from the cosmology that he has just produced, Ficino perhaps simply picks it up from the common stock of ideas on the relative worth of sensory experiences. He thus concludes that the first two senses belong to the spirit and the following three to the body, obliterating in this way the finer discriminations he had introduced in the previous discussion on the composition of the universe.

Whatever its origin, this very important divergence between more spiritual and more material senses is significant to Renaissance discussions on love which contrast physical love as less worthy and less pure than spiritual love. The germs of this rather rough contrast can easily be found in Ficino, who goes on to compare the sort of love that is "'honest," with that "venereal rage, i.e. lust . . . which is in fact the very opposite of love," describing it as "so vehement and furious that it puts the mind out of its place and perturbs man."[14]

But again, we would be wrongly underestimating the subtlety and richness of Ficino's ideas if we were to conclude that, once having posited a demarcation such as this, he is content to work schematically along the same lines. If we puruse the text for indications of a more complex universe, we will be able to discover indications sharply contrasting with the previous condemnation of lower sensations. Only a few pages after having declared that "with the other senses (that is to say with taste, smell and touch) we possess not the beauty that love desires, but rather something else that is needed for the body,"[15] Ficino employs an extraordinary and unexpected metaphor which explains how the human soul, although incapable of knowing God, has, however, a confused groping towards him: "Lovers don't know what they desire or are looking for, because they don't know God, whose hidden taste has put in his works a very sweet smell by which all day we are excited. And we smell that perfume but we cannot feel the taste."[16] Why would Ficino choose that very metaphor of smell and taste concerning God if it were not in order to correct the previous schematism distinguishing proper sensations from debasing sensations? Once more we have the confirmation of the circulating, ever-changing nature of the universe that Ficino, perhaps only for didactic reasons, describes as rigidly vertical.

But, however much we modify the hierarchy of the senses, in Ficino's system (and in neo-platonic discussions on love), sight and hearing remain the most perfect instruments for knowing love, while, invariably, at the bottom we find touch. In Bembo's *Asolani* (1505), Lavinello responds to the relaxed attitude of Gismondo who, although prizing sight and hearing, has not been able to abstain from the pleasures of the other three senses, by reminding him that there are only two windows for the flight of the soul towards beauty.[17] In Leone Ebreo's *Dialogi d'amore* (published in 1535, but known in manuscript form many years before), Sofia is made to question Filone: "You take sight to be more excellent than all other senses taken together; but, despite this, the others, and particularly touch and taste, are more necessary to man's life," giving Filone the opportunity to reply: "Necessary to the life of the body, while sight is so to the spiritual life of intelligence." Filone then classifies the senses according to the medium in which they function: pure air for sight, air broken by high and low notes for hearing, vapour for smell, humidity for taste, and passive qualities for touch. This is a classification that goes, of course, qualitatively downwards.[18] In later treatises, Ficino's distinction is assumed and repeated, at times verbatim. So in Castiglione's *Courtier* (1528), it is stated that "it is impossible for touch to perceive beauty, just as it is impossible to smell with the ears," whereas "beauty is the proper object of the faculty of sight."[19] In Betussi's *Il Raverta* (1544), sight and hearing are said to appreciate harmony, whereas the other three "lower" senses "belong rather to a sort of rage and fury than to anything else"; and in his *La Leonora* (1557), "touch, taste and smell cannot be said to be beautiful."[20] One can here recognize Ficino's very words. And again in Tullia d'Aragona's *Della infinità d'amore* (1547), Varchi declares: "Nothing can be understood except through the senses, and of them the most noble and most perfect is sight."[21] The same idea also appears in Flaminio Nobili's treatise (1567), approvingly commented upon by Tasso in 1570.[22]

Equicola's treatise was finally published in 1525, a few months before his death. Equicola, however, had been working on it since his youth.[23] Within this lengthy span of some twenty-five years many of his ideas must have changed. This poses a special problem to his readers, because we have no way of ascertaining if some of the apparent contradictions are indications of changes of mind. Which parts were written in his youth? Which in later years? As he did not excise them at the moment of printing the final version, we must view them as being all constituents of a completed thought. However, much light could be shed on some considerable difficulties, and certain obscurities in the development of the arguments would perhaps disappear, if only we knew the circumstance of the writing.

Equicola opens his treatise with a survey of previous and contemporary discussions on love. This account occupies, in fact, the whole of the First Book.[24] One section of this survey deals with Ficino's *De amore*. Equicola's analysis of Ficino is, however, singularly unfocussed.[25] Ficino's ideas, which attempt to encompass all the discourses on love and integrate all its phenomena within a single system, are described by Equicola as a rather remote philosophy, as though he had been unable to find any substance for his meditation on the true nature of love. Equicola does not criticize Ficino's cosmology or dismiss it, but mentions it as though it were totally alien to his own type of pursuit. Rather than starting from a survey of the universe, Equicola's point of departure is the question of what and why the individual human being loves.

What, then, is this feeling of love? Equicola produces a very straightforward answer. Not only the root of love but also its essence is the innate instinct of keeping ourselves alive and well: "Nature has given us an instinct, which we cannot deny, to keep ourselves alive and maintain ourselves in the best conditions of existence. This necessary and immutable law was not found by man, nor inspired by heavenly power, but is inborn in us, grows with us, becomes old with us."[26] All actions can be attributed, thus, to this all-powerful instinct: "Everyone loves himself; and this love which remains in us all our life explains our desire for useful, glorious, pleasurable things, while we only appear to love others, who are merely the instruments of these personal gains."[27] As a proof that this is so, Equicola invites us to verify its truth through the testimony afforded by introspection. It may be difficult at first to admit it, but we will have to accept it in the end:[28] "Nature has given us this inborn and unshakable desire to obtain what we believe is good for us, and avoid what we are persuaded is bad."[29] As a convinced Benthamite "avant la lettre," Equicola reiterates this inescapable law of nature which has yoked us to these two most cruel tyrants, hope and fear, and makes us aware of the opposite paths of pleasure and pain.[30]

But Equicola is not content with the broad outline of a utilitarian world view. In a series of examples he examines the nature of altruistic love in order to expose its pretensions. Thus, liberality, fortitude, temperance and justice, just as much as fraud, perfidy, calumny and all the rest, can be shown to have their origin in this simple instinct of self-love. For instance, no other reason (according to Equicola) is necessary to explain why, in ancient times, man instituted religious rites, but that he could in this way pay homage to his former benefactors. The cult of animals in certain civilizations can be explained in this same way. And it is not only pagan religions that can be thus accounted for—all social institutions, continues Equicola, are disguised forms of self-love that take on the garb of justice.[31] Finally, in the last steps of this rationalistic explanation of human institutions, Equicola takes up the two most sacred ones, the family and religion. A mother may seem motivated by altruistic love, but it is not so. She loves her creatures for the pains undergone; if her children will not return her affection, her own love will quickly change.[32] The same can be said of fathers toward their children and of children toward their parents.[33] As for religion, our pretended love of God is again disguised self-love: "this is true and praiseworthy love of ourselves, since the eternal prize is everlasting life and the possibility of seeing God."[34]

Here we have, then, the foundation stone of Equicola's philosophy of love. Not the whole pervading feeling of the Universe, as in Ficino's system—the desire of all creation to die and to be reborn in others in its quest for the creator—but a very realistic and individual wish to survive, painted in some of its crassest terms by an author who must have realized that in his analysis he was swimming against the current neo-platonic idea of a supposedly natural instinct to love other than oneself. That this foundation of his philosophy of love was a departure is made clear by Agostino Nifo, who, writing his own *De amore*, published only a few years after Equicola's, in 1529, devotes a whole chapter to the refutation of "self-love."[35] Nifo proclaims himself "amicissimus" of Equicola in the preface to the treatise, and affirms that our author has written about love in a more than satisfactory way.[36] But he must have drawn the line at the idea of self-love, because to the disproof of Equicola's arguments (which consist in essence, as we have seen, of an appeal to introspection), he opposes a full array of logical arguments aimed at revealing what is significantly un-Christian in Equicola's idea that love for God is narcissistic.[37]

But the idea of self-love was not unique to Equicola. It represented part of a general philosophical position, except that his approach to the question of man's position in the universe, as contrasted to Ficino's strategy, is anthropocentric. What the cosmological discourse is to Ficino, psychology, or the discussion of the soul, is to Equicola. It constitutes his doctrinal foundation. Its importance is clearly indicated by the central position it holds in Book II, right in the middle of the analysis of self-love as the essential concept in the philosophy of love, after which it is left aside, to reappear two books later as an introduction to the discussion of the senses.

Unfortunately this section of Equicola's discourse is particularly opaque. Very briefly, Equicola seems to be arguing for a total integration of body and soul. There are not two souls in man, but only one, he concludes at one point.[38] And later on he will exclaim that the soul responds to, and only to, all the solicitations of the body, suffering through it, rejoicing through it.[39] This is a far cry from Ficino's idea of the independence of the intellective soul, totally immune to the events of the flesh. For, in Ficino's system, besides the body, there are two entities that constitute the totality of the individual, the "anima" and also the "spiritus," this latter being the element capable of allowing communication between body and soul.[40] The "anima," on the contrary, is strictly independent of the body in its intellective function.[41]

It is tempting to interpret the hesitations and the obscurities of the account of the soul given by Equicola[42] (who goes so far as to describe the belief in the mortality of the soul "like the truth, even if not true"),[43] as indications that he knew he was treading on dangerous ground. The reference is, of course, to the public burning of Pomponazzi's *De immortalitate animae*, in 1516, while Equicola was still composing his treatise. Pomponazzi had run afoul of orthodox beliefs because he had held the soul to be mortal.[44]

From 1509 onwards the lives of Equicola and Pomponazzi were closely intertwined. In that year Pomponazzi, after the closure of Padua's Studium, moved to Ferrara and, later that same year to Mantua, while Equicola spent some months in Mantua and then moved back to Ferrara. From 1510 to 1512 both resided in Mantua, where Equicola had become the teacher of Isabella d'Este, an admirer and also supporter of Pomponazzi in the troubled period following the publication of his treatise on the soul.[45] The question, then, is whether Equicola shared Pomponazzi's views on the soul but was afraid of declaring them too openly. If we hold to the hypothesis that the discrepancies in Equicola's account of man's soul are due, not to the wavering of his mind, but to the fear of incurring ecclesiastical censorship, then we are free to look for his actual beliefs not so much in the programmatic declarations (such as the one concerning the immortality of the soul, which is infused for a time into man's body), but in the beliefs attributed to other people used as mouthpieces (as for instance when he writes that some people claim that Homer describes the soul to be corporeal),[46] in hinted truths (that the soul's direct connection with bodily conditions, even if not true, seems true), and in hidden sarcasms of the opposite views (that the soul, although immortal, is afraid of dying and has doubts of failing, although it is not subject to defect).[47]

In this light we can then see emerging from the treatise a consistent analysis of the human condition in which the individual is depicted as an integrated being, not partly divine and partly human, but totally human and totally mortal. On this first philosophical foundation, Equicola develops his philosophy of love. As the individual is without immortal aspirations, so is he basically interested in his survival on earth. Hence his fundamental instinct is for self-preservation, his search for pleasure, and his fear of pain.

If such is man, then it is obvious that a distinction of the senses based on some other, extraneous, criterion would be meaningless. Equicola's analysis is consistent with his philosophical premises. It is true that he begins in a conventional way by stating that the five senses have been disposed by Plato and Aristotle in a hierarchical ordering, and that, furthermore, he himself treats them in that same order, beginning with sight, and following with hearing, smell, taste, and touch, as tradition required. But there are not two categories of senses, one more intellectual, the other more bodily. How, in fact, could such a distinction be maintained in Equicola's materialistic system?

The most shocking proposition (to a platonist) comes with the discussion of the sense of touch. This, although dealt with last, is bluntly declared to be the principal sense.[48] All the other senses are given by nature as ornaments of the essence of man, whereas touch was given for his very existence.[49] Indeed, the only criterion for distinguishing among the senses can be found in their usefulness. Each of them is supremely important in its natural task to help in the survival of the individual.[50] All are essential, certainly, but none so much as touch: "If the other senses break down, the whole animal does not break down; but if touch breaks down, then life stops, for without it the animal cannot be or exist."[51] In his treatment of the sense of touch, besides placing it before the other senses in utter disregard of Ficino's cosmological ordering, Equicola seems to have been unable to resist a last provocation. Reflecting on the connection of the senses with the four elements, he exclaims (surely tongue in cheek): "I would like to say that touch belongs to ether, the fifth element."[52] Touch, the sense that according to the Ficinian tradition tended to make brutes of men, and traditionally placed at the bottom in the vertical ordering of the five senses, is, by Equicola, associated with the extra element, unknown to man but posited above the other four, the only uniquely heavenly element.

But is man, then, for Equicola, in respect to the senses, not more than an animal? There is a big difference, in reality, between animal and man. Although they equally depend on the use of the senses for their survival, man adds another dimension to their use, an aesthetic one. Animals see natural and artificial things just like men; but men, besides, delight in colors and proportions. Only man, in addition to hearing, smelling, and discriminating between edible substances, is capable of taking delight in music, pleasant smells, and refined tastes.[53] And so it is, of course, for the sense of touch: "Touch was given to them to breed, to us, just like them, to maintain the human species, but also in order to give us varied, many-sided and continuous pleasure."[54] Pleasure, then, is the ultimate goal of life, and the capacity to enjoy it the aspect that sets us apart from the beasts. And love, of course, is the most powerful way of achieving it. Equicola's philosophical foundations of his entirely earthly theory of love are thus concluded.

The University of Alberta, Edmonton

NOTES

1 For Ficino's *De amore* see *Opera Omnia* II, 1 (Basileae, 1576; rpt. Torino, 1959), and Ficino's own translation into Italian (Milano, 1973). Equicola's *De natura de amore* was first published in Venice in 1525.

2 This facile classification does not surprise when found in handbooks or histories ("L'ispirazione ficiniana è evidente," E. Bonora, in *Storia della letteratura italiana*, eds. E. Cecchi, N. Sapegno (Milano, 1966), as an example), because one assumes that the authors have, at best, only glanced through Equicola, but it is astonishing when it is held by those who have read him. Nesca A. Robb, *Neoplatonism of the Italian Renaissance* (London, 1935), despite a careful analysis of *De natura de amore*, still wants to place Equicola in the wake of Ficino ("it marks a further stage in what one might call the secularization of Neoplatonism," p. 189).

3 The hypothesis that Equicola had been a student in Florence is in D. Santoro's remarkable biography, *Della vita e delle opere di Mario Equicola* (Chieti, 1906). That he was a student of Ficino appears in M. Aurigemma, *Il Cinquecento* (Bari, 1973), who perhaps takes it from G. Toffanin, *Il Cinquecento* (Milano, 1954) who writes: "Anch'io—diceva egli—come 'il mio dilettissimo Diacceto' vengo dalla scuola del 'nostro venerando Ficino'." But whereas the two small quotations are almost correct, the key part, on the discipleship, is Toffanin's, and I was unable to find grounds for it in the text. Equicola says of Diacceto that he was a disciple of Ficino (p. 24); he does not say it of himself. The only evidence, for this claim, that I can find is the expression found in *De natura de amore*: "il nostro venerando Marsilio," but it seems very slender evidence.

4 The long excursus on the "murder" of the person in love which is automatically perpetrated by the loved one, and the following witty argument on the right to exact revenge for it (Oratio II, ch. 8, p. 1327), is but the first example that comes to mind, but they could be multiplied.

5 Indispensable for Ficino's philosophy is, of course, P.O. Kristeller's monograph, of which many editions are available. See also J. Festugière, *La philosophie de l'amour de Marsile Ficin* (Paris, 1941) and Saitta, *Marsilio Ficino* (Bologna, 1954).

6 "Ad Deum . . . quodam appetitu convertitur." (Oratio I, ch. 3, p. 1322v).

7 See *Republic* VI (507d.) and *Timaeus* (45c).

8 Even the systoles and diastoles of the universal organic pulsation are made evident in Ficino's prose by a delightful rhetorical device. After the description of the movement from God to the outer regions of the periphery ("In the beginning God creates the substance of the Angelical Mind . . . and this, for a certain innate appetite turns toward God, its source, and is enlightened by God, and approaching God receives the forms . . . " and so on), Ficino proceeds immediatley to redescribe the very same act of creation but backwards ("But before the angelical Mind was given the ideas by God, it approached him, and before it approached him, its appetite to approach him was already incensed, and before its appetite was incensed . . . " and so on). Even the functioning of the universe is thus mentioned twice, first as it is acted by God, and, immediately subsequently, as it is acted upon by the created world. In chapter 3 of the First Oratio the first description begins: "Mens angelica . . . " and the second: "Sed idearum conceptionem a formante Deo . . . " (Oratio I, ch. 3, p. 1322).

9 Oratio I, ch. 3, p. 1322.

10 Oratio I, ch. 3, p. 1322.

11 "Amor vero sit fruendae pulchritudinis desiderium: Amor semper mente, oculis, auribus est contentus. Quid olfactu, quid gustu, quid tactu opus est?" (Oratio I, ch. 4, p. 1322).

12 Oratio VI, ch. 2, pp. 1334–35.

13 Oratio VI, ch. 2, pp. 1334–35.

14 "Voluptas itaque, gustus et tactus, quae usque adeo vehementes furiosaeque sunt, ut mentem e suo statu dimoveant hominemque perturbent, amor non modo non cupit sed abominatur." (Oratio I, ch. 4, p. 1322).

15 Oratio I, ch. 4, p. 1323.

16 "Deum namque ipsum ignorant, cuius sapor occultus odorem quaedam sui dulcissimum operibus suis inferuit. Quo quidem ardore quotidie excitamur. Odorem quidem sentimus. Saporem procul dubio ignoramus." (Oratio II, ch. 6, p. 1329).

17 Gismondo's speech is in chapter 30 of Book II, and Lavinello's rebuke is in chapter 6 of Book III (he goes on to say: "alla bellezza dell'animo aggiungere, né fiutando, né toccando, né gustando non si può, così non si può né più né meno eziandio, a quelle del corpo"); see P. Bembo, *Prose e rime*, ed. C. Dionisotti (Torino, 1966).

18 From the third dialogue of Leone Ebreo's, *Dialoghi d'Amore*, ed. S. Caramella (Bari, 1929).

19 In Book IV of *Il libro del cortegiano*, ed. C. Cordie (Milano-Napoli, 1960),

pp. 348–49.

20 G. Betussi, *Il Raverta*, in *Trattati d'amore del Cinquecento*, ed. G. Zonta (Bari, 1968), p. 12; *La Leonora*, ibid., p. 337.

21 Tullia d'Aragona, *Della infinità d'amore*, in *Trattati d'amore del Cinquecento*, p. 230.

22 "Le altre sentimenta [other than sight] possono bene caldo et freddo, tenero et duro; dolce et amaro, odorifero et suo comprendere, ma proportione di parti . . . non mai"; and on the margin Tasso wrote: "la bellezza non altrimenti che guardando e contemplando"; in Flamino Nobili, *Il trattato dell'amore humano, con le postille autografe di Torquato Tasso*, ed. P.D. Pasolini (Roma, 1895), p. 13. The only discordant note that I have found (apart from Equicola) to this unanimous chorus, is Agostino Nifo (about whom see later), who, undoubtedly influenced by Equicola, affirms the possibility of the sense of touch experiencing beauty: "Experientia docet quod aliquando per solum tactum deferatur pulchri species ad animam" (p. 103); adding as an example the case of the delightfulness of bodily contacts with women not beautiful who force ("rapiunt") one to love. We are not astonished, as a consequence, that Nifo received so much opposition to his theories on sensuality.

23 See Santoro's biography for the details. Equicola mentions some of the vicissitudes in the Preface. As a young man he had engaged in no little armed service, and in his maturity, as secretary to Isabella d'Este and then to the reigning Duke of Mantua, had to alternate these duties with diplomatic missions, but also with more war service, which must have been painful as he had grown quite corpulent.

24 It is, in fact, the only section of the treatise to have attracted the attention of a modern editor: see Mario Equicola, *La natura d'amore: Primo Libro*, ed. Neuro Bonifazi (Urbino, 1983).

25 The relevant part (omitting the direct quotations from Ficino) can be found in P.O. Kristeller's *Supplementum Ficinianum* (Florence, 1973), vol. II, pp. 235–36.

26 "Ha quella (natura) datone instincto al quale repugnare nol sapemo di conservare noi stessi in vita, mantenerne in optimo stato di vivere. . . . Questa necessaria et immutabil legge, non fu da homini trovata, non inspirita da potentia celeste . . . ma dal nascimento datane con noi facta, con noi cresciuta, con noi invecchiatasi," pp. 42b–43a.

27 "Ama dunque ciascuno se stesso, et tale amore sempre restando in noi, tanto pare fora extenderse quanto la inclinazione ne tira al utile, al honore o voluptà, percioché pare amemo quelli che di tal cose desiderate ni possono esser datori o auditori in conseguirle," p. 43a.

28 "Examine prima ciascun se stesso et poi circa ciò nostra opinione reprehenda. . . . Pare dura cosa nel primo aspecto de affirmare che noi non amamo se non noi stessi et che per noi mostramo amar altri," p. 43a.

29 "Da natura ne è insito e inseparabilmente dato desiderio di conseguire quel

credemo ci sia bene, ed evitare quello che ne persuademo ci sia male," p. 47b.

30 "Doi crudelissimi tyranni," p. 48; "Lo principio, capo, radice et fonte del appetere o fugire, esser voluptà et dolore," p. 47b. And compare with the first page of Jeremy Bentham's *Principles of Morals and Legislation* for exactly the same concepts and terminology. Of course the basic idea of self-love, "philautia," must have come to Equicola from Aristotle (the discussion is contained in the *Nicomachean Ethics*, IX, 8 (1168a), but also from Cicero's *De officiis*, I, 11: "Principio generi animantium omni est a natura tributum ut se, vita corpusque tuetur declinet ea quae nocitura videantur omniaque quae sint ad vivendum necessaria anquirat et paret." And many of the ideas on pleasure (but also on the connection of the body and soul) may have come from the life of *Aristippus* in the *Lives* of Diogenes Laertius.

31 "Li legislatori quello chiamano iusto . . . che è pubblicamente utile. Per la qual cosa se non volemo dissimulando cavillare, confessaremo noi per la magior parte amar altri per lo amor et benivolenza che havemo a noi medesmi," p. 50b.

32 "Per le patute fatiche le matre amano li figlioli" and "Matre . . . che sia fuor de speranza di non haver . . . honore, victo et amore, subito mutasi . . . et quel che havea più a caro alle volte ha più a vile," p. 52.

33 "Se con acerbe reprehensioni li loro piaceri sono impediti, non solamente li hanno in odio et la morte con desiderio aspectano," p. 52b.

34 "Questo è il vero et più laudabil senza comparazione amor di noi stessi, essendone premio preposto eterno, sempiterna vita, et di veder colui in ciel nome sempre . . . se implora," p. 55b.

35 Chapter LXXII, titled "A philautia non omnem amorem proficisci." I am using the edition of Lyon, 1549.

36 "fertilissime de amore scripsit," p. 91.

37 Furthermore, writes Nifo, if we reduce "good" to "useful," we involve ourselves in a contradiction, because we will always be able to ask of any useful action whether it is good. It is exactly the same argument levelled against utilitarians in contemporary discussions of the issue.

38 "La verità, la quale è: nel nostro corpo non esser doe anime, ma una, la qual il corpo vivifica et ministra ragione." p. 49.

39 "Infermo il corpo, più de le volte se impediscono le operationi de l'anima. Se dole del dolore del corpo, grida et si lamenta. Ha paura di morire, et è immortale. Dubita di mancare, et non pò pater defecto. . . . Se allegra del viso, se allegra de l'harmonia; Se fa giocunda nelli odori, se recrea del gusto, se fa lieta nel tacto," p. 122. Perhaps the image of the soul that complains is a quotation, as suggested above, from Diogenes Laertius' *Aristippus*, in which the school of Hegesias is said to have held that "the soul suffers with the body," *Lives of Eminent Philosophers*, ed. R.D. Hicks (Loeb Classics, 1966), p. 94.

40 "Tria . . . in nobis videntur: anima, spiritus atque corpus. Anima et corpus, natura longe inter se diversa, spiritu medio copulantur, qui vapor quidem est tenuissimus et perlucidus, per cordis calorem ex subtilissima patre sanguinis

genitus." (Oratio VI, ch. 6, p. 1344).

41 "Si generare . . . dicimus, anima tamquam pater . . . ipsum (hominem) augit. . . . Si sentire, anima per sensuum instrumenta, quasi fenestra, percipit . . . " but "Si intelligere, anima per se ipsam sine aliquo corporis veritatem assequitur." (Oratio IV, ch. 3, p. 1322).

42 Hesitations, because the discussion on the soul had started on perfectly orthodox lines: "L'anima dal ciel discesa cosa incorporea, mente incorruttible, spirito immortale . . . alli nostri corpi in terminato tempo infusa. . . . L'anima primo confusamente per lo universale discorre. . . . Appresso lo universale divide in particulari, connecte insieme le differentie . . . ," p. 43b. Does this first description of the soul, which perfectly conforms to platonic philosophy, represent a first stage in Equicola's thought? Or is it the facade under which are hidden the materialistic views that he will carefully develop later?

43 "Chi indusse tanti preclari homini ad tale opinione? Se non vera, verisimile? Se non l'amicizia grande et unione la quale tral corpo vedeano et l'anima," p. 122.

44 I am using Gianfranco Morra's edition (Bologna, 1954).

45 See Santoro's life of Equicola, and, for Pomponazzi and Isabella's interest in him and desire that he be her son's teacher in Bologna, A. Luzio and R. Renier, *La cultura e le relazioni letterarie di Isabella d'Este* (GSLI, 1899), who reproduce also Isabella's letter to Pomponazzi.

46 "Homero la natura de l'anima (secondo alcuni) corporea canta," p. 122.

47 "Ha paura di morire, et è immortale; dubita di mancare et non pò pater defecto," p. 122.

48 "De sensi alcuni credeno principe il tacto," p. 123b.

49 "Vedemo li altri sensi esser dati da natura per ornamento de la essenzia, questo è dato necessario per lo esser," p. 123b.

50 "Havemo il viso ad inventione accomodatissimo, per cognoscere le differentie de le cose, per evitare precipitii. Havemo lo udito apto ad farne scientifici et per prender da altri le discipline. Per l'odorato, da longi sentuto bono odore, convertimo in alimento. Il gusto, come terreo, è, unitamente col tacto, per appetere et refutar le cose, secondo nostra salute recerca," p. 125b.

51 "Questo è causa del nutrimento, il qual è più differente che li altri sensi. Iudica caldo, fredo, umido, secco, grave, leve, duro, molle, aspero et lene. Corrupti li altri sensi, non pate corruptione tutto lo animale; corrupto il tacto manca la vita, ché senza quello, non pò essere né consistere lo animale. Senza tacto la spetie humana et animali perfecti cesseriano," p. 125b.

52 "Se me fosse licito, che la arroganzia di quelli che le parole più notano non me retenesse, diria il tacto essere di tutte quelle parti celesti da Platone etere, da Aristotele quinto elemento nominato," p. 123b.

53 "Usano questi il viso nelle cose naturali et artificiale. Essi belleza di cosa alcuna non discerneno. Noi gratia, colore et proportione di membra dilecta. Lo odito è dato a questi per congregatione. A noi per unirne et che habiamo

piacere de voci et musice harmonie. Hanno lo odorato, acciò sentano lo bono et non bono odore. A l'homo è stato concesso per il medesmo, et per recreare li spirti de varii et suavissimi vapori. Ha quelli natura dotati del gusto, per cognitione de le cose utili et nocive al corpo. Noi per simil effecto, et che se piglie voluptà de varietà de cibi et condimenti diversi," p. 123.

54 "Il tacto è dato a quelli per generare prole et in quella multiplicare. A noi, sì come loro, per augmentare, conservare et mantenere la humana spetie; et che havessemo vario, multiplice et continuo piacere," p. 124.

Lina Bolzoni

The Art of Memory And The Erotic Image in 16th and 17th Century Europe: The Example of Giovan Battista Della Porta

1. Medicines for the Memory

I would like to invite you on a voyage to realms very distant from us, from our experience, and from our sensibility: a voyage into the realms of the art of memory. Today, in fact, it is very difficult for us to imagine even why this art was so assiduously cultivated for centuries in the West, why it was considered literally indispensable and why, particularly in the sixteenth and seventeenth centuries, it fascinated so many men and condensed in itself so many myths.[1]

Not only did the masters of memory in the sixteenth century make direct use of the erotic image in practising their art, but in an even wider sense we find that both the mnemonic techniques and the various remedies for love of the period (designed to curb or to stimulate passion) bring us into a complex territory where body and spirit interact, where medicines are utilized in conjunction with techniques acting on the *imaginatio* to control and to direct the images of the mind.

Let us move on to the person who will be our guide on this voyage—Giovan Battista Della Porta (1525–1615). He was an important scholar and scientist who lived for the greater part of his life in Naples, but who in his youth completed many voyages which took him to Puglia, Calabria, and Venice, and even further afield to France and Spain.[2] He was a central figure in the cultural life of Naples in this period, when political, social and religious tensions were generating an intellectual climate of unusual intensity and vigor. Numerous academies were created which the Spanish viceroys as quickly tried to suppress; books prohibited by the Inquisition circulated widely; and magic, scientific research, astrology, and the expectations of a universal renewal were to be found closely intertwined. Such personages as Giordano Bruno and Tommaso Campanella passed formative periods of their lives in Naples, and it was there that the young Giovan Battista Marino recorded his first literary experiences.[3]

This complex culture was mirrored in the work of Della Porta, which was destined to enjoy an enormous fame throughout Europe. Not only was he an impassioned investigator into the infinite secrets of nature through his role as magician, alchemist, and expert in optics, hydraulics and agriculture, but he was also a student of cipher languages and a prolific writer for the theater.[4] With these wide-ranging interests, Della Porta cultivated a vast network of friends and associates throughout Italy and Europe. Under the patronage of Cardinal Luigi d'Este, he frequented the circles of Fulvio Orsini in Rome; in Venice he became a friend of Sarpi's; he helped Cardinal Federico Borromeo to set up his famous library; and he corresponded regularly with the great naturalist, Ulisse Aldrovandi of Bologna. The emperor Rudolph II was also his patron and corresponded with him, and the young prince Federico Cesi asked him to collaborate in the founding of the Accademia dei Lincei, that illustrious academy of which Galileo was also a member.[5]

As the exponent of a culture undergoing profound transformation, a culture thus characterised by a curious mixture of the old and the new, Della Porta also occupied himself with the art of memory in various contexts and using a multiplicity of approaches. Let us first examine his medical and naturalistic approach. In the work *Fisonomia dell'uomo*, the problem of memory appears several times; it is treated from various points of view reflecting Della Porta's struggle to organise the vast and somewhat chaotic mass of material which he had at hand. In Book I, chapter 8, a good memory is taken to be an important indication of the nature of a man's temperament, the "complexion" of his brain, and, consistent with this orientation, Della Porta significantly places "imaginatione, cogitatione e memoria" side by side.[6]

In Book V, which is a veritable museum of physiognomies, a gallery of the various human types, we find in chapter 8 the "figura dell'huomo ricordevole e smentichevole" [the face of a man gifted with a retentive memory and that of another prone to forgetfulness] accompanied by a careful description of the physical signs which characterise these two types. In Book VI, chapter 2, after an ample review of the relationship between memory and the temperament of the brain, we find various recipes useful in treating forgetfulness. In these pages, a good memory is linked to a moderately humid complexion of the brain. Too much humidity, however, may induce a dangerous melancholy, and, while humidity renders one more receptive to "phantasms," or the mental representations of real objects, these images which are so easily impressed on the memory may disappear with equal ease. Conversely, a dry brain may be a sign of great intelligence, but an excessive dryness, while guaranteeing the conservation of memories, on the other hand, renders learning difficult. As proof of the link between a humid temperament and a retentive memory, Della Porta reminds us of the fact that we learn and remember much more easily during those periods of our lives and in those parts of the day where humidity prevails; that is, during our youth (our ability ever diminishing as we grow older, until we reach the final decay of dry old age) and in the morning, when sleep (as Hippocrates and Aristotle taught us) has restored humidity to the brain.

The portrait of the "uomo ricordevole" is derived from the pseudo-Aristotelian work *Fisiognomica*: the upper parts of his body are small, well-arranged, and "dimostrano poco vapore per la siccità del cervello" [show little vapour due to the dryness of the brain]; "carnose, non grasse, ma ben vestite di carne" [fleshy, not fatty, but well encased in flesh]. To this portrait is appended an amusing note by Della Porta: "gli giongemo noi l'orecchie grandi" [we added the large ears].[7]

The remedies against forgetfulness proposed in Book VI are of various types; we can find in it recipes for making pills, for preparing decoctions to be dissolved in water and used to wash the head or the feet, advice on diet and food ("guardarsi di carne di castrato, che per occulta proprietà rovina la memoria, da i cibi fumosi, come agli, porri, cipolle e legumi" [avoid the meat of the wether, which due to its occult properties may weaken the memory, and also vapour-producing foods such as garlic, leeks, onions and other vegetables]), and on sleep ("fuggire il molto dormire, le lunghe vigilie" [avoid both too much sleep and overlong vigils]). He also explains how to prepare an ointment to be spread "nella parte di dietro del capo [over the back of the head] . . . perché è stato conosciuto per esperienza che [è] quella parte del cervello dove risiede la memoria" [because it has been learned from experience that it is in this part of the brain that memory resides].[8] Della Porta here revives an antique conception which placed the faculty of memory in a precise location within the brain.

Similar recipes to improve the memory are presented as part of the countless secrets contained in the work *Magia naturale*; in proposing them Della Porta declares that he has included only the most efficacious of these among the many remedies available. Evidently there existed a flourishing market for these types of medicines, but our author seems disposed to keep his distance from them: "gli altri secreti vedi nella Phitognomica nostra, che ve ne sono assai. Ma io loderei l'arte del ricordare, che è assai meglio che porsi a rischio d'impazzirne, e io n'ho scritto un libretto, che va assai a torno" [there are many other secrets contained in my *Phitognomica*. But I would recommend practising the art of memory, which is vastly preferable to subjecting oneself to the risk of going mad through the use of medicaments, and on this subject I have written a short book which has enjoyed much success].[9] Della Porta is here referring to a treatise of his which was first published in the Italian vernacular in 1566 called *L'arte del ricordare*; an expanded version in Latin, embellished with a considerable iconographic apparatus, came out in 1602 and was entitled *Ars reminiscendi* (fig. 1). In the excerpt quoted above we see Della Porta (even if he was primarily motivated by the desire to publicise his own book) warning the reader of the very real dangers connected with certain drugs for the memory, drugs which were very popular at the time, but which "posed the risk of driving one mad." His comments here are all the more interesting when we contrast them with the preface to Book VI of his *Fisonomia dell'uomo*, in which he exalts the wonderful efficacy of certain medicines in controlling the passions and vices of man. In earlier works, Della Porta writes, he has demonstrated how one may recognise from certain outward physical signs a man's innermost moral character, and:

> resta che in questo ultimo libro si tratta di cosa più mirabilissima, e degnissima di questa, nuova e degna d'esser amata e desiderata, cioè che conosciuti i tuoi o gl'altrui vitii, possi levarli via e scancellarli del tutto. A che dunque ci gioveria questa arte, se conosciuti i tuoi difetti, non potessi quegli convertirgli in virtudi? Ma ciò non con pensieri, imaginationi, o persuasioni di morali filosofi, che per lo più vane riescono, ma con purgationi, locali rimedii, e natural virtù di herbe, pietre et animali, et occulte proprietadi.
>
> [it thus remains for this last book to deal with that thing which is most admirable and most worthy of this art since, once you are acquainted with your own faults or those of others, it becomes possible to remove and eliminate them all. Still, what benefit may be derived from this art if, even with full knowledge of all your defects, you are unable to convert them into virtues? For it is not with thinking, imaginings, or the persuasions of the moral philosophers, for the most part worthless, that you will succeed, but rather with the purgatives, local remedies and the natural virtues of herbal, mineral and animal essences and their occult properties.][10]

This is a revealing passage. In order to defend himself against the accusations of the Inquisition, Della Porta affirms repeatedly that his principles of physiognomy do not contradict the Church's doctrine of free will and that man, gifted with reason and volition, could always find the way to salvation. However, the contrast which Della Porta presents in this passage between the efficacious remedies offered by "natural magic" to combat the vices of man, and the nostrums, "for the most part useless" prescribed by the "moral philosophers," reveals instead his genuine convictions.

The very potency of these "natural" remedies, their capacity to act not only on a physical but also on a psychic and moral plane, carried yet another source of risk, however. Numerous passages from the works and the personal correspondence of Della Porta testify to the admirably detached spirit of inquiry with which he carried out his investigations into drugs and poisons, conducted for the most part on slaves, but at times extended to unfortunate friends as well. For example, the second chapter of Book VIII of his *Magia naturale* is entitled "come si possino far impazir gli huomini per un giorno" [how one may drive men mad for one day], and describes what Della Porta assures us is "un giocondo spettacolo" [the merry spectacle] of hapless subjects who, after having swallowed a concoction based on belladonna, believe themselves to be fishes or birds: "ricordo che essendo giovane sperimentava queste cose ne' schiavi di casa mia" [I remember how in my youth I used to experiment with these substances on the slaves in our household]. Some of them floundered desperately, believing themselves to be drowning, and another thought he was an ox in the midst of a herd of cattle, and as a result "gli pareva ch'era percosso con le corna da loro" [it seemed to him that he was being struck by their horns].[11]

These studies carried out by Della Porta and his friends on the effects of certain medicines on the psyche or, to use Della Porta's term, the "imaginationi," were thus a curious mixture of pure scientific research and a cruel sort of game, a detached and uninhibited *divertissement*. The passage from *Magia naturale* which was cited earlier is one of the few occasions in which the limits to the remedies offered by "magia naturale" are considered. Thus, after cautioning the reader that certain drugs for the memory could drive one mad, Della Porta invites him to adopt another technique, one that would act directly on the mind rather than on the body and its "temperament." In contrast to the "essentially worthless" remedies offered by the moral philosophers, those of the art of memory have behind them centuries of proven efficacy, and a large part of them are guaranteed—Della Porta assures us—by long practice in these arts by the author himself.

2. *Memory and the Interplay of Images (*ut pictura poesis *and* ut pictura memoria*)*

In Della Porta's treatise on mnemonics we can find only the briefest of allusions to the fact that diet and medicine may improve the memory; in fact, here he moves on to an entirely different plane, that of the construction of *loci* and of *imagines agentes*. Within the tradition of the art of memory, the writings of Della Porta are not particularly innovative; we see little of that complex thread of magic and encyclopaedism, or any of the other new ideas which were animating the sixteenth-century revival of the arts. He took as his basis only the most orthodox components of the tradition; that is, the necessity of establishing an ordered series of *loci*, each of which was to be invested with a set of *imagines* that were capable of linking to themselves, via the complex interplay of associations, those concepts and words that had been consigned to them, so that they could later be recalled when needed. However, as so frequently came about in works of this nature, Della Porta's treatise, apparently made up only of the most traditional of components, in fact became something more and different than a simple sum of its parts. Conventional ingredients were recombined in intriguing new ways, resulting in a work that reflected not only the artistic and literary experiences of the author, but various new orientations in the tastes and sensibility of the period as well.

The iconographic apparatus of Della Porta's treatise *Ars reminiscendi*[12] includes figured numbers (fig. 2) and alphabets (fig. 3), as well as a complete sonnet rebus (fig. 4), all of this material freely plundered from other texts, in keeping with the piratical tradition which characterised so many of the contemporary publishing houses. This material carries us directly into a realm where the art of memory intersects with the language of ciphers, and with experimentation in "poesia per gioco" [poetry for amusement].[13] Here we find Della Porta engaging in a search for a new language, one that would unite the visual and the legible where fragments of word and image could coexist.

This reduction of the literary text to pure writing, and its elements to material objects cunningly arranged on the page so as to lend themselves to elaborate metamorphoses and divers recombinations, not only forms the basis of the sonnet rebus, but plays a primary role in the treatise itself. It made possible the transformation of the topos of *ut pictura poesis* into something which may be called *ut pictura memoria*. The processes that are set into motion by the art of memory are, in fact, continually compared by Della Porta to those triggered by the visual image: the *imaginatio* which transmits images to the memory, he says, is like the artist who paints these images on a canvas. The scholar who subsequently recalls the previously fixed images to mind in order to use them is similar to a painter restoring a work faded and ruined by the passage of time, and so on. In order to remember the story line of a poem or theatre piece, Della Porta instructs us to fix the salient moments in a series of mental "pictures" which follow one another in a predetermined order, corresponding to the *dispositio* (action) of the text.

This section of Della Porta's treatise is of great interest because it offers vivid testimony regarding a certain attitude which characterised the culture of sixteenth- and seventeenth-century Europe. The literary text came to be visualised and actually projected into space, *ut pictura poesis* developing into an analogy between the poem and an edifice decorated with images, between the poem and a gallery. Galileo, for example, compared *Orlando furioso* to "una guardaroba, una tribuna, una galleria regia, ornata di cento statue antiche de' più celebri scultori, con infinite storie intere, e le migliori dei pittori illustri" [a guardaroba, a tribune, a royal gallery decorated with a hundred antique statues by the most celebrated sculptors, and paintings recounting entire stories in infinite number, by the best and most illustrious of painters].[14] We know that these analogies did not exist solely in a limbo of literary metaphor, but were amply sustained by the visual experience of the period; it should suffice to recall the vast art collections of the sixteenth century in which the figurative and the literary traditions mirrored one another, or the great fresco cycles created for the villas and palaces of the period.

Della Porta combined this interlacing of picture and poetry with the more practical dimension of the mnemonic art. For his purposes he did not hesitate to borrow heavily (and without suitable acknowledgement) from one of the most famous treatises on painting of the late fifteenth century—*De pictura* by Leon Battista Alberti, a widely disseminated and highly influential work, which just in this period came to be translated into the vernacular. The part of the treatise which Della Porta copied almost word for word was a section describing the procedure which a painter must follow in order to represent a *historia*; in fact, where the artist is seeking to concentrate an entire narrative sequence in a single scene.[15]

We can see in this act of plagiarism by Della Porta a cultural process come full circle. Alberti, the refined humanist, had adapted to painting in its various phases the same rhetorical system that tradition had reserved for literary compositions; thus, he succeeded in re-elaborating the topos of *ut pictura poesis* in such a way as to bestow on the painter the same dignity as the poet. Della Porta re-uses Alberti's ideas in the context of the art of memory; here the mannerist code serves to associate, from a rhetorical point of view, the experience of the poet with that of the painter and that of the practitioner of the art of memory.

It is also interesting to examine the strong component of the theatre which characterises the art of memory in Della Porta. In his choice of *imagines agentes*, in fact, he limits himself exclusively to images of persons, carefully instructing the reader on how to construct a veritable miniature theatre of the mind. To begin, he says, we must first fix a suitable series of *loci*, and then arrange in these *loci* the personages we wish to utilise, placing them in sequential order based on precise criteria (for example, by age). They must be posed with their arms hanging, and standing against a wall, either completely nude or dressed in white. Since the play is about to begin and our actors, or more exactly our marionettes, will be transformed into *imagines agentes*, we must re-animate them. Their faces must take on expression, their arms and legs and hands must be disposed in appropriate positions and gestures, they must be dressed in clothing of various pattern and colour, and significant objects should be placed either in their hands or nearby. Absolutely nothing, he notes, ought to be left to chance; gestures, expression, clothing and colours all must be associated with each figure in a manner that is not only convincing, but that also closely reflects the exact type of the personage before us, adapting itself to his mores—that is, to his physical, moral and psychological characteristics.

We see once again how the rhetorical canons of the period permitted a complex interlinking between literary experience, artistic experience, and the art of memory. By the second half of the sixteenth century the typology of mores was already well-established in contemporary treatises. In particular, the rebirth of the "commedia classica" led naturally to the widespread use of certain highly topical personalities (the young lover, the old man, either in his role as miser or rendered ridiculous in love, the sponger, the braggart soldier, etc.). Their mores, the particular physical characteristics and behaviour which formed the basis for the various "maschere" (types) of the commedia dell'arte, were quite familiar to Della Porta, as may be seen from his plays.

The painter has an analogous problem to that of the practitioner of the art of memory, for he too is seeking to depict his figures in such a way that their outward visual aspect transmits a conception of their internal disposition according to a code which is common to both the artist and his public. The art treatises of the second half of the sixteenth century shed a very interesting light on this theme, particularly since this period is also marked by the popular use of ever more broad and varied systems of types: one need only consider the prevailing vogue for caricatures, for ugly, deformed and monstrous faces, and for those "pitture ridicole" which were linked to the lowly characters of the commedia dell'arte.[16]

Thus, when Della Porta writes that the art of memory requires a thorough knowledge of the "personarum mores," he is demanding a skill identical to that of the painter or writer. At the same time, because the creative processes involved were so similar, and because a highly evolved typology of mores was already to be found in the literary and artistic works of the period, the practitioner of the art of memory could draw directly on this large depository whenever he was in need of *imagines agentes.* In fact, Ovid, Virgil, Titian and Michelangelo are specifically cited by Della Porta as potential sources of mnemonic images. He also suggests using the repertoire of mythography, the hieroglyphics of the pseudo-Orus Apollo as annotated by Piero Valeriano, and the other great dictionaries of images from this period which presented antique tradition, filtered and fragmented into mosaic *tesserae* ready for use by the artist and scholar.[17]

3. The Typology of Mores: Between Body and Spirit, Between Nature and Culture

The art of memory as conceived by Della Porta operates on the level of mental images using a sophisticated re-elaboration of traditional ingredients. It would seem therefore to be located on a completely different plane from those techniques which were discussed earlier, where diet and medicines were prescribed to treat the memory. If we look more closely, however, we see that this dichotomy is only an apparent one. Instead of treating separately the territories of the body and the spirit, a large part of Della Porta's work is dedicated to retracing the "signs" that unite these two realms, the paths that bring them into communication with one another, and that we must follow if we wish to act on the body or the spirit or both.

For example, Della Porta insists that an intimate knowledge of the mores which characterise the various human types is absolutely essential to the practice of the art of memory. In his mnemonic treatise, the typology of mores is drawn from a wide variety of cultural sources—iconographic, literary, and mythological. However, as we examine his other works, we realise that Della Porta's cultural sources do not offer an exhaustive catalogue; he has, rather, used the systems of mores already in existence—

neatly sorted, well-established in the collective memory, they offered a convenient source of images ready for use.

In contrast, the sources utilized by Della Porta for his work *Fisonomia dell'uomo* are much broader and much more interesting. Here he is attempting to retrace the physical signs which would permit one to individuate the moral and psychological qualities of a man, to penetrate into his innermost parts and thereby to realize the ancient Socratic dream of a window opening onto the very heart. Thus, the *Fisonomia dell'uomo*, as we have already noted, offers a rich and comprehensive gallery of the various human types, together with the mores which distinguish them one from the other. Significantly, the typology of sources which he draws upon is very wide. Della Porta integrates those conceptions contained in the already existing tradition of physiognomy with his own direct analyses of various subjects—for example, the cadavers of men who, as he explains in *Chirofisonomia*, in their lives had given free license to their baser natures. To this end he studied the bodies of the hanged, and others who had died violent deaths; he describes in analytical detail the bodies of prostitutes; and he frequented the public hospitals and prisons where, as he wrote "è racchiusa gran moltitudine de' facinorosi, ladri, parricidi, assassini di strada" [were confined great numbers of ruffians, thieves, parricides, highway assasins].[18] These observations, more or less pre-Lombrosian in nature, were interwoven with others derived from the animal world, where the connection between physical form (as pertaining to a particular species) and character appeared to be clear, distinct, and immutable—and therefore easily decipherable.

This diverting interplay of reflections in the mirror held up between the animal world and the human was not limited by Della Porta solely to an analysis of criminal types, however, for he believed that instructive analogies could be drawn for all types of men. To reconstruct this complex system, he had recourse to elements derived from literary tradition: the descriptions of typical personages from the theatre, novels, and poetry; the allegorical images created by poets and artists; the descriptions of important figures handed down to us by historians, and the direct testimony provided by antiquity (in the form of coins, statues, bas reliefs, etc.). Here the task of analysing these mores was facilitated, and the result in a certain sense guaranteed, for the course of these great personages from history has already been run and all one needed to do was to re-connect—as symbol to its signification—the physical traits of these figures with those moral qualities which had influenced their destinies. Since Della Porta believed, however, that the roots of man's most significant physical traits were actually to be found in the animal world, he established a kind of "double gallery" in which a "scientific" portrait of an animal was paired with that of a historical personage copied from antique collections (figs. 5–6).[19] For his physiognomies, in fact, he drew on the vast repositories provided by both nature and cultural tradition. From this chaotic and fragmented mass of material, Della Porta isolated those elements which could enable one to reconstruct the strands of the complex chain of correspondences and the vast network of "signs."

4. The Magic Power of the Image

According to Della Porta, the human world could trace its roots back directly to the animal world. Therefore, through an apposite analysis of the mores of a man (his psychological disposition and moral habits) one should be able, not only to penetrate the rapport between the body and the spirit, but also to glimpse, behind and inside him, the figures of the animals which he resembles.

Here we are treading on slippery ground, however, for a study of similitudes not only permits one to recognise the network of correspondences, but—tied as it is to the overpowering magical force of the image—it may actually bring about strange metamorphoses. One need only recall the mythical figure of Circe who so fascinated the late sixteenth-century world; this sorceress, with her ability to transform men into beasts, was actually doing nothing more than bringing to light pre-existing similitudes, images already latent in these men. Della Porta himself shows that the boundaries between the animal world and the human could be precarious. The fact that a human being may be like a certain animal implies the possibility that he may actually become that animal should the force of his passions overwhelm him. In *Fisonomia dell'uomo*, Della Porta revives certain elements which were already well-established in the tradition of lovesickness,[20] endowing them, however, with a magical meaning. He cites, for example, "licantropia" and "cinantropia," the antique conceptions of a malady in which man may assume the form and characteristics of a wolf (lycanthropy) or a dog as extreme examples of the reciprocal influence existing between body and spirit: "Nella cinantropia e licantropia infermitade, il volto si muta in cane, gli occhi divengono infocati; con grigni minacciosi e naso acuto, escono di notte, vanno intorno i sepochri, né si sente altro da loro che latrare, ringhire, et altre cose che raccontano Aetio e Paulo Egineto." [In the maladies of lycanthropy and "cinantropia," the face transforms itself into that of a beast, the eyes become inflamed;

with keen noses and threatening grimaces they venture forth at night, roaming among the sepulchres, and one hears naught but their howls and their growls, and other things as recounted by Aetius and Paulus Aegineta]."[21]

In an analogous way—precisely because they are impressed into the very structure of the individual and form potent *signaturae* linking the body with the spirit—these mores may function autonomously, transmitting their essences as if by contagion, much like a sickness, or like the magnet which can transfer its properties to the inert substance iron. In *Magia naturale* for example, Della Porta declares that the qualities of impudence and lustfulness which characterise the prostitute may communicate themselves to the mirrors and the articles of clothing which she habitually uses, and may thence spread to all who come into contact with these objects.[22]

Following a traditional doctrine (one strongly indebted to Avicenna), Della Porta designates the *imaginatio* as the point of intersection between physical reality and the reality of the psyche. It is there that the "phantasms" or images of things come to be deposited: it is there that our perception of external reality takes form and is incorporated into our internal world, with whatever positive—or devastating—effects this may have. Conversely, and especially through the power of concentration and the irresistable pressure of desire, the *imaginatio* can transform the very nature of reality, constraining outward form to mutate according to one's will. The *imaginatio* is the place where man succumbs to the power of enchantment and spells, and from there he may in turn project these magical forces outward.

The *imaginatio* also has a primary role to play in the process of falling in love. According to the most widespread medical doctrines of the period, which Della Porta himself shared, tiny visual "spiritelli" (sprites) may fly from the eyes of the beloved directly to the heart of the lover; seated there, they go to work reconstructing the form, the very image, of the beloved object. Thus, in the *imaginatio* a species of animated statue is created, a living phantom which must be continually nourished, even if—as in the case of unhappy love—it brings the ill-fated lover to madness and death. This conception of love suggests to our author various remedies designed to treat the physical and psychological ills brought about when the passions are unable to find their proper outlet. At the same time this concept functions on a rhetorical plane; in the theatre, for example, it contributed to enrich the topos (also traditional in the love lyric) of the beloved woman whose image is engraved on the heart of her faithful lover. "Mi doglio," says Erotico in Della Porta's *Sorella*, "ch'io non posso aperto mostrarle il cuore, ch'ivi vedrebbe risplendere la sua bella imagine, come in un lucido e polito specchio, e star tanto occupato e ripieno di quella, che non v'è più luogo per altre, e che son chiuse le vie a tutte" [I'm sorry that I cannot open and show her my heart, where she would see shining forth her resplendent and beautiful image, as if in a bright and polished mirror; it is so taken up and filled with this image that there is no longer space for others and the way is closed to all]. Soon afterwards he adds that even if he cannot see his beloved, he constantly speaks with her due to the "continua memoria che ho di lei, e quel ritratto, che mi sta nel cuore dipinto per man di amore col pennello della imaginazione, sta più vivo nel mio cuore, che non ci sta l'anima istessa" [the constant memory that I have of her, and that portrait which dwells in my heart, painted by the hand of love with the brush of the imagination, she remains more alive in my heart than my very own soul].[23] We see in this way how medicine and philosophy contribute to enrich the conceptual variations of a literary image.

5. *Images of Love and Images of the Memory*

To return to the theme which was the starting point of our voyage, it seems clear that Della Porta considered the two modes of treatment—one acting on the body through the agency of medicines, diet and drugs, and the other acting on the mind through the use of mental images—not as two parallel and separate paths, but rather as two different means of operating on a single reality. And both of these approaches could be used, not only to treat the human passions, but to act on the memory, as well. In fact he observes that the art of mnemonics is located in a region somewhere between instinct and rationality, between the conscious and the unconscious, where the free play of associations in the mind is at the same time countered by forces attempting to block and control them.

However, there are even more profound and specific ties linking the phantasms of love and the images of the memory. The phantasm of the beloved person feeds on recurrent and obstinate memory; thus the love lyric has from its very origins been used to express the anguish of the lover suffering from the lack of a single moment of respite, of forgetfulness. On the other hand, the practitioners of the art of memory, who were constantly in search of new *imagines agentes*—images which could stimulate the emotions and thus effectively reactivate the chain of memories—quickly realised that the erotic image could be exploited to great advantage in this context.

Della Porta introduces this aspect in his work *Arte del ricordare*; we read, in a chapter dedicated to *loci*:

Nec mihi videor persuadere tam hebetis ingenii hominem posse reperiri, quin per locum transiens, in quo ei aliquid vel summe bonum, vel malum evenerit, illico illius rei non recordari; Darii equus per locum transiens, ubi pridie ante conflictus diem equae admissus fuit, cognito loco, ex Veneris voluptate, hinniit, et faelix auspicium domino dedit, ut Darium Persarum regem salutarint.

[I cannot imagine the man so insensible and stupid that, when passing by a certain place, he will not remember, even if he has no wish to do so, things which he may have done or which may have happened to him there, however pleasant or unpleasant they may have been. The horse of Darius, passing on the eve of a battle by that place where it had earlier made love to a mare, immediately recalled this fact and neighed loudly, thus giving an auspicious sign to his rider that he would afterwards be crowned king of Persia.][24]

Thus, we see that the association of place and erotic scene may be extremely evocative; in humans this linkage functions automatically, but the same phenomenon may be encountered in the animal world, as well.

It is therefore clear that this technique may be used as an extremely effective tool in the practice of the art of memory, although it is equally clear that one must try to avoid such types of associations when one is seeking to forget. Already in *Remedia amoris*, Ovid counsels the bereaved lover to remove all portraits of the beloved and to keep his distance from those places where he has made love to her.[25] Ariosto's Orlando reaches the stage of desperation, clinically speaking the stage subsequent to that of unhappy love, precisely when he finds himself in that place where Angelica and Medoro had earlier made love. Our hero's situation is triggered when he comes into contact with the evocative signs emitted by the fountains, cottages, and trees around him, and even more exactly at that moment when the story is recounted to him by the shepherd, thus lending to these images an inescapable meaning, and transforming them into devastating internal phantasms.[26]

In Della Porta's treatise, consistent with his original premises, he describes the highly satisfactory results which may be obtained when one uses as *imagines agentes* the images of young maidens, since these may give rise to memories of the most pleasant kind:

Mox qui eiusmodi regulas periclitabitur, videbit quanta iucunditate et animi hilaritate ad loca pervenitur, ubi amatae et optatae personae repositae sint, et qualiter universa memoria commoveatur: nam ubi usuales aegre et negligenter, illae duos integros versus vel totius sententiam praestabunt.

[He who puts our rules to the test will see, if he makes association with a certain place a person whom he has enjoyed or desired, how clearly and easily this association will call forth an entire verse or even two, whereas other persons will bring back the memory of just one word]. Further on he recommends that one arrange in the *loci* "da diece a venti donne bellissime, le quali habbiamo godute, o amate, o reverite" [ten or twenty beautiful women, whom we have possessed or loved or revered.][27]

In justifying his technique, Della Porta could have invoked, not only his own personal experience, but the tradition of the art of memory itself. He might have cited, for example, Pietro da Ravenna, the great fifteenth century jurisconsult who wrote a treatise on mnemonics, *Phoenix*, which enjoyed a considerable vogue throughout Europe during the sixteenth century. Da Ravenna declared: "Ego communiter pro literis formosissimas puellas pono: illae enim multum memoriam meam excitant" [I generally arrange, in place of the letters of the alphabet, a series of beautiful maidens; this, in fact, helps greatly to stimulate my memory].[28] He goes on to add that, from his youth onwards, he has always used the image of a beloved young maiden to help him to remember things. In this way, he assures us, everything becomes less arduous and more pleasant; it is an expedient of great efficacy which only modesty has prevented him from revealing earlier. Of course, this technique would not serve one who hates and despises women: "sed isti huius fructus difficilius consequentur" [but they will find it more difficult to profit from this art]. In other words, to men who are hard of heart or cold in temperament, insensible to the enchantments of feminine beauty, the paths of the art of memory are closed as well, since this technique demands an impressionable *imaginatio*, one sensitive to the interactions between the areality of the senses and the interior world of the mind.

The use of lovely young maidens as a mnemonic support must have become quite commonplace if in 1603, during the height of the Counter Reformation, the Franciscan Minorite, Gerolamo Marafioto of Calabria, in his *Ars memoriae* felt no hesitation in advising the reader to go forth into the streets, to look attentively at the most charming girls, and to fix in his mind their gestures and the movements of their bodies, using these as *imagines agentes*. He himself had tested the efficacy of this technique, although only towards the most edifying of ends, of course; for example, to recall the soul he used the nude image of a beautiful girl whom he had known.[29]

Fair maidens who have been loved, or even simply desired, were not the only component present in the erotic imagination of Della Porta's treatise.

In fact, he departs from the traditional precept which denotes as *imagines agentes* any image which may act effectively on the emotions, going on to develop new typologies which reflected a decided taste for the comic, the grotesque, the cruel, and even the obscene. In his search for efficacious images, he resolutely set aside any inhibitions or concern for the dictates of decorum or lofty idealism. We will remember, he remarks, the story of the love between the matron and the ass, as recounted by Apuleius, much better than any of the tales of heroism of the ancient Romans. And thus

> si amantis meminisse voluero, non figurabo loci personam egregiis vestibus ornatam, comptamque suspirantem, et similia, quae nobilem amantem decent, sed configurabo qualem Ovidius Polyphemum describit, falce radentem barbam et rastro caput pectentem, in aqua se speculantem atque inusitato musices instrumenti genere pulsare et canere. Nam si ridiculosas configurationes imaginibus accomodabimus, faciemus ut rerum facilius meminisse possimus.
>
> [If I wish to remember a lover, I won't imagine a well-dressed and well-groomed figure, sighing and doing all the other things proper to a gentleman in love, but rather would depict him as Ovid described Polifemus in love, shaving himself with a scythe, combing his hair with a rake, regarding his reflection in the water and playing a musical instrument of strange form, and singing. Because this image is so ridiculous, it will stimulate all the more easily my memory.]

Laughter, as he explains earlier, "nascitur . . . ex admiratione, inhonesta et egregia aliqua turpitudine insignia, potius memoriam commovent quam honesta et bona" [is born of marvels and it is things unreal and ugly that make us laugh, rather than good and beautiful things]. "Horribilia et terribilia etiam recordandi praebent ansam, nam nostrum animum percutiunt terrentque: potius eorum meminimus, qui horribili carnificina, quam qui febri, aut peculiari aliqua pereunt infirmitate" [Horrible and frightening things give us even more reason to remember, because the horribleness of the fact remains impressed upon the spirit for a longer time; we remember much more vividly those who have died the most atrocious deaths by the hand of justice than those who have died of the fever or other sickness].[30]

Therefore love, above all in its obscene and grotesque aspects, and the shivers of pleasure to be derived from cruel and bloody spectacles, appear to offer the most effective sources of images to animate the interior theatre of the memory. Della Porta shows that he fully shares in the sensibility of his age, which was one characterised not only by an edifying taste for knowledge, but also by the sophisticated tastes of the slightly bored and spoiled spectator. These influenced his observations and experimentation in those complex areas where—as in memory and in love—the body and the psyche meet and interact.

Università di Pisa

NOTES

1 Two works which have become classics in the field of the history of the art of memory are: Paolo Rossi, *Clavis universalis. Arti della memoria e logica combinatoria da Lullo a Leibniz* (Milan and Naples: Ricciardi, 1960), and A. Frances Yates, *The Art of Memory* (London: Routledge and Kegan Paul, 1966). Cfr., as well, Morris N. Young, *Bibliography of Memory* (Philadelphia and New York: Chilton Company, 1961), and Lina Bolzoni, *Il teatro della memoria. Studi su Giulio Camillo* (Padova: Liviana, 1984), and "Memento. Tecniche della memoria e dell'oblio," *Kos*, 30, 3 (April-May 1987).

2 Biographical information on Della Porta may be found in: Francesco Fiorentino, "Della vita e delle opere di Giovan Battista de la Porta," in *Studi e ritratti della Rinascenza* (Bari: Laterza, 1911), pp 235–93; Giuseppe Gabrieli, "Giovan Battista Della Porta Linceo. Da documenti per gran parte inediti," *Giornale critico della filosofia italiana*, 8 (1927), pp. 360–97; and Giovanni Aquilecchia, "Appunti su G.B. Della Porta e l'Inquisizione," *Studi secenteschi*, 9 (1978), pp. 3–31.

3 On the cultural life of Naples during this period, cfr. Nicola Badaloni, "Fermenti di vita intellettuale a Napoli dal 1500 alla metà del '600," in *Storia di Napoli*, V, 2 (Naples: Società Editrice Storia di Napoli, 1972), pp. 643–89; Lina Bolzoni, "Note su Giulio Cortese. Per uno studio delle accademie napoletane di fine 1500," *La rassegna della letteratura italiana*, 77, no. 3 (1973), pp. 475–99; Amadeo Quondam, *La parola nel labirinto. Società e scrittura del Manierismo a Napoli* (Bari: Laterza, 1975); M. Simona Pezzica, "Una galleria di intellettuali nel poema inedito di Giulio Cortese," *La rassegna della letteratura italiana*, 88, nos. 1–2 (1984), pp. 117–45.

4 On Della Porta as magician and naturalist, see Antonio Corsano, "Per la storia del pensiero del tardo Rinascimento, III. G.B. Della Porta," *Giornale critico della filosofia italiana*, 38 (1959), pp. 76–97; Nicola Badaloni, "I fratelli Della Porta e la cultura magica e astrologica a Napoli nel '500," *Studi storici* 1 (1959–60), pp. 677–715; Luisa Muraro, *G.B. Della Porta: mago e scienziato* (Milan: Feltrinelli, 1978); Gabriella Belloni, "Conoscenza magica e ricerca scientifica," forward to G.B. Della Porta, *Criptologia*, Gabriella Belloni, ed. (Rome: Centro internazionale di studi umanistici, 1982). On Della Porta's works for the theatre, see Louise G. Clubb, *G.B. Della Porta: Dramatist* (Princeton: Princeton University Press, 1965); Raffaele Sirri, *L'attività teatrale di G.B. Della Porta* (Naples: De Simone, 1968); Paola Gherardini, "Problemi critici e metodologici per lo studio del teatro di G.B. Della Porta," *Biblioteca teatrale*, 1 (1971), pp. 137–59; Carmelo Greco, "G.B. Della Porta fra improvvisazione e tradizione comica," *Critica letteraria*, 2 (1974), pp. 240–75; Giovanni Iovane, "Fantasia

verbale e manipolazione linguistica nella commedia di G.B. Della Porta," *Critica letteraria*, 11 (1983), pp. 313–34.

5 Information on Della Porta's extensive network of friends and colleagues may be found in the references already cited above. See, in addition: Giuseppe Campori, "Gio. Battista Della Porta e il Cardinale Luigi d'Este," *Atti e memorie della R. Deputazione di Storia Patria per le Provincie Modenesi e Parmensi*, 6 (1872), pp. 165–90; Giuseppe Gabrieli, "Federico Borromeo e gli Accademici Lincei," *Acta Pontificiae Academiae Scietiarum Novi Lyncaei*, 87 (1933–34), pp. 164–83; Robert W.J. Evans, *Rudolf II and his World. A Study in Intellectual History. 1576–1612* (Oxford: Clarendon Press, 1973); Giuseppe Gabrieli, "Il 'Linceo' di Napoli. Lincei e linceabili napoletani. Amici e corrispondenti della vecchia Academia dei Lincei nel Mezzogiorno d'Italia," *Rendiconti della R. Accademia Nazionale dei Lincei, Classe di scienze morali, storiche e filosofiche*, 6.14 (1938), pp. 499–565; Giuseppe Olmi, "'In essercitio universale di contemplatione, e prattica': Federico Cesi e i Lincei," in *Università, Accademie e Società scientifiche in Italia e in Germania dal Cinquecento al Settecento*, Laetitia Boehm and Ezio Raimondi, eds. (Bologna: Il Mulino, 1981), pp. 69–235.

6 Giovan Battista Della Porta, *Della fisonomia dell'uomo* (Padova: Pietro Paolo Tozzi, 1627), 10r. Concerning the numerous editions of this work in existence, as well as the complex situation regarding the edited and unedited works of Della Porta, see Giuseppe Gabrieli, "Bibliografia lincea, I. Giambattista Della Porta. Notizia bibliografica dei suoi manoscritti e libri, edizioni, etc., con documenti inediti," *Rendiconti della R. Accademia Nazionale dei Lincei, Classe di scienze morali, storiche e filologiche*, 6, 8 (1932), pp. 206–77, and idem, "Spigolature dellaportiane," ibid., 6, 9 (1935), pp. 491–517.

7 *Della fisonomia dell'uomo*, 181v.

8 *Della fisonomia dell'uomo*, 208r.

9 Giovan Battista Della Porta, *Della magia naturale libri XX* (Naples: Bulifon, 1677), p. 281.

10 *Della fisonomia dell'uomo*, 205v.

11 *Della magia naturale*, p. 280.

12 Giovan Battista Della Porta, *Ars reminiscendi* (Naples: Giovan Battista Sottile, 1602), pp. 17–20, 39–41. In addition to the published editions, in both the vernacular and in Latin, of this treatise on mnemonics, there exist two manuscript copies of the vernacular text: Vatican Library, cod. Vat. lat. 5347, 77r–107r, and the National Library of Paris, cod. 10166 (cod. ital. 589), 257r–97r.

13 See Lina Bolzoni, "Riuso e riscrittura di immagini: dal Palatino al Della Porta, dal Doni a Federico Zuccari, al Toscanella," in *Scritture di scritture. Testi, generi, modelli nel Rinascimento*, Giancarlo Mazzacurati and Michel Plaisance, eds. (Rome: Bulzoni, 1987), pp. 171–206 (in particular, pp. 171–89), and Giovanni Pozzi, "Poesia per gioco," in *Poesia per gioco. Prontuario di figure artificiose* (Bologna: Il Mulino, 1984).

14 Galileo Galilei, *Considerazioni alla Gerusalemme liberata*, in *Le opere*, t. 15 (Florence: Società Editrice Fiorentina, 1856), p. 131. Other examples of analogies drawn between poems and edifices may be found in Paola Barocchi, "Fortuna dell'Ariosto nella trattatistica figurativa," in *Critica e storia letteraria.* Studies in honour of Mario Fubini (Padova: Liviana, 1970), 1, pp. 388–405.

15 "In historia id vehementer approbo [Alberti wrote] quod a poetis tragicis observatum video, ut quam possint paucis personatis fabulam doceant. Meo quidem iudicio nulla erit usque adeo tanta rerum varietate referta historia, quam novem aut decem homines non possint condigne agere" [In their *historie* I find it very pleasing what the tragic poets do regularly, for they use the minimum number of personages possible. In my opinion no *historia* is so complex and varied that it cannot be perfectly well represented by 9 or 10 personages] (Leon Battista Alberti, *De pictura* [Basel: Cratander, 1540], pp. 74–5). And Della Porta, in explaining in chap. 6 how one may go about constructing the mental framework which would help one to recall a story, wrote, "Id vehementer placet quod a poetis tragicis et comicis observatum video, ut quam paucis personis possint fabulam monstrent, neque ulla erit tam rerum varietate referta historia, quam novem aut decem personae optime repraesentent" [It pleases me very much what the tragic and comic poets do regularly, representing their tales with the minimum number of personages possible. No *historia* is so complex and varied that it cannot be perfectly well represented by 9 or 10 personages] (Giovan Battista Della Porta, *Ars reminiscenti*, p. 10).

16 Barry Wind, "Pitture ridicole: Some Late Cinquecento Comic Genre Paintings," in *Storia dell'Arte*, 20 (1974), pp. 25–35.

17 *Ars reminiscendi*, p. 8.

18 Giovan Battista Della Porta, *Della chirofisonomia overo di quella parte della humana fisonomia che si appartiene alla mano* (Naples: Antonio Bulifon, 1677), p. 25.

19 The two figures were taken from Della Porta, *Della fisonomia dell'uomo*, 115v, 116r.

20 Massimo Ciavolella, *La "malattia d'amore" dall'antichità al Medioevo* (Rome: Bulzoni, 1976).

21 *Della fisonomia dell'uomo*, 4r.

22 *Della magia naturale*, p. 26.

23 Giovan Battista Della Porta, *La sorella*, in *Teatro*, III, Raffaele Sirri, ed. (Naples: Istituto Universitario Orientale, 1985), pp. 144–45.

24 *Ars reminiscendi*, p. 5.

25 Ovid, *Remedia amoris*, pp. 724–30.

26 Ludovico Ariosto, *Orlando furioso*, 23, 92 ff. On the links between Orlando's madness and the corresponding tradition in medicine, see Marina Beer, *Romanzi di cavalleria. Il Furioso e il romanzo italiano del primo Cinquecento* (Rome: Bulzoni, 1987), chap. 2.

27 *Ars reminiscendi* 8, pp. 7–8.

28 Pietro da Ravenna, *Memoriae ars quae phoenix inscribitur* (Vienna: Matteo Bonhome, 1541), 9.

29 Gerolamo Marafioto, *Ars memoriae* (Frankfurt: Matteo Becker, 1603), 19 and 66. Using the body of a beautiful young woman to help one to recall the spirit is a variation on an antique iconographic tradition, one in which the souls are represented by nude bodies. Frequent references to this type of iconography as a source of images for the memory occur in the text of Marafioto.

30 *Ars reminiscendi*, 16.

(*Article translated by L. Chen*)

Paolo Cherchi

A Dossier for the Study of Jealousy

Jealousy, just like love, is a passion experienced and known by western man at least since the day he was able to record his own feelings in writing. Indeed ancient literature teems with stories motivated by a passion which we would not hesitate to call jealousy. But however many these stories may be, the definitions of this passion are scanty and no extended treatment of it exists. We can recall definitions such as Chrisippus' "jealousy is a grief at the possession by another of that which one desires for oneself";[1] or Cicero's: "*obtrectatio*, in the meaning of the Greek word ζηλοτυπία, is the sadness that comes from seeing another possessing what we have desired,"[2] and a few more; but we would hardly fill a page with them. Moreover, in these definitions no specific reference is made to the erotic passion which we normally associate with the notion of jealousy today. It seems that jealousy was never a problem for our remote ancestors. The Greeks coined the word *zelotypia* but didn't make any effort to explain its psychological traits. The Romans didn't even have a specific word to indicate jealousy: *obtrectatio*, *aemulatio*, *invidia* and other synonyms were used, all of which have a vast semantic field which could include many passions together with jealousy. Even a work like St. Cyprian's *De zelo et livore*, which in the title promises to tell us something about jealousy, is simply a treatise on envy with no mention whatsoever of jealousy aroused by erotic love. Thus it is safe to say that jealousy is a problem only for modern man, a problem born simultaneously with a notion of love which was quite different from the ancient one: this is courtly love which seeks to draw virtue from erotic love. It was a timid birth, but the offspring was destined to grow big and loud as the discussions on love proceeded through the centuries. And jealousy became a problematic companion of love: it was never clearly settled whether erotic love and jealousy were consubstantial passions or capital enemies. Whatever the case, the fact is that jealousy became a pervasive theme in the literatures of the sixteenth and seventeenth centuries and produced unforgettable prosopopeias in Ariosto, Spenser, Lope, Shakespeare and

Marino, and nurtured characters like Othello, Orlando, and the *Celoso extremeño*. The purpose of this dossier is to highlight a few moments of that growth and discussion. For the sake of clarity and economy, this dossier will concentrate as much as possible upon Italian materials up to the end of the sixteenth century and exclusively upon discussions of jealousy, without dwelling on their particular influence on literary creation.

Unlike love, jealousy, perhaps because of its monstrous nature, has not gained the attention of scholars. With the exception of the work by Madaleine Bertaud,[3] which is limited to a few decades of French culture, there is no study on jealousy. A collection of essays on eros and anteros seems to me the most appropriate place to introduce this lady who at times was seen as an inseparable companion of eros and at other times as its implacable enemy.

The passion we call jealousy got its name at its modern birth. But from where did it come? An autoschediastic attempt at an etymology would suggest *zelotypia* as the immediate root of the Romance words. But a thorough study by Margot Grzywacz[4] has proven that *jalousie*, *gelosia* and *celos* are back-formations from the word *jalous*, *geloso* and *celoso* which come from *zelotus*, frequently found in the Bible meaning "a person with zeal" but also "a person who expects exclusive love"; in the latter sense God himself is called jealous. Whatever the case may be, it is certain that the troubadours knew the theme of jealousy[5] and it was highly dramatized in an episode of the late Provençal *novela* entitled *Flamenca*, where Archimbald, the husband *gelos*, suffers an attack of jealousy which brings upon him the highest form of melancholy, namely the *cucubut*.[6] But, we must follow our program of disregarding literary utilizations of jealousy, and look into what is the first modern definition of this passion. We find it in Andreas Capellanus, the first polemical interpreter of courtly love. In his *De amore*, he presents two characters, a man of the higher nobility and a noble lady, who discuss jealousy. The man maintains that love cannot exist between married people; neither can jealousy because it "is of the nature of love itself and without which true love cannot exist" and "is wholly rejected between husband and wife, and must be always expelled by them as a harmful bane. But lovers must embrace it always as the mother, so to say, and nurse of love."[7] In a subsequent phase of the discussion, the aristocrat gives a definition of jealousy:

> it is a genuine mental emotion which provokes sharp fear in us that the substance of our love is being diminished through a failure to serve the wishes of the loved one. There is anxiety that love is not evenly poised, and suspicion against a lover is aroused, but this is accompanied by base thoughts. So it is quite clear

> that jealousy has three aspects. The truly jealous man is perpetually afraid that his service cannot be adequate to preserve his love; he fears that his love is not reciprocated to the same degree; and he reflects on the harsh pains he would have to suffer if his partner took another lover, though he believes that this could not possibly happen. It is quite obvious and clear that this third contingency could not happen to married couples. A husband cannot suspect his wife without having unworthy thoughts about her. Jealousy in its pure form, if applied to a husband, is defiled through the defect in the substance in which it has its place, and ceases to be what it was. . . . But jealousy is said to preserve love between lovers, for all three roles earlier allotted to jealousy are judged necessary to the lover, and so jealousy between lovers themselves is not condemned. However, many people are plainly deceived in this matter. They mistakenly maintain that base suspicions are jealousy, and accordingly a considerable number who know nothing of its source and description are very often misled and drawn into intractable error. Even between an unmarried couple this false jealousy can claim a place.[8]

Andreas, or rather his characters, are never a model of clarity. But the meaning of this long quotation may be made clearer by recalling the definition of love which opens the *De amore*. Essentially love is striving for the sexual possession of the beloved. And in that striving dwells jealousy, namely all the fears of inadequacy, of not doing enough to deserve requital. Hence jelousy is a positive force which always improves the moral qualities of lovers. Jealousy cannot exist between married people simply because that striving of love is no longer necessary or existent. In a married couple jealousy's place is taken by base thoughts which in fact have nothing to do with jealousy which is really "mater et nutrix amoris" as the following two rules of love preach: II, "Qui non zelat amare non potest," and XXI, "Ex vera zelotypia affectus semper crescit amandi."[9] The first of these two rules became proverbial and even Erasmus recorded it in his *Adagia*. Jealousy was born as a dignified lady, always present where love is present and always absent from marriage. The truthfulness of these ideas will be often debated in the sixteenth century. Some disagreement with Andreas' position was already voiced in the Middle Ages. A theologian of St. Thomas's stature doesn't differ very much from Andreas in understanding jealousy as related to erotic love; but his judgement on this lady-friend of love was not equally favorable. In the *Summa Theologiae* 1–2, quaestio 28, St. Thomas analyzes the effects of love. In the first article he debates "utrum unio sit effectus amoris"; in the following, "utrum mutua inhaesio sit effectus amoris"; in the third he asks himself whether the "extasis" is an effect of love, and in the fourth, which concerns us here, "utrum zelus sit effectus amoris." In order to understand this passion, it is important to follow St. Thomas in the distinction between two loves: one is "benevolentia" and the other "concupiscentia." Jealousy belongs only to the second one. Love is a movement toward the object which is loved, and it tries to exclude everything that opposes this movement. But, again, one must distinguish between two kinds of love. The love for a friend opposes everything which impedes the well-being of a friend; whereas the love for a lover opposes everything that impedes one's own enjoyment of the person he loves. This is the jealousy which exists between lovers: thus in the last analysis it is simply love for oneself. Jealousy is a form of selfishness, different from envy although it shares some traits with it. St. Thomas's explanation of jealousy as self-love will be echoed for a long time; one can hear it as far away as in Descartes.

Feared or revered, lady jealousy soon enlists the greatest poets and writers to proclaim her great powers. Who doesn't remember the role jealousy plays in *Le roman de la rose*? Who doesn't remember the powerful prosopopeia created by Boccaccio in his *Filocolo*?[10] The young writer gives this old and ugly lady a house very similar to the one Ovid had given to Envy.[11] This is a sign of the difficulty anyone faces in distinguishing these kindred passions. Even more important is Petrarch's testimony. He not only wrote a letter to a friend exhorting him to tame jealousy by using good sense,[12] but he mentioned jealousy several times in his love poetry. His attention to jealousy is quite important because his texts will provide one of the strongest supports in later discussions of the relationship between love and jealousy.

The Quattrocento had its share of poets who admit to being tormented by jealousy. One need only refer to Boiardo's *Amorum libri* to see how privileged Madame Jealousy is. Also she had her exorcizers in doctors like Benedictus de Nursia who in his *Pulcherrimum et utilissimum opus ad sanitatem conservationem* (Bologna, 1477) warns against this passion because it causes severe physiological problems such as difficulties in digestion, shortness of breath, insommia and serious symptoms of melancholy.[13] Similar warnings, even if not physiological in nature, are to be found in many works on marriage, such as *De re uxoria* by Francesco Barbaro, in the chapter "De obsequendi facilitate." Yet, all this attention not withstanding, the fifteenth century was not rich in discussions on jealousy. The reason—it seems to me—is that humanistic culture was quite averse to romance literature and above all to its exaltations of erotic love. Where love has no acolytes there is not much room for jealousy either. Treatises like Alberti's *Ecatomfila* and *Deifira*, Platina's *Dialogus contra amores*, Edo's *Anterici*, Fregoso's *Anteros* and Calandra's lost work *Aura*, are manifestos against erotic love. The last of these works mentioned is known to us only through the references made by M. Equicola,[14] in which one perceives a fondness for discussing "questioni d'amore," among which this one is interesting: "whether love can be without jealousy." This is a question for which there is no answer from Calandra, but one which will elicit many differing answers in later times. Besides the disinterest, on the part of the Humanists, in love and erotic love, there is another important reason for relegating jealousy to the shadows. It is the appearance on the horizon of a new kind of love which its founder, Marsilio Ficino, calls "Platonic love." His *Comento* on Plato's *Symposium* is a fundamental work in the history of love in western civilization. It inspired works such as the *Dialoghi d'amore* by Leon Ebreo, the *Asolani* by Bembo, the *Tre libri d'amore* by Francesco Cattani Diaccetto, and some sections of *Il cortegiano* by Castiglione, just to mention some of the most illustrious followers of this tradition. Platonic love is eminently spiritual and rational, so it is not surprising if in these treatises very little or no place at all is reserved for jealousy, which is an irrational passion. Only the last representative of this tradition, Giordano Bruno, spends some time discussing jealousy in his *Eroici furori*.[15] Commenting on a sonnet by Tansillo, Bruno has the opportunity to classify jealousy as the second of the nine forms of "blindness" which impede the attainment of what he calls "heroic love."

Platonic love, however, was not to reign undisputed. Mario Equicola, who didn't disregard erotic love, knew how important a role jealousy plays in it. Accordingly, he devoted several pages of his *Libro de natura de amore* to clarifying this passion. Jealousy, he says, is caused by the coldness of the beloved, or by the fact that she loves another person. It is impossible that a person can divide love into equal parts; it is impossible to love two persons at the same time; thus a lover knows that love for him cannot be shared. Hence comes jealousy. This feeling is more or less intense according to one's culture: it is less so among northern people, and more so among southerners. Because all animals in love are affected by jealousy, one must conclude that it is necessary for the reproduction of species. Jealousy must be cured through dissimulation: if there is hope of prevailing over the rival, the lover behaves in a generous, liberal way towards the beloved; if there is no hope, then despair, rage and animosity are aroused, all of which are contrary to love. Mario Equicola is one step away from defending jealousy since he is so prone to understanding it as a natural passion. Perhaps his ties to Platonic love theories prevented him from taking this step. Equicola's ideas were repeated, often verbatim, by Agostino Nifo, a philosopher of Aristotelian extraction, who is decidedly opposed to Platonic love, and is also concerned with jealousy.[16] It seems as if a more natural or Aristotelian way of understanding love was the key to allowing jealousy to survive. Varchi and Tasso, we shall see, move in this direction. Paradoxically, however, jealousy found an unexpected and indirect vital support in Platonic love even before Aristotelianism came into the picture. It all happened because Bembo restored the dignity of vernacular poetry by seeing in Petrarch the forerunner of Platonic or neo-platonic love. Bembo was instrumental in the creation of a new poetical trend which is known as Petrarchism. In reviving Petrarch's teachings and themes, he revived jealousy as a poetical theme as well. This theme is omnipresent in the *canzonieri* of the sixteenth and seventeenth centuries, especially among those of the southern poets from Sannazaro, to Epicuro, to Rota, to Tansillo, Tasso and Marino.[17] But love's adversarial sister had her singers among the northern poets as well, the most celebrated of them being Giovanni Della Casa. This intense attention to jealousy brought with it two consequences. One is what seems to be a peculiar trait of the Italian discussions on jealousy: poets are treated as the authorities on the subject to such an extent that it is not infrequent to find a treatise on jealousy which is just a commentary on a specific poem. The other consequence is more philosophical, but it is strongly tied to the notion of authority which was just mentioned: if we find so many poets who sing about their loves and at the same time admit to experiencing jealousy, does it mean that love and jealousy coexist? Or do they annul each other? The problem is not new, for we already saw it in Andreas and in Calandra. What is unprecedented, however, is the intensity of the discussion it creates now, especially at the moment in which Platonic love seems to have spent its creative energy. In just three years, from 1542 to 1545 appear four important contributions to the discussion. Alessandro Piccolomini, in his *De la institutione di tutta la vita de l'huomo* of 1542, rejects the possibility that love and jealousy go together: love, he maintains, is essentially hope and jealousy kills it. Love is always accompanied by a certain fear which may be called a feeling of reverence which inspires the lover to improve his moral qualities. This fear cannot be confused with jealousy, which never produces any moral improvement. In the same year Sperone Speroni published his *Dialogo d'amore* whose first part is devoted to a discussion of jealousy. Through a subtle argumentation, Gracia, one of the dialogue's characters, persuades his interlocutors, Bernardo Tasso and Tullia, that jealousy, which kills hope, cannot coexist with perfect love. What his interlocutors claim to experience as jealousy is actually a fear which may be more accurately called reverence and hope. Speroni, thus, reaches the same conclusion as Piccolomini. The same is true in Betussi's dialogue *Raverta* of 1544 where the question "se amor può esser senza gelosia" is debated and where, again, a distinction is made between fear or reverence and jealousy.[18] But in 1545 we hear a discordant voice: it is the voice of Benedetto Varchi which therefore deserves closer attention. His *Lezione d'amore*, published as a pamphlet, enjoyed a noticeable prestige, perhaps because it was the first publication entirely devoted to the subject of jealousy or because of its ideas. It was widely read and even translated into English by Robert Tofte with the title *The blazon of jealousie*.[19]

Varchi's "lezione"[20] was read in 1543 in the academy of Padua, that is in the same city where Speroni and Betussi were active. The "lezione" is presented as a commentary on Della Casa's sonnet "Cura, che di timor ti nutri e cresci," but many other poets, especially Petrarch, are quoted. The subtle distinctions and the argumentation clearly show Varchi's Aristotelian inclination and convictions. For him jealousy as a general feeling is not limited to erotic love, because one can be jealous of a sister, a friend and so forth. Being a fear or suspicion that others may enjoy the beauty we love, jealousy can be said to be a kind of envy, but not all forms of envy are jealousy, whereas all jealousies are a kind of envy. Varchi, however, limits his subject only to jealousy related to erotic love. This jealousy is born out of cupidity which can be of four types: of pleasure, of possession, of property, and of honor. The first type of jealousy takes place when the pleasure one derives from his lover is so much that he cannot accept sharing it with anybody else. The jealousy of possession exists where one desires to possess the beloved person just for himself and fears losing that person. The jealousy of property arises when one possesses the person he loves and wants her exclusively for himself. The fourth and last type, the jealousy of honor, depends on the estimation of the shame which follows from the loss of a lover to someone else. This type of jealousy changes from person to person, from culture to culture, from country to country: southern countries are known to be affected by jealousy more than northern ones. Jealousy, like all passions, can decrease and grow according to four factors: people, place, time and occupation. As far as people are concerned, one must distinguish among people who are jealous (there are persons more prone to jealousy than others), the people of whom one is jealous (there are persons who according to their behavior cause jealousy more than others) and the quality of the people of whom one is jealous (a woman of low class and poor intellectual qualities is less likely to arouse jealousy than a superior woman). As for place, jealousy grows or decreases according to its qualities: a church is less likely to arouse jealousy than a theatre, and carnival is a time when the occasions for jealousy are more frequent than in Lent. Regarding occupation Varchi says that busy people are less jealous than lazy ones. All these things are true both for men and women because they are both capable of loving with the same intensity, although women, being less prudent and less judicious, are, more often than men, victims of jealousy. This awful feeling has its physical consequences. *Gelosia* and *gelo* (ice) seem to be related. Jealousy indeed makes its victims pale and cold. This happens because fear contracts and weakens the heart, so that nature, in order to protect the noblest part of the human body, sends to it the blood from the upper and the lower parts: hence the cold. Jealousy makes one tremble because the heart trembles for fear. Jealousy is an unbearable pain; it doesn't allow one to rest or sleep and keeps one in a constant state of anxiety. After these physiological and philosophical elucidations, Varchi finally comes to the old question: can love exist without jealousy? He is unequivocal in his answer: love and jealousy can never be separated. If love is the desire of generating in the loved person a simulacrum of oneself, which also means loving only one person, then it is impossible to conceive that the person one loves can in turn love someone else at the same time. Love, in other words, is desire of possession, it is possession, property and honor, so jealousy can never be separated from it. Moreover, it is a natural feeling, because animals experience it. If such is the case, why then blame jealousy? One must only blame its excesses, as one must blame the excess of eating and drinking which in moderation are healthy and necessary. The excesses of jealousy can be cured only if its causes are; but one should not cure the *just* form of jealousy because that would be tantamount to eliminating love.

Varchi's ideas seem quite original; in fact, he based his *lezione* on a chapter of the *De anima* by Luis Vives, precisely on a chapter which became quite influential in similar discussions. Varchi often copies him word for word. None of his contemporaries were aware of it, nor are his modern editors. It should be noted, however, that Vives doesn't defend jealousy as does Varchi. In any case, Varchi's ideas were new in Italy and they were opposed to Ficino's notion of love. Jealousy for the first time, after several centuries, found its champion.

For a while Varchi's fight was a lonely one. The conclusions reached by Piccolomini, Speroni and Betussi were defended by Michelangelo Serafini who in 1550 wrote a short book commenting on a sonnet by G.B. Strozzi on jealousy and in so doing he imitated the form of Varchi's commentary if not his conclusions.[21] In 1565 Levantio da Guidacciolo Mantoano wrote a long book entitled *Antidoto della gelosia* (Brescia) which also belongs to the genre of commentary on poems inaugurated by Varchi. In this *antidoto* all of the *improperia* against jealousy are based on Ariosto's *Orlando furioso*. As late as 1585 Annibale Romei in his *Discorsi* found nothing positive to say about this companion of love.[22] But in defense of Varchi's thesis came none other than Torquato Tasso who touched upon the subject of jealousy on several occasions. In his *Conclusioni amorose*[23] we read that "jealousy is not a daughter of love, but a sister of it; that it is not an affection born from love, but one born after love is born." We read also that: "jealousy is a very certain sign of a very ardent love and increases it; but it cannot be denied that jealousy doesn't destroy love." Finally, we read that: "a jealousy which is in the lover, if it depends on a defect [of hope], is not a lover's defect but rather a defect of the beloved one." Then to our subject Tasso devotes one of his dialogues, *Il forestiero napoletano, ovvero della gelosia*, and a lengthy discourse entitled *Della gelosia*. It would take too long to follow the subtle argumentation of the dialogue so I shall look instead at its main thesis. Jealousy is the fear of losing love and honor, but this fear—if not immoderate—stimulates us to improve ourselves. Jealousy, thus, far from being a despicable vice, is a moral virtue which promotes other virtues, and it is a purgative virtue insofar as it purges us from vices. Jealousy, not love, turns a stingy man into a liberal one, a coward into a brave man, etc. Jealousy is like a shadow which always follows love. The *Discorso sulla gelosia* is more straightforward and less paradoxical than the dialogue. It is also more extended so that we must content ourselves with highlighting its main assertions. Love is desire of beauty; the movement towards beauty is love; the desire of overcoming all impediments which prevent that movement is what is called jealousy, which is, thus, not a daughter of love, but a sister of it, born from the same cause, namely beauty. We can say it in different words: love is an inclination towards goodness; jealousy is the withdrawal, the escape from the bad. Jealousy is not envy, although it resembles it in some respects. It is fear, but one which is mixed with hope, because where there is no hope there is no jealousy. One is not jealous of the husband of the woman he loves because she loves each one of the two men in a completely different way. Conversely what one calls a husband's jealousy is actually a form of zeal. Jealousy always accompanies love and grows as love grows. Jealousy is a passion and it is normal in all men. One is not jealous of the goodness which can be shared by many (for example: God, science, wisdom, etc.); but one is jealous of those goods which cannot be shared, such as the body of the person he loves. Man's love is always directed both to the body and to the mind of a woman: the first one cannot be shared and, consequently, even the love for her mind cannot be happily shared with other people. Tasso concludes his essay by recalling Boccaccio's description of jealousy in his *Filocolo*. It is a description worthy of the best emblematist. One thing in it can interest us here: why is jealousy portrayed as a woman? Tasso says it is because women, having a body temperature colder than that of men, and having more subtle spirits, are more subject to fears and jealousy than men. This sketchy summary of Tasso's ideas is enough to give a sense of the sophistication the discussion had attained. Perhaps many of the new things found in Tasso's writings reflect current discussions; perhaps the problem of whether one is to feel jealousy for a lover's husband was the object of a dispute; if so, I don't know where; perhaps the image of jealousy as a sister of love is not so new, but I don't know who was the first to use it. Obviously much more research needs to be done. The results, however, whatever they may be, will not modify in any substantial sense the impression one has from reading Tasso's work on the theme of jealousy. It is clear that Platonic love has become a pure memory by the end of the sixteenth century. We are clearly in the world of Mannerism where passions are not only acknowledged but also exalted. And in Tasso the presence of honor is stronger than in any previous author. This may be due to the already advanced form of new-feudalism brought about by the Counter-reformation with an exaltation of aristocratic values which have a touch of the medieval world; it is perhaps not a mere coincidence that in Tasso's defense of jealousy one senses a revival of Andreas Cappellanus' ideas.

With Tasso breaking a lance in defense of jealousy, we have reached the end of the sixteenth century and our dossier comes to a close. Whether jealousy survived in the following century as a sister or an enemy of love, or as both, is a matter of a new investigation. Varchi's and Tasso's position probably fared very well if one considers as sufficient proof *I vanti della gelosia* written by Francesco Berni in 1658 as a discourse of his *Dell'accademia.*[24] But it may very well be that Berni's voice was one of the very few which was raised in defense of our much maligned lady in all of the seventeenth century. To complete this dossier one must collect endless materials, and, if possible, not only in Italy but in other countries as well in order to assess through a comparison the originality and uniqueness of these discussions in Italy. A first impression would suggest that they were widespread all over Europe and that the same arguments were used everywhere. In France, for example, discussions of jealousy were frequent. One recalls Montaigne's repeated touching upon the problem in his *Essays*,[25] or Descartes's analysis of this passion,[26] or Bodin's[27] observations on the jealous nature of southern people. These few indications show the frequency and the quality of the discussions. In France, as in Italy, there was even a René Bary who wrote what he calls a "paradox" entitled *Défence de la jalousie*, a defense which came much later than in Italy.[28] A first impression also suggests that in France jealousy between married people was a problem much more debated than in Italy; it is enough to look at Tiraqueau's *De legibus connubialibus et iure maritali*, where book XVI is devoted to jealousy, or at André Courtin's *Traité de la jalousie ou moyen d'entretenir la paix dans le marriage* of 1674.

In closing this dossier I am aware that it would be much bigger if it included legal texts and above all medical texts, where jealousy appears as either a cause or an effect of melancholy. Doctors tell us that jealousy comes from impotence, ugliness and laziness. They also tell us that it can be cured in the same way in which *amor hereos* is cured: with company, good sense, and activity. One should not forget to include the astrologers because some, like Pontanus, believe that jealous people are born under a special conjunction of the stars. Fortunately, as a point of departure for these and many other things, one can refer to Robert Burton's *Anatomy of Melancholy* where jealousy is studied in a long encyclopedic chapter of part 3 section 3. Undoubtedly, a dossier with any historical validity should relate the problem of jealousy to the problem of honor and women's role in society, because in the literature we have seen some of these problems. But, to begin with, any dossier has to have a beginning. Its closing must be postponed until all the documents and facts are in order.

University of Chicago

NOTES

1 In Diogenes Laertius, *Lives of Eminent Philosophers*, ed. R.D. Hicks (Loeb Classics, 1925, 1966), 7:111.

2 *Tusculanae disputationes*, ed. J.E. King (Loeb Classics, 1950, 1968), 4:18.

3 *La jalousie dans la littérature au temps de Louis XIII* (Geneva: Droz, 1981).

4 *"Eifersucht" in den Romanischen Sprachen*, in "Arbeiten zur Romanischen Philologie," nr. 42 (Bochum-Langendreer: H. Pöoppinghouse, 1937).

5 E. Kahler, "Les Troubadours et la jalousie," in *Mélanges . . . J. Frappier* (Geneva: Droz, 1970), 543–59.

6 On this episode see M. Ciavolella, *La malattia d'amore dall'antichità al medioevo* (Rome: Bulzoni, 1976), 116.

7 *Andreas Capellanus on Love*, trans. P.G. Walsh (London: Duckworth, 1982), 147 and 149.
8 *Andreas Capellanus on Love*, 149 and 151.
9 *Andreas Capellanus on Love*, 282.
10 Book 3, ch. 24; see also *De Genealogia Deorum*, 1:18.
11 *Metamorphoses*, 2:760 ff.
12 *Variarum*, ed. Fracassetti, ep. XXI.
13 In ch. 96 of the ed. quoted.
14 *Libro de natura de amore* (Mantua, 1525), 40r.
15 Dialogue I.
16 *De pulchro et de amore* (Lugduni, 1549), bk. 2, 221–218, ch. 88: "De zelotypia et conrario," 221–28.
17 See E. Raimondi, "Il petrarchismo nell'Italia meridionale," in *Atti del convegno internazionale sul tema 'premarinismo' e 'pregongorismo'*, Accademia dei Lincei (Rome, 1973), 105–7.
18 The *Raverta* is published in *Trattati d'amore del '500*, edited by G. Zonta (Bari: Laterza, 1912) reprinted by M. Pozzi (Bari: Laterza, 1975); the *questione* is on p. 100 of the reprint.
19 On the bibliography on this work see R.C. Melzi, "Un contributo alla storia del petrarchismo in Inghilterra: Robert Tofte e il *Blazon of jealousie*," in *Il lettore di provincia*, 17 (1986), pp. 17–40.
20 *Lezione di M. Benedetto Varchi nell'accademia di Padova sopra un sonetto del Casa e sulla gelosia.* This lesson was given in 1543, but it was published first in Mantua in 1545. It can now be read in *Opere di Benedetto Varchi* (Trieste: Lloyd Austriaco, 1859), 570–82.
21 *Sopra un sonetto della gelosia di M. Giovanbattista Strozzi* (Firenze: Torrentino, 1550).
22 Discourse II: "Dell'amore umano," which can be read in A. Solerti, *Ferrara e la corte estense nella seconda metà del secolo decimosesto—i discorsi di Annibale Romei* (Città di Castello: S. Lapi, 1891), 46.
23 The *Conclusioni*, the dialogue and the discourse are all found in the eighth vol. of the complete *Opere* of Tasso (Venice, 1729–1743) respectively on pp. 161–65 (the conclusions we have translated are on nos. 45–47), pp. 36–42; 231–42.
24 This work was published in Ferrara and the *Vanti* are on pp. 176–205.
25 Especially in bk. 2, ch. 12, and bk. 3, ch. 5.
26 *Les passions de l'âme.* The articles 167–69 are devoted to jealousy.
27 *Method for the Easy Comprehension of History*, trans. B. Reynolds (New York: Octagon Books, 1966), pp. 85 ff.
28 See on this book, published in 1642, M. Bertaud, *La jalousie dans la littérature au temps de Louis XIII*, pp. 177–85.

Domenico Pietropaolo

Love, Sex, and Eugenics in the *City of the Sun*

Among the features that distinguish Campanella's *City of the Sun* from other utopias, the chief one is undoubtedly its Ministry of Love. Here is the blueprint for a radically different social order, built on some of the fundamental implications that eros can have for the structure of society as a whole and including an entire ministry to take charge of it and to regulate all activities that are even remotely related to it. Together with its two equal counterparts, the Ministries of Power and Wisdom, the Ministry of Love owes its existence to Campanella's analogical imagination, which patterned the city's high bureaucracy on the model of the Trinity. But it derives its political significance from the principle that love is the basis of human assortment and thus the internal binding force of a community. Whatever its philosophical, religious, and medical significance may be, there can be no doubt that sociologically love works like a gravitational force that draws people together into social nuclei, compels them to devise conventions for the expression of friendship and for the regulations of sexual behaviour, and hence links those nuclei into an organized community with its own institutional network. An adequate understanding of community dynamics requires, therefore, some comprehension of the sociological implications of love, which is to say of its capacity to constitute social relations, while any plan to proclaim a new form of society on the basis of that understanding must include the design of an institutional order to care for it. Hence the Ministry of Love.

The inhabitants of the City of the Sun are most famous for their aversion to private property and to the single family unit, both institutions viewed as outward projections of the self in a manner that infringes on the minimum social and material space required by the other members of the community. The founders of the City of the Sun redistributed this space in equal measure by legislating away both private property and the family. The concepts are clearly related, but the first of these—private property—lies entirely outside the scope of this paper, whose purpose instead is to examine Campanella's institutional mechanism for the control and legitimation of sexual intercourse against the background of the social reality of the time.

In the City of the Sun women are common to all men and men are common to all women. To the extent that a system governing socially legitimate sexual intercourse is a form of marriage, the sexual communism of the City of the Sun may be described as a form of regulated communal or group marriage—that is to say, a form of marriage in which each woman becomes potentially married to all the men and each man to all the women upon reaching physical maturity. It is a system of simultaneous polyandry and polygamy, requiring no special ceremony for religious or juridic legitimation, but governed by a principle of selection without which it would degenerate into sexual anarchy. This internal regulating principle is the system's eugenic orientation. Sexual relations in the City of the Sun have one of two purposes: they are either intentionally procreational, in which case they are designed to ensure racial continuity in progressively improved generations, or else they are not procreational, which is to say that they are quite simply meant to satisfy individual psychophysiological needs for coital union.

Of these two objectives of the system, the procreational one is by far the more important, and undoubtedly the one more familiar to readers of *La città del sole*. English-speaking students of the Renaissance and Counter-Reformation usually come into contact with this aspect of Campanella's thought in Frances Yates' justly famous book on *Giordano Bruno and the Hermetic Tradition*, in which they find no mention of the non-generative function of sexual relations and an exclusively hermetic account of procreation. Yates, who is so precise and enlightening on a daunting variety of subjects, does not exhibit her usual standard of rigour when she analyses this issue in Campanella. By stating, as she does, that human breeding in the City of the Sun is only a question of hermetic astrology, that it is exclusively "concerned with choosing the right astrological moment for conception, and with mating males and females in accordance with their astrological temperaments,"[1] she assimilates Campanella to Bruno, forcing him to conform to the conceptual paradigms that sustain the latter's thought, and thereby gives the mistaken impression that there are no sexual relations other than the procreational ones tightly controlled by the city's priestly astrologers.

But the text could not be clearer on this point. First of all, the moment of pairing for procreational coital union is determined, not by an astrologer alone, but by an astrologer and a physician working together and with equal authority—both deputised to this task by the Minister of Love. And the factors that they take into account in their deliberations are by no means exclusively astrological. In addition to calculating the astrological propitiousness of a given moment for a given couple, the physician and the astrologer take care (i) to match partners of comparable sexual development, (ii) to pair fat girls with thin men and thin girls with fat men in order to guarantee hybrid vigour in the offspring, (iii) to pair tall beautiful girls with tall, handsome and brave men, in order to maintain homozigosity or purity of lineage when biological and psychological excellence is already found in the sexual partners, (iv) to provide—just prior to the sexual act—the women with the opportunity to contemplate statues of such excellent men as might induce arousal by visual suggestion, and (v) to check that both partners have properly digested their supper and offered appropriate prayers to God before making love. Most of these concerns are medical rather than astrological and represent the rudimentary speculation on inheritance and genetic continuity of which the science of the time was capable. If we do not read Campanella's dialogue "with an eye to Bruno,"[2] the procreational system of sexual union appears to be steeped in medical reflection and directed to a theory of society grounded in medicine as much as it is in religion and magic, fields that then overlapped in more than one area and hence lacked the conceptual autonomy and hierarchical relations to which we are accustomed. From such an interdisciplinary base, Campanella eventually arrived at Solarian eugenics.

In our purview of reality, variously coloured by science fiction and vulgarized smatterings of genetic engineering, eugenics may conjure up the nightmare of a society of healthy and handsome clones, devoid of selfhood and compassion, under the control of tyrannical institutions that are ready to push some absurd principle of racial superiority to frightening extremes. Certainly there is no doubt that the morality of Francis Galton, who introduced the term eugenics into the common vocabulary at the turn of the century, "is the morality of the gas chamber."[3] Therefore we, mindful as we are of the great lessons of history, feel entirely justified in approaching with suspicion any eugenic scheme. The Europeans of Campanella's time did not have the same experiences, but they showed a similar aversion to selective sexual pairing as being somehow dehumanising. But the Solarians, who do not lack compassion, who do not practice any form of racism, and who must be convinced that science *per se* is morally neutral and can be used either *in bono* or *in malo*, laugh condescendingly at their contemporary Europeans, who breed their dogs and horses with great care but leave to chance the biological quality of their own progeny.[4] The eugenic system of the City of the Sun is based on the principle that spontaneous assortment for love-making results much too frequently in the tragedy of an infant unable to survive or destined to live out his life in great suffering. Spontaneous assortment is replaced by selective pairing on the basis of eugenic compatibility, and the natural right to privacy in erotic relations is altogether annulled.

As for non-procreational relations, Campanella devised a scheme that enabled individual Solarians to express, and to seek fulfilment of, sexual desires and needs which social custom and moral theology had long called on everyone to suppress in the Western world, though always tolerating a certain degree of polygamy. But to the extent that a utopia represents an ideal redressing of the imperfections in the real world, it is a liberating vision of reality under all of its aspects. In the case of healthy sexual fulfilment, the only condition on such liberation is that sexual intercourse must not result in a medically undesirable pregnancy. Non-procreational sex is, therefore, as institutionalised as its eugenic counterpart. However, the services of this institution are not available to all of the adult female population at the same time and with the same degree of freedom that they are available to men. For only pregnant women and women who have proved sterile—after several attempts at conception with different men—can actually have intercourse with a given partner without first passing the test of eugenic compatibility. Fertile women who are not pregnant must either be predisposed to fulfill their sexual needs with an assigned partner in eugenic conception or else must suppress their feelings until they are pregnant, at which time they become eligible for intercourse with a consenting partner of their choice. The risk of conceiving a biologically weak child with an incompatible partner must at all costs be avoided. Consequently the system is unfair to fertile unpregnant women, who must exercise greater self-discipline than anyone else. Bold as he was in his utopian vision of reality, Campanella restrained his medical imagination from devising a method of state-regulated contraception that could fully democratise non-procreational sex and eliminate the imbalance between polygamy and polyandry sanctioned by the institution in its present form.

It is however quite remarkable by any standard that Campanella—who was himself a priest and a theologian, and who built into his utopia a great deal of his experience of monastic life—did in fact realise that the prolonged suppression of sexual feelings for whatever reason could, on the one hand, cause unnecessary distress to the individual and, on the other hand, constitute a potentially disruptive social force. With respect to the individual, that is why, in Campanella's liberating vision of life, non-procreational sex is allowed in order to satisfy both needs and simple wants, "per delizia o per servire alla necessità."[5] Need ("necessità") refers to distress on account of love. Those who are most deeply entrenched in such a state, "quelli più molestati da Venere,"[6] need only describe their predicament to the officials in charge, and arrangements for therapeutic coitus are made with the approval of the chief physician and as expeditiously as possible, before eros can show its dark side in Solarian life. Pleasure ("delizia") refers to enamourment that has not (or not yet) produced any great distress. When a young man falls in love with a young woman, he is encouraged by Solarian custom to express his love by engaging in conversation and harmless jest with her and by sending her verses and garlands. Sexual intercourse, as the ultimate expression and consummation of that love, is readily allowed if there is no danger of undesirable conception. But it is strictly forbidden if there is no such certainty, and in that case the young man must transfer his desire onto another eligible partner—evidently Campanella's eugenic preoccupation would never allow him to accept the notion that the erotic desire for one woman cannot be satisfied by another. Sex for pleasure pure and simple, however, is more of a privilege than a right, and consequently it may be withheld by the law as a form of punishment for such transgressions as ingratitude, malice, refusal to help others, and lying.[7] Young people who have preserved their chastity until the age of 21 are honoured with poetry and songs, as examples—one infers—for those who would abuse or take for granted this gift of nature. Priests do not seek sexual intercourse other than for therapy, "per medicina del corpo." Magic, verbal tricks, and the imagination have absolutely no status in Solarian erotic therapy.

With respect to society, it is noteworthy that in the City of the Sun there is no rape, there are no crimes of jealousy, and there cannot be adultery or incest. Obviously Campanella believed that if young people are initiated into a healthy sexual life upon reaching physical maturity, and if a young man's sexual needs are not allowed to remain unfulfilled and to become suppressed to the point that they distort his self-understanding and his vision of reality, rape can have no material or psychological cause. Similarly there cannot be any jealousy among the Solarians, for, in a sociological perspective at least, jealousy is none other than the sense of having exclusive rights to the love and erotic disposition of another person, and Solarians know from birth that in the institution of communal marriage each woman is legally married to every man and vice versa. No one has exclusive rights to the attentions of anyone else. If we consider that in terms of institutional conditioning, a person may be defined as "the internalization of organized social roles,"[8] we can readily see how the Solarians cannot experience jealousy, and hence are not driven to commit any of the crimes that are associated with this passion. The same reasoning applies to the question of adultery. Whether they are procreational, therapeutic, or simply for pleasure, all sexual unions occur within the bounds of communal marriage. Physical maturity and citizenship make one *ipso facto* married to the entire adult community of the opposite sex. Unlike the institution of marriage prevalent in most of contemporary Europe, the Solarian one did not have to tolerate some degree of selective polygamy or polyandry—that is to say, adultery—since it excluded no one from the marriage relation. The same is true of incest, or the exclusion of blood relatives from institutionally sanctioned intercourse. In the City of the Sun, sexual intercourse is possible between brothers and sisters as well as between parents and fully grown children, since consanguinity does not constitute an ethical problem in group marriage, though it may well constitute a biological one—but the Solarians are not aware of this. In the Solarian institution everyone is either a brother or a sister to the others, and that is why they call each other brother and sister, mirroring in their society a monastic practice well known to Campanella. Being a brother or a sister to the community of the opposite sex is in fact the necessary and sufficient condition of eligibility for communal marriage and hence for legitimate sexual relations, whether for procreation, therapy, or pleasure.

The question now arises whether all of this is only artificial speculation, a kind of philosophical construct on assumed principles, divested of significant links with the world of real social history and destined to remain enclosed within the sphere of political wishful thinking, such as is characteristic of the merely philosophical utopias built on the Platonic archetype as well as on the millenarian and golden age traditions. Certainly this literature was known to Campanella, and there are ample traces of it in his conception of the City of the Sun. But questions of intertextuality and rhetorical transumption aside, the point at issue is whether Campanella's advocation of sexual communism could not also, or even principally, have been suggested to him by examples of real communities in which the institution of group marriage had been fairly put to the test. In this context, references to authoritative sources of philosophical stratagems and fictional designs would be of little concern and totally devoid of weight next to allusions to history or to historiographic texts that purport to give an accurate account of empirical data. We are not here concerned with the process of textualisation, but with what has already been textualised and with its relation to situations perceived as real as opposed to situations perceived as merely fictional or literary. From this vantage point a reference to Plato's *Republic* would be insignificant next to an allusion, say, to Herodotus' and Caesar's accounts of group marriage among the ancient barbarians and the ancient Britons.[9]

Of course, Campanella knew of ancient Jewish polygamy (Gen. XVI, 4; XXV, 16), and he took into account that the early Christians practiced a form of communism. He even refers to the controversy among the early fathers regarding the precise scope of that principle of sharing, since some, like Tertullian, denied that it covered sexual relations, while others, like St. Clement of Rome, believed that it did.[10] In Campanella's time the orthodox view was that any communal possession of women constituted institutionalised fornication, though both Luther and Melanchthon had ruled that polygamy was not against the law of God.[11] Campanella's view of sexual life in the City of the Sun is anything but orthodox moral theology, but he is very careful not to mention any sources and parallels other than those which, by reason of their philosophical dignity, could not give rise to suspicions of heresy—the legend that Socrates took two wives allegedly in response to an Athenian law meant to increase the population[12] and Cato's decision to share Marcia with Hortensius so that she might bear his children as well. Herodotus and Caesar are not mentioned, and there are no discernible textual allusions to more recent social history.

But the fact is that the political and religious turmoil of recent history alone offered more than one example of sectarian attempts to institutionalise the common possession of women. That none of these is mentioned in the text does not constitute proof of irrelevance, especially since the groups in question were condemned as cases of mass heresy. By way of example we may recall the Brothers and Sisters of the Free Spirit, a heretical sect rooted in France which advocated the abolition of paired marriages and the practice of absolute sexual freedom; the Adamites, or radical wing of the Taborite movement in Bohemia, who dissolved the institution of the separate family and shared their wives in democratic fashion; and the later Münster Anabaptists in Germany, who avoided adultery by taking advantage of the institution known as the Companions of the Wives, that is to say a legal system that compelled unmarried women and widows to seek the guardianship of a man and to share the duties of his wife, including that of providing erotic services. The City of the Sun, which Campanella had originally proposed to found in Calabria at the culmination of an uprising against the Spanish authorities, falls naturally in context as the last potential example of the Renaissance heretical movement towards sexual communism, though with a different religious orientation and with none of the contempt for women that the heretical sects propounded.

The political understanding of eros in all of these cases was very probably a consequence of the unfair distribution of wealth and of hard economic thinking, rather than the result of philosophical speculation, which in all likelihood was part of the effect rather than the cause. The combination of these two factors, in conjuction with the principle that fairness means equality, can bring one readily to advocate not only the communal possession of the means of production, which would be fully compatible with paired marriage and the single family institution, but of all goods of consumption as well, a system of distribution that ultimately leads either to monastic celibacy or to the communal possession of women.

Of the heretical sects that I have mentioned the one that comes closest to the City of the Sun is that of the Adamites. Campanella undoubtedly knew about them from Enea Silvio Piccolomini's account in his history of Bohemia.[13] Here he could read that the Adamites lived on an island in the Luznic river, and that they practiced total community in wives, for procreational purposes as well as for erotic gratification, and always with the approval of the Chief Elder, after he had been informed of the sexual desire that prospective lovers had for one another. He would simply exhort them to be fruitful and to replenish the earth. In the City of the Sun, which is also located on an island, though not in a river, the institution of communal marriage was organised along more scientific lines. The function of the Chief Elder is carried out by the physician and the astrologer—jointly in the case of procreation, and by the physician alone in other cases—both in possession of a technical knowledge and of skills that the Adamite Elders, in all their wisdom, could not possibly have. And to the simple "go, be fruitful and multiply" of the Chief Elder, there corresponded the eugenic iron rules of the Ministry of Love. It was perhaps this organizational superiority that had given Campanella the false confidence of succeeding where others had failed.

Part of this superiority derives no doubt from the eugenic orientation of the system, not so much from its appeal as a scientific theory, as from the practical manner in which it allowed Campanella to face the threat of demographic crisis which loomed large over Europe in general and Southern Italy in particular throughout the sixteenth and seventeenth centuries. We modern North American and European readers, used as we are to longevity and to an infant mortality rate of about 1%, and afraid as we are of the dangers of overpopulation, rightly dismiss all eugenic thinking as the dream of a madman. But would we be so bothered if the infant mortality rate occasionally approached 40%, if over half of the children born in any year were destined to die before reaching the age of marriage, if the average life expectancy calculated at birth were just over thirty years, and if women did not marry until they were approximately 25, thereby reducing their period of fertility to just a few years? And this account does not make excessive allowance for epidemics, which in the sixteenth and seventeenth centuries came with predictable frequency to disrupt any semblance of demographic balance, sometimes literally decimating the population. Add to this sketch the fact that 15% of all marriageable girls never married, that during epidemics marriage was postponed by a few years if the prospect was not altogether abandoned, that during the penitential periods of the year the Church advised abstention from all sexual activity, and the fact that the population density in Southern Italy was anyhow one of the lowest in Western Europe[14] —add all of this and you have an acceptably accurate picture of the demographic reality in the face of which Campanella set himself the task of designing a better social and political order.

A utopia compelled to tolerate an occasional infant mortality rate of up to 40% would be no utopia at all, no matter how attractive its other features. Therefore, the first thing that Campanella did in his design was to lower the age of marriage to 19 for women and 21 for men—a little later if they had a frail constitution—in order to increase the women's period of fertility and to ensure sufficient vigour in the men. Then, to improve the children's chances of survival, he devised an appropriate eugenic system built on a science that knew no difference between religion, magic and astrology, on the one hand, and biology, medicine and genetics, on the other hand, each of which was to evolve as an autonomous field of research much later in history. In order to ensure that the birth rate was sufficiently higher than the death rate, he provided that sexual intercourse should occur three times a week throughout the year. And to increase the children's stamina and capacity to survive through adolescence to adulthood, he prescribed personal hygiene, good food, and plenty of exercise. To prevent adults from falling into a state of deep melancholy, he devised the stratagem of liberal therapeutic sex, while to dispel incipient sexual anxieties he allowed sex for the mere pleasure of it. And finally, in order to ensure health and longevity, he added to his design every possible hygienic precaution, including the cremation of the dead. In the city represented by this blueprint, he thought, people could live happily for a long time, some perhaps reaching the ripe age of 200.[15] But all of this required a supreme sacrifice, which was impossible to make without relinquishing one's humanity at the same time: yielding one's eros to the state. This was indeed the dream of a madman—but it would be very difficult to deny the reason in his madness and to disregard the concern for the human condition in which it is firmly grounded.

However, this reason and this concern for the human condition cannot emerge unless we look at the work in a purview fixed on the social reality of the time, on the assumption that a text always has extra-textual affiliations that enable it to reach beyond the formal confines of the genre in which it is cast, and on the principle that the critical act has also the responsibility of seeking out these affiliations. In the world of vertical intertexuality, distributed along the evolutionary axis of the genre in history, some of the issues that I have raised in this paper can easily be reduced to manneristic variations on other texts, beginning with Plato's *Republic*. In horizontal inter-texuality, they might just as easily be described in terms of parallel passages in medical, literary, and legal texts of the time. But in both cases the critical act would limit itself to demarcating a locus of meaning somewhere in other texts, altogether disregarding the question of reality. On the other hand, when we move out of these contexts—which can aid us in the study of the text as a construct but are of no help in the analysis of its motivating ideology—and we fix our gaze on social reality, those same issues begin immediately to vibrate with life. My purpose in this paper has been to show that this life is real and that it derives great ideological significance from correlative phenomena in social history. The communal possession of women, considered only a precious good of consumption, is a direct consequence of the attempt to abolish private ownership of all products of consumption; and the eugenic teleology of social institutions is an equally logical result of the effort to facilitate survival by improving the biological quality of all citizens. Once these two principles appear necessary in the face of social reality, the rest is a matter of derivation *more geometrico*.

University of Toronto

NOTES

1 F. Yates, *Giordano Bruno and the Hermetic Tradition* (New York: Vintage, 1969), p. 369.

2 Yates, p. 362.

3 P.B. Medawar and J.S. Medawar, *Aristotle to Zoos: A Philosophical Dictionary of Biology* (Cambridge: Harvard UP, 1983), p. 87.

4 T. Campanella, *La città del sole: dialogo poetico / The City of the Sun: A Poetic Dialogue*, bilingual edition by D.J. Donno (Berkeley: California UP, 1981), p. 36.
5 Campanella, p. 56.
6 Campanella, p. 52.
7 Campanella, p. 40.
8 H. Gerth and C.W. Mills, *Character and Social Structure: The Psychology of Social Institutions* (New York: Harcourt, Brace and World, Inc., 1964), p. 83.
9 F. Engels, *The Origin of the Family, Private Property and the State* (Peking: Foreign Languages Press, 1978), p. 46.
10 Campanella, p. 65.
11 K. Kautsky, *Communism in Central Europe in the Time of the Reformation* (New York: Augustus M. Kelley, 1966), p. 272.
12 Diogenes Laertius, *Vitae philosophorum*, ed. H.S. Long (Oxford: Oxford Classical Texts, 1964), 2.V.26.
13 Kautsky, p. 61.
14 R. Mols, S.J. "Population in Europe, 1500–1700," in *The Fontana Economic History of Europe*, ed. C.M. Cipolla (Glasgow: Fontana Books, 1974), pp. 38–38, 68–74.
15 Campanella, p. 88..

Francesco Guardiani

Eros and Misogyny from Giovan Battista Marino to Ferrante Pallavicino

The author of a recent study entitled "Misogyny or Feminism?" concerning the poetic treatment of women in the Renaissance concludes that no clear answer to this question exists.[1] If, however, we pose the same question for the Baroque, there would be no ambiguity in the answer: works from this period are generally characterized by unequivocal misogyny. Of particular interest is the relationship between erotic drive and misogynist rejection in the literature of the early seventeenth century. The erotic drive is no longer camouflaged by idealistic feelings, and the traditional feminine rejection of the lover becomes a sign of woman's perversity: it is from this new perspective that misogyny is born, as we shall see in considering some prominent writers of the time. The boundaries of the territory of research as declared in the title "From Marino to Pallavicino" are not intended simply as chronological limits, but more specifically as "poles of reference" between two relevant and different trends. In Marino, the misogyny is ultimately expressed by a tendency to turn away from women in order to avert the miseries of heterosexual relationships. The canonical petrarchist distress of the lover becomes, for him, realistic suffering to be avoided. The grace and gentleness of neo-Platonic madonnas is attributed to androgynous young men, and therefore a dimension of homosexuality, although never overt and plain, arises in most of his works, particularly in L'*Adone*. Ferrante Pallavicino, on the other hand, openly declares his radical misogyny, which in fact takes on violent and provocative expression.

In the historical and cultural milieu of the time, disputes over the alleged inferiority of women and the peculiarity of their psyche were commonplace and have been subsequently well documented. After the early reviews of the various positions by Giovan Battista Marchesi,[2] and Benedetto Croce's comments on the "Donne letterate del seicento,"[3] we rely today on the more analytical essays of André Rochon, Ginevra Conti Odorisio and Gabriele Muresu,[4] just to name a few. It is important to realize that at the beginning of the seventeenth century there was an insurgence of a certain sense of liberation from the axioms of neo-Platonic Petrarchism and, in general, from a very erudite and dogmatic tradition. "Non vuol filosofia de l'amar l'arte" [the art of loving rejects philosophy], denounces Scipione Errico in a poem significantly entitled "Contra l'amor platonico" [Against Platonic Love].[5] Consequently, there was a wide-spread rebellion against the typical Renaissance concept of love in favour of a realistic mode of representation.

In the following pages I will be speaking, essentially, of literary descriptions of love situations in an age that was dominated by rhetoric.[6] However, as Luigi Baldacci discovered, and as Giulio Ferroni confirmed, the rhetorical code of Petrarchism corresponded to an actual manual of social behaviour.[7] If this is true for the entire Cinquecento, it must be true *a fortiori* for the following century when a strong realism of representation entered in the treatement of love. The Baroque insistence on the presentation of the woman with all her human faults has to be considered as the effect of a revolutionary attitude born from and still attached to the general vision of life during the Renaissance. Baroque writers turned to misogyny to reject what they perceived as the hypocritical way of life of their Renaissance predecessors; they inherited the language of Petrarchism, but they used it to demystify all the essential metaphors pointing to ideal beauty and perfection in women.

The most important work that certified and defended this new tendency was L'*Adone* by Giovan Battista Marino, published in Paris in 1623.[8] Even before this "masterpiece of the century," to which I will soon return, there were open manifestations of this new important trend. Tommaso Stigliani's canzoniere, *Rime*, is a relevant case in point.[9] Stigliani felt the inadequacy of the poetic situation of the petrarchists, but unlike his Neapolitan friend and later adversary Marino, who responded with an ambiguous and meditated attitude, he reacted vehemently, attacking the core itself of the neo-Platonic concept of love—the metaphysical essence of the woman in poetry. Stigliani's position can be clearly retraced in the section entitled *Amori giocosi* of his canzoniere. The book was soon censored by the Church primarily because of this section, and later the collection was allowed to circulate without it. The quotations that I am about to present are from a rare copy of the early print, kept in the Biblioteca Angelica in Rome.[10] *Amori giocosi* contains not only obscene riddles characterized by a vulgar sense of humour, but also several innovative compositions worthy of consideration by every scholar interested in the development of Baroque literature.

Two short quotations must suffice to indicate Stigliani's radical position. Here is a madrigal on the common theme of the death of the lover demanded by an ungrateful madonna. It is entitled, "Sopra il morire" [On Death].

Ed altro non bramate
Donna che il morir mio?
Picciol certo è il desio
verso il gran merto di tanta beltade.
Voi sapete che dentro al vostro petto
il mio cor ha ricetto.
Se mi volete spento,
passatel con un stral, ch'io mi contento.[11]

[So, woman, you desire
nothing but my death?
Certainly the desire is small
compared to the greatness of your beauty.
You are aware that within your bosom
my heart has its dwelling.
Well, if you wish me gone,
drive a blade through your chest
and I'll be happy.]

The following madrigal, entitled "Meretrice che fila," [Wool-Spinning Whore] reminds one of similar poems of the "rimeria barocca," among which is a "Donna che fila" [Wool-Spinning Woman] by Marino himself.[12] Stigliani's criticism of this common poetic theme is tinged by a crude erotic realism; his misogyny appears violent and destructive in its hilarious obscenity.

O de' sensi d'Amore
mercenaria sentina,
che perpetuo disnore
sei del femineo sesso:
dimmi, mentr'or tu fili a un tempo stesso
le vite degli amanti col pensiero
e lana con la man bavosa e sporca:
sei una Parca o una Porca?[13]

[Oh you, den of vice,
mercenary of love,
perpetual dishonour to the female sex,
tell me, as you spin

the lives of lovers with your thoughts
while you spin wool
with your drooling and dirty hands,
are you a Parca or a pig?][14]

This particular position of the poet, as far as I know, had no overt following among the intellectual *élites* of the seventeenth century and, in fact, the new poets preferred to align themselves with the more urbane and polite Marino; but it is exactly the nonconformity of the *Amori giocosi* that makes these lyrics critical, because they brought about the realization that Stigliani's new attitude concerning the treatment of women had no place in poetry. The same attitude became relevant, instead, in prose, especially in the works of Ferrante Pallavicino, as we shall see.

Marino's position is more meditated and complex than Stigliani's: the basic misogynist feeling remains, and is charged with a more pronounced erotic drive, but humour and vulgarities disappear. To present the point of view of the great Neapolitan, it may be useful to recall a short passage from Canto XI of L'*Adone*; the section is dedicated to Maria de' Medici, Queen of France and Marino's benefactress.

Questa è l'eccelsa e gloriosa donna,
ch'accoppia a regio scettro animo regio,
gran reina de' Galli e dela gonna
e del sesso imperfetto eterno pregio (XI, 109).

[This is the excellent and glorious woman
who combines royal authority with royal soul,
great queen of the Gauls and of all females
eternal glory of the imperfect sex.]

The queen is said to belong to the *imperfect sex*, and the fact is here emphasised to contrast with her magnanimity and greatness. From the passage, we can also infer that the inferiority of women is universally accepted—not forgetting that this was the century during which it was debated whether or not women even possessed a soul.[15] Marino's basic concept is not, therefore, a novelty; but the common notion develops particular consequences in the mind of the poet. We find the general idea of the alleged inferiority of women, already with some theoretical implications, in several idylls of *Sampogna*.[16] In *Piramo e Tisbe*, for instance, the poet says that in women "minor naturalmente / suol esser la ragione" (213) [reason is / naturally inferior]. Throughout the *Sampogna* we are led to believe that it is precisely the inferior intellectual capability of women that renders difficult, if not virtually impossible, a perfect relationship with men. In the idyll *La ninfa avara* [The Greedy Nymph], which consists of a dialogue between Fileno (the poet himself) and Filaura (i.e. she who loves gold), the nymph does not hide the irresistable attraction she feels for gold and shamelessly associates her avarice with her vanity:

venga pur l'oro
in qualunque lavoro,
anel, vezzo, o maniglia,
o cintura, o pendente;
sia pur d'oro il presente
in moneta battuto o in massa accolto
di ciò non mi cal molto (270).

[Let gold come
in every form or shape:
ring ornament or bracelet,
or perhaps belt or pendant;
let the present be of gold,
whether coins or bullion
I don't much care.]

Fileno is very patient as he talks to the nymph elaborating on the natural beauty of the sentiments of love; but she interrupts him claiming that she does not understand, and actually takes pride in her inherent ignorance:

or con sentenze argute e detti gravi
dottrine alte e sublimi
filosofando esprimi.
Io, che semplice e roza, il basso ingegno
negli studi profondi
ho per natura a specolar mal atto,
quanto tu più ti sforzi
farmi le tue ragioni
ragionando capir, t'intendo meno (257).

[Now, with witty sentences
and profound words,
you talk like a philosopher
of great and sublime doctrines.
I, a simple and rustic woman,
have by nature a small brain
incapable of understanding
profound studies.

So, the more you try to make me
understand with reasoning,
the less I follow you.]

For Marino-Fileno, at this stage of the "dialogue," there is only one last avenue open should he decide not to renounce the pressure of love. The "ninfa avara" herself suggests that he should look elsewhere:

conviene a non vulgare
spirito peregrino
dal segnato sentier sviarsi alquanto,
e per novo cammino
dietro a novi pensier movere il corso (262).

[It is proper
for a unique and witty spirit
to stir away from the common path,
and to open new roads
following new thoughts.]

Filaura is the archetype of the woman who is avaricious and vain, who demands jewels and money in return for her love. Marino-Fileno rejects the abhorred *conditio sine qua non* and turns to where his feelings can be understood and shared. He turns to homosexuality and becomes Orpheus in another idyll.

Mai d'altra donna agli occhi suoi non piacque
vista leggiadra, e mai
di novella beltà fiamma non l'arse,
sol mostrando sen gia con versi molli
ai giovani pastori
dolce cantando, i puerili amori (25).

[He never liked again
to look at beautiful women,
never again his heart was lit
by a new lovely flame.
He would only go about
singing sweet verses
of adolescent loves
to young shepherds.]

What is remarkable in the new "puerili amori" [adolescent loves], the love stories sung by Marino-Orpheus, is that all of them (as well as some others of the same kind) are presented again in the *major poem*: the stories of Atteone, Ganimede, Giacinto, Adone himself, Attide, Narciso and Pampino.

In L'*Adone*, "the poem of the century," Marino's theory of love is presented in its mature and complete form. The entire poem could be seen as a meditated demonstration of the impossibility of gaining happiness through a heterosexual relationship. Adonis and Venus are portrayed as the archetypes of perfect lovers: he is the most handsome adolescent of all time, a virgin just out of puberty (Marino specifies that he is fifteen years old); she is the most beautiful and lovely woman ever imagined by mankind. She falls in love with the youth and her love is fully returned. But, in spite of this, the relationship does not work. Nature herself, who dictated their love, is incapable of guaranteeing their continued happiness: the extraordinary power of Fate, mysterious and implacable, intervenes to block the dream of erotic perfection:

> Vuolsi goder mentre si pote e lice,
> ma che giova cozzar col fato avverso? (XV, 76).
>
> [One wants to enjoy love
> when it is possible and permitted,
> but what can one do against the adverse Fate.]

says the poet. Homosexual love, admittedly, does not correspond to another dream of perfection in love; it is instead an expedient remedy for a mind that has not lost a basic optimism for life and recognizes that it is better to turn to an imperfect form of love, rather than to renounce it completely. The "amori imperfetti" [imperfect loves] (but not tragic), be they homosexual or heterosexual, are so abundant and described with such an intense participation in Marino's work as to suggest that it is only through them that the poet could feel at peace. Their presence is, furthermore, an indication of a certain refinement of feelings that Marino considered to be essential.

> Sempre quel ch'è vietato e quel ch'è raro
> più n'invoglia il desire e più n'è caro (V, 109)
>
> [That which is forbidden and rare
> is always the most desired and precious]

says Adone, and the poet himself comments,

> Ombreggia il ver Parnaso e non rivela

> gli alti misteri [of love] ai semplici profani (I, 10).
>
> [The true Parnassus shades and ne'er reveals
> its mysteries to the simple and profane]
> (Trans. H.M. Priest)

All this, together with the sentence that follows,

> Smoderato piace termina in doglia (I, 10),
>
> [Immoderate pleasure terminates in grief]
> (Trans. H.M. Priest)

which is perhaps the most famous of the entire poem, leads us to recognize a balanced and suffered moderation in the attitude of the poet in regard to love: on one hand there is the impossibility of reaching perfect happiness, on the other, the pressure of erotic passion. Notwithstanding the common ideas concerning misogyny held by the two writers, Ferrante Pallavicino's position is essentially the opposite of Marino's. Several preliminary considerations are necessary before trying to establish a comparison between these two prominent intellectuals of the seventeenth century: different are the literary genres in which they express themselves (Marino in poetry, Pallavicino in prose), different are the social environments in which their works came to light (the court of France *versus* the Republic of Venice), and probably different are the ideal audiences they envisioned for their works. I will not deal with these problems specifically, but concentrate on showing how their common misogynist feelings could create two different attitudes in regard to women.

It is from the time of Benedetto Croce's erudite writings on Baroque prose works that some importance has been attributed to the novelists of the seventeenth century, but only recently has there been considerable attention devoted to Pallavicino.[17] We owe, for instance, to Armando Marchi, a precise critical edition of Pallavicino's most important work, *Il corriero svaligiato* [The Robbed Courier];[18] and it is with a remark by Marchi on the general perspective offered by Pallavicino that it seems appropriate to start the discussion on the position of the Baroque novelist. Marchi states that with *Il corriero svaligiato* "occorre fare il contrario di quello che si usa fare con un testo barocco . . . sollecitare risposte storico-ideologiche" [it is necessary to do the contrary of that which is usually done with a Baroque text . . . search for historical and ideological answers].[19] Pallavicino, in fact, is mostly interested in exposing what he considered to be "the two major impostures of the time", the political and the ethical. I am not concerned with the first. The problem the writer confronts, with respect to the "moral imposture", is primarily that of the hypocritical behaviour in the man-woman relationship. Prostitution was rampant at the time; it has been calculated that there were approximately 20,000 prostitutes in Venice. The convents were full of nuns forced into monastic life by their parents in order to save the great expense of a dowry. Luxury was excessive and considered a social necessity. Platonic love was still present in poetry but nowhere in actual life. Women were seen as the culprits of the general debauchery by Pallavicino and by most intellectuals. It is important to realize that his attitude was not dictated by a spirit of renewal of ancient values or by a spirit of reform. His criticism was mostly destructive and designed to shake the conscience of his readers with no concern whatsoever for the consequences. His attacks are especially vehement against prostitutes. In opposition to their practice he recalls the type of relationship regulated by the law of nature, and he argues that since nature had been more generous to men, their superiority should not be questioned. He sees the idealization of the woman in the neo-Platonic dream of perfection as a great deception. His misogyny is based on the idea that women have overturned the law of nature to their advantage and have created a form of love that is cruel and mercenary. The position of the writer is radical, but simple and straightforward, and this is why we find in his works "allusioni oscene, epiteti infamanti: una misoginia popolaresca, un eros animalesco . . . sesso ingiusto e discortese, donne perfide[20] [obscene allusions, slanderous epithets: a misogyny of the common, bestial eroticism . . . unjust and discourteous sex, treacherous women] and so on. The writer very rarely touches on philosophical arguments. He fights an imposture that should be clear to everyone without supporting documentation. In his forty-fifth letter of the *Corriero*, "Sopra l'uso del pagar le puttane" [On the Custom of Paying Prostitutes], he has this to say:

Questo è l'uso non so da chi introdotto di pagar le puttane con tanto pregiudizio dell'uomo, e della superiorità del sesso maschile, obligato a pagare ciò che la femina, come soggetta, ha debito di donare a nostro compiacimento. . . . Dovrà l'uomo tolerare le insolenze di questa schiava, alla formazione di cui dando una costa l'ha annodata con una catena d'obbligazione, come comprata col suo? . . . A ragione potrebbero gli uomini invidiare lo stato dei bruti, e desiderare l'autorità, con cui soprasede il maschio alla femina nella nostra specie, mentre ovunque lo scorge stimulato dall"appetito, monta, cavalca, gode, né senza altro riscontro s'obbliga a dar la paga de'suoi gusti. Un povero amante dovrà dunque essere peggio trattato d'un cane, e quando non abbia denari sarà privo di que' piaceri che non si negano ad una bestia? Maledetto istituto, conforme il quale a suono di preziosi metalli si regola l'amorosa danza, posta la gabella sopra quelle dolcezze, che sì abbondandemente dona la natura).[21]

[This is the custom, introduced by God-knows-whom, so harmful to men and to the superiority of the male sex, who is forced to pay that which the woman, as subject, has the duty to give for our satisfaction. . . . Must man tolerate the arrogance of this slave to whose creation he contributed by giving a rib and in so doing establishing her obligation to him, her dependence upon him? For a good reason, then, men could envy the state of the brutes and desire the authority that brutes have over females in our species; in fact, men see the brutes that mount, ride and enjoy sex with no other payment for the woman besides their own pleasure. Must a poor lover, then, be treated worse than a dog, and when he has no money must he be deprived of those pleasures that are not denied to a beast? Cursed institute! According to which the amorous dance follows the rhythm of the sound of money. Cursed institute, that taxes those sweet pleasures so abundant in nature.]

The misogyny of the author becomes more subtle in other letters. In the most famous one, "Contra le donne" [Against Women], for which he got an angry reply from Suor Arcangela Tarabotti, he mantains that the major problem with women is their lack of intellectual capabilities: "in ragione di differenza [rispetto agli uomini] essa non ha punto di ragione, perché, senza senno, opera quasi bruto, non quasi ragionevole.[22] [with respect to man, woman has no reason at all because, lacking intelligence, she acts like a brute, not like a reasoning human being]. It is difficult to believe, he continues, that women possess no reason at all, because (and he agrees with the more liberal minds in this) they must be granted a soul. The only conclusion he can come to, then, is that their minds are inherently malevolent and opposed to the benevolent minds of men.

These are not Pallavicino's most rhetorically effective arguments, which I think should be retraced in the ironic outburst of his discourse, especially in the *Retorica delle puttane*,[23] but they are his typical points. In a broad cultural sense, he should be seen as a great fighter in the name of anti-Platonism; he definitely stands against the values instituted by the lyrical tradition since the wicked women he condemns are the same ones, "celebrated" by poets, who

Nella gioventù, se sono amabili tormentano, se odiose annoiano, se amano tiranneggiano, se non amano uccidono. . . . Nella vecchiezza poi, con molto maggior discapito della ragione, concertano la perversità dei costumi coi progressi del tempo.[24]

[In their youth, if they are lovable they torment, if they are obnoxious they are boring, if they love they act like tyrants, if they don't love they kill. . . . Then, in their old age, with greater detriment of reason, they, combine the perversity of customs with the progression of time.]

In fact, we can find the same women in many Baroque *canzonieri* in which, however, the condemnation will be rather oblique and subtle.

With Pallavicino, we really see the high tide of seventeenth-century misogyny. His dramatic denunciation of women had the potential to create a constructive reaction, to involve the intellectuals of the time in a broad debate on ethical issues. But the dialogue never came; there were no alternative proposals and the reactionary forces prevailed. That which remained was the ambiguity of Marino's position with the pursuit of imperfect forms of love, and this is why throughout the century we encounter a long series of beautiful women, some with missing teeth, some with their hair full of lice, some with their speech impaired or with other similar disenticements. The language and imagery of neo-Platonic Petrarchism remained and the revolt expressed itself through an inner deformation of the themes.

To Pallavicino's denouncements the only rebuttal came from the resentful pen of Suor Arcangela.[25] Her work certainly presents historical relevance, revealing the author to be a truly inspired *ante-litteram* feminist; but in reality the exchange with the outspoken misogynyst never took off and remained only on the level of polemics. It wa a sterile confrontation because the nun, understandably, could never relate to (or agree with) Pallavicino's position on the globality of his thought, which was innovative, libertarian and modern.

Perhaps only in our time, now that the positive value of the Baroque erotic drive has been indisputably recognized, can we begin to understand that Pallavicino and Suor Arcangela, together with Marino, were fighting the same enemy on the same front: the reactionary power of the establishment, barricaded behind conservatism and indifference.

University of Toronto

NOTES

1 Luigi Monga, "Misogyny or Feminism? A Topos in the Early Renaissance Novella," *Fifteeenth-Century Studies* 10 (1984), pp. 121–33.

2 Giovan Battista Marchesi, "Le polemiche sul sesso femminile ne' sec. XV e XVII," *Giornale Storico della Letteratura Italiana* 25 (1895), pp. 362–69.

3 Benedetto Croce, "Donne letterate del Seicento," *Nuovi saggi sulla letteratura italiana del Seicento* (1931; Bari: Laterza, 1968), pp. 155–72.

4 André Rochon, Francois Glenisson and Silvia Fabrizio-Costa, *Au pays d'Éros. Littérature et érotisme en Italie de la Renaissance à l'âge baroque*, primière sèrie (Paris: Université de la Sorbonne Nouvelle, 1986). Ginevra Conti Odorisio, *Storia dell'idea femminista in Italia* (Torino: Eri, 1980); by the same author, see also *Donna e società nel Seicento. Lucrezia Marinelli e Arcangela Tarabotti* (Roma: Bulzoni, 1979). Gabriele Muresu, "Chierico e libertino" *Letteratura italiana*, ed. Alberto Asor Rosa, vol. 5 (Torino: Einaudi, 1986), pp. 903–42.

5 In *Marino e marinisti*, ed. Giuseppe Guido Ferrero (Milano-Napoli: Ricciardi, 1954), p. 788.

6 Cf. Giovanni Pozzi, in Giovan Battista Marino, *L'Adone*, Giovanni Pozzi ed., 2 vols. (Milano: Mondadori, 1976), vol. 2, p. 13.

7 Cf. Luigi Baldacci, *Il petrarchismo italiano nel Cinquecento* (Milano-Napoli: Ricciardi, 1957), pp. 86–164; Giulio Ferroni, Amedeo Quondam, *La "locuzione artificiosa". Teoria ed esperienza della lirica a Napoli nell'età del manierismo* (Roma: Bulzoni, 1973), pp. 13–20.

8 A new interest for this work of Marino is certified by two recent critical editions, one by Giovanni Pozzi (see footnote n. 6) and the other by Marzio Pieri: Giovan Battista Marino, *Adone*, 2 vols. (Bari: Laterza, 1975–1977). The English reader may find selections from the poem in *Adonis*, translated and with an introduction by Harold Martin Priest (Ithaca N.Y.: Cornell University Press, 1967).

9 Tommaso Stigliani, *Rime* (Venezia: Ciotti, 1605).

10 I am indebted to Giorgio Fulco, whom I wish to thank here for the generosity he demonstrated in helping me to acquire a copy of the rare section of Stigliani's Rime.

11 Stigliani, *Rime*, p. 265. The following translations are mine unless otherwise specified.

12 In *Lira*, 2nd part (Venezia: Ciotti, 1602), p. 90.

13 Stigliani, *Rime*, p. 268.

14 The madrigal centers upon the play on words between "Parca" (Fate) and "Porca" (sow), which cannot be rendered in English.

15 The point was debated, for instance, in the exchange between Suor Arcangela Tarabotti and Ferrante Pallavicino, discussed later in this paper.

16 Giovan Battista Marino, *La sampogna* (Venezia: Giunti, 1621).

17 Extremely relevant to the work of Pallavicino are the bibliographical data presented by Laura Coci: "Bibliografia di Ferrante Pallavicino," *Studi secenteschi* 24 (1983), pp. 221–306; "Ferrante a Venezia: nuovi documenti d'archivio," *Studi secenteschi* 27 (1986), pp. 263–316. See also Albert Mancini, *Romanzi e romanzieri del Seicento* (Napoli: SEN, 1981); "La narrativa libertina degli Incogniti. Tipologia e forme," *Forum italicum* 16, 3 (1982), pp. 203–29; "Stampa e censura ecclesiastica a Venezia: il caso del *Corriere svaligiato*," *Esperienze letterarie* 10, 4 (1985), pp. 3–36.

18 Ferrante Pallavicino, *Il corriero svaligiato*, ed. Armando Marchi (Parma: Università di Parma, 1984).
19 *Il corriero svaligiato*, p. x.
20 *Il corriero svaligiato*, p. xii.
21 *Il corriero svaligiato*, p. 113.
22 *Il corriero svaligiato*, p. 11.
23 Ferrante Pallavicino, *La retorica delle puttane*, (Villafranca [i.e. Amsterdam], 1673). There are some doubts concerning the authorship of this work, which was, nevertheless, clearly inspired by the analogous "treatise" by Pietro Aretino; Coci, however, attributes it to Pallavicino.
24 Ferrante Pallavicino, *Il corriero svaligiato*, cit., p. 13.
25 Galerana Baratotti [Suor Arcangela Tarabotti], *La semplicità ingannata* (Leida: 1654).

Winfried Schleiner

Ethical Problems of the Lie that Heals in Renaissance Literature

While the Hippocratic oath is evidence that speculation about the ethics of medical curing is old, reference to the oath, as also to the aphorism *primum non nocere*, seems today more like a bow to the academy of learning than a bow to the learning of the academy. The *Journal of Medical Ethics*, which has contributed significantly to raising our sensitivity to ethical issues in doctor-patient relationships as well as also to circumscribing the kinds of documents (e.g., medical cases) best used to elicit and teach ethical concerns, has done little to illuminate the historical dimension of the subject. My present contribution is a modest attempt to illustrate by one single instance or problem what texts of the past from different genres can and should be assembled in the absence of a consciously self-reflexive discipline of medical ethics and to salvage for historical purpose a few distinctions of provisional certainty from the steadily eroding body of literary scholarship. That my texts are from the Renaissance is not entirely an accident: for while it would still have to be proven that for the history of medical ethics that period was one of the *wendezeiten* (to use Karl Jaspers' term for a pivotal period of change), I think we can agree that the Renaissance brought the analysis of ethical dilemmas to new heights in the discipline of moral casuistry, of which entire shelves of books on cases of conscience are the evidence. It would be entirely misleading to think of these books as merely a short-lived and perhaps parochial Jesuit phenomenon, ridiculed out of existence through Pascal's *Provinciales*. Some recent studies have shown that cases of conscience were collected and discussed on both sides of the Channel and, even more importantly, that English writers of imaginative literature as different as Donne, Shakespeare, and Defoe conceived of the determinants of moral action in ways similar to the moral casuists.[1]

It would certainly be interesting to write a history of the ethical issues of curing vexing us now, which include: the rights of the human embryo; euthanasia (and the obligation to prolong life); secrecy; doctor-patient relationships (particularly in psychiatry and psychoanalysis); and the use of deception for healing. Such a history would reveal, for instance, that the Renaissance gave some attention to the problematics of interrupted pregnancy. The dangers of such an account are the dangers besetting any approach to medical history: not only that we let our present concerns dictate what we want to see of the past (which to some extent is unavoidable, for I admit that I am drawn to the topic of deception by my interest in imaginative literature with its assertions of disputed truth value), but that we become absorbed with determining how closely so-called "advanced" thinkers of the past anticipate present solutions. In older works on the history of medicine and literature of the Renaissance almost the general approach (and occasionally still to be found in journal articles), this latter perspective is now discredited, and rightly so, since it involves what may be called a mixing of paradigms.[2] On the other extreme, Derrida's strident critique of Foucault's historical work on madness for failing to present such a history "from within," i.e., Derrida's attempt to out-Foucault Foucault, shows the difficulty of any such project, but does not point to an alternative to reconstructing the past system of ideas (i.e., the past paradigm) at least as a point of departure.[3] While it may be more readily granted that such reconstruction is necessary when the past system is radically different from ours, this preliminary activity is at least just as important in the presence of *faux amis*, key terms that form part also of later systems but have acquired a different "value" (in the sense of Saussure's *valeur*) since they are part of a different paradigm.

In trying to determine the role in the Renaissance of what a modern writer on medical ethics has called "the lie that heals," we are guided by Renaissance medical works to their sections on the imagination. Quite different from any post-Romantic notion of imagination, this faculty is generally conceived of in that period as the lowest of the mental faculties as spacialized and visualized, for example, in Spenser's House of Alma (*Faerie Queene*, II, ix, 50–52). The imagination fed reason the images it worked upon and in this process could easily deceive. Ultimately therapy of patients with fixed delusions aimed at restoring the supremacy of reason and was based on a few theoretical assumptions shared by most medical writers. In his section "Of the Force of the Imagination" (pt. 1, sec. 2, mem. 3, subs. 2) and throughout his *Anatomy of Melancholy*, Robert Burton accurately records a Renaissance trend to assign the causes of melancholy to the imagination. He agrees with Nicholas Piso and other medical authorities in saying that the fountain of distempers is *laesa imaginatio* (wounded or injured imagination) and draws upon Thomas Feyens (Fienus), who in an eminently interesting book called *De viribus imaginationis* held that melancholic humors result from *prava imaginatio* (distorted imagination). Hence, says Feyens, they cannot be expelled from the body except by inducing other and contrary images in the imagination. In the resulting therapy, the healers become stage managers and actors who act within the fiction of the patient, even expanding it. Thus one finds scores of reports like those of people who believed they contained frogs or snakes and were cured by a physician who pretended to extract the animals from their innards, of patients who thought that antlers were growing on their heads and were healed by a clever physician's simulated operation, or (possibly the most frequently rehearsed case) of a voluntary retentive, who refused to urinate for fear of submerging his town and was coaxed to empty his bladder by a simulated fire threatening his town.

Unfortunately Renaissance medical writers rarely comment on the ethics of such cases, which I have described in greater detail elsewhere.[4] Often emphasis is on the ingenuity of the "lie," i.e., the fiction with which the patient's behavior is modified. The narration of the medical case or exemplum usually breaks off with some initial success. In most cases (as most clearly in the instance of the voluntary retentive where therapy maybe said to preserve life) it is simply assumed that the end justifies the means. Even what is one of the most elaborate medical cases of this sort I have read, Platter's very instructive account of dealing with a man who believed he harbored frogs in his body, does not really question the ethics of pretense, although in this case manipulation fails: since the patient has studied medicine he is alert to Platter's trick of slipping a frog into his stool during the purge.[5] His reaction "You can't do that to me" expresses not moral dismay at the "lie," but offended medical pride. The practised therapy is not called into question, at least not by the medical writers, although its ambiguities are explored in imaginative literature (for instance in *Don Quixote*).

Are we entitled to take notice when a particular form of deception is not called into question, i.e., can we construe an argument from silence and give weight in our context to elements that do not call for Renaissance comment (*Cum tacent clamant*)? While it may be legitimate to apply any ethical question whatsoever to a text of the past in order to tease out its hidden assumptions, I will argue that passages that themselves problematize medical deception take a certain precedence in our context. Fortunately there are two areas (which overlap to a degree) where medical writers occasionally do foreground the ethical question of curing the imagination through the imagination, although in both areas the more memorable treatments of the question may again be in *belles lettres*: these areas are witchcraft and sex.

1. Sexual Dysfunction Cured by Pretended Magic

It does not take much historical sense to realize that any healing by magic would have been looked upon with suspicion by the Church authorities almost anywhere in Europe during the Renaissance, for such healing could be seen as invoking the devil. Nevertheless it is worth noting that in that period a medical doctor and skeptic in most matters of alleged witchcraft could find that a cure by pretended magic works and yet condemn its use.

The sixteenth-century physician Jan Wier, one of the most courageous defenders of alleged witches, reports an experience narrated by someone *en une lettre imprimeé* of how a certain nobleman overcame his temporary impotence:

> Jay souvenance, dit il, d'avoir oui iurer a un gentilhomme qu'il estoit lié et encorcellé tellement qu'il ne pourroit plus avoir campagnie de femme: enquoy ie le voulus aider, taschant par divers argumens de luy arracher ceste imagination. Or voyant que ie ne gaignois rien, ie fis semblant d'estre de son avis et le confermer, en monstrant le livre de Cleopatra de la beauté des femmes, et y lisois une recepte contenant que l'homme lié seroit guéri s'il faisoit un onguent d'oeuf de corbeau mesle de l'huile de navette, et qu'il s'en frotast tout le corps. Luy oyant cela, se confiant es paroles du livre, fit l'experience de l'onguent, et recouvra l'envie d'habiter avec les femmes.[6]

Wier is explicit in his disclaimer that the ointment might have any power on its own, but reasons nevertheless "pource que l'imagination estoit preoccupee de fausse opinion, il falloit la guerir par un remede qu'elle troivast bon" (II, 450). The wording of this reasoning draws on medical tradition in the treatment of certain kinds of "melancholy" characterized as *laesa imaginatio*. Significantly the speaker *pretends* to agree with the patient and offers the ointment as a placebo.

But while the traditional cure of the melancholic imagination through the imagination is the context in which both Wier and his informant see this case, Wier is quite aware that the cure of impotence by pretended magic is of a different order from the cures of melancholics who refused to eat or to urinate and had to be tricked into performing those life-preserving activities by elaborate schemes. Though Wier is unquestionably aware of the threat of the Inquisition, his reservation about such a cure is different from the objections of the ecclesiastical inquisitors. His concern seems to be less that evil forces might be invoked (for in this case the skeptic Wier does not see them operating at all), but rather that the use of magic on the part of even the skeptic and lucid therapist might confirm a belief in witchcraft. Therefore, after reporting how the concocted ointment healed the gentleman of his temporary impotence and after referring to the principle quoted earlier that an element of imagination has to be cured through the imagination, he adds: "Et pourtant ie desire que les adversaires torchent de leurs yeux ceste brouée de superstitieuse crédulité qui leur offusque le iugement" (II, 250).

To this case reported by a physician, I would like to add one narrated by someone who in this instance acted as a lay therapist. In his essay on the "Power of the Imagination," throughout conceived as a negative force that interferes with proper perception, Michel de Montaigne tells the case of a French earl whom he himself helped to overcome his temporary impotence by a ruse. Haunted by fears of witchcraft and particularly of one man who had been the bride's suitor and was coming to the wedding, this lord had engaged an aged relative to celebrate the wedding at his house. When this relative communicated these concerns to Montaigne, he asked her to leave the matter to him, for by some good fortune he had a certain piece of flat gold engraved with celestial symbols effective against a variety of conditions. It was held in place by a ribbon that could be tied under the chin. I quote the rest of the story in Florio's translation:

> I tolde the Earle, he might happily be in danger, and come to some misfortune as others had done, the rather because some were present, that would not sticke to procure him some ill lucke, and which was worse, some spitefull shame; but neverthelesse I willed him boldly to goe to bed: For I would shew him the parte of a true friend, and in his neede, spare not for his good to employ a miracle, which was in my power; alwayes provided, that on his honour he would promise me faithfully to keepe it very secret; which was onely, that when about mid-night he should have his candle brought him, if he had had no good successe in his businesse, hee should make such and such a signe to me. It fel out, his mind was so quailed, and his eares so dulled that by reason of the bond where with the trouble of his imagination had tied him, hee could not runne on poste: and at the houre appointed, made the signe agreed upon betweene us, I came and whispered him in the eare, that under pretence to put us all out of his chamber, he should rise out of his bed, and in jesting maner take my night gowne which I had on, and put it upon himselfe (which he might well doe, because we were much of one stature) and keepe it on till he had performed my appointment, which was, that when we should bee gone out of the Chamber, he should withdraw himselfe to make water,

and using certaine jestures, I had shewed him, speake such wordes thrice over. And every time he spake them he should girt the Ribbond, which I put into his handes, and very carefully place the plate thereto fastned, just upon his kidneys, and the whole figure, in such a posture. All which when he had accordingly done, and the laste time so fastened the ribbond, that it might neither be untide nor stirred from his place, hee should then boldely and confidently returne to his charge, and not forget to spreade my night-gowne upon his bed, but so as it might cover them both.[7]

The "magic" worked, or as Montaigne puts it (playing on one of Ficino's distinctions), the magic characters proved more venerean than solar: the earl was able to perform properly.

Like most of the examples in Montaigne's essay on the powers of the imagination, this story shows how some misalignment in perception may lead even to physical dysfunction. But in addition it proves that the power of "magic" lies in the believer and illustrates how this power lends itself to manipulation by the lucid skeptic. Montaigne realises that manipulation is morally ambiguous and closes the case with a subtle palinode:

Ce fut une humeur prompte et curieuse qui me convia à tel effect, esloigne de ma nature. Je suis ennemi des actions subtiles et feinte, et hay la finesse, en mes mains, non seulement recreative, mais aussi profitable. Si l'action n'est vicieuse, la routte l'est (ed. M. Rat, p. 99).

End and means are unadjusted at least in theory; the moral dilemma remains acute.

Both Wierus and Montaigne show a higher awareness of the ethical tension field of such cure or attempted cure than Robert Burton, who while collecting the recondite and bizarre, appears to stint any latent ethical dilemma. On the principle of cures by magic he merely says: "'Tis not permitted to be done, I confess; yet often attempted."[8]

2. *Let them have their desire–or imagine so*

Burton devotes a long section to the ultimate cure of love melancholy: "The last refuge and surest remedy, to be put in practice in the utmost place, when no other means will take effect, is to let them go together, and enjoy one another" (Pt. 3, sec. 3, memb. 5, subs. 5; III, 228). Of course he is aware of difficulties: hardness of heart of one of the parties involved, unreasonable parents, the practice of enforced marriages, etc. Since the two persons' enjoyment of one another is not conceivable to him outside of marriage, the question of cure (of love melancholy) becomes to Burton in effect a *question de mariage*, which he debates at extraordinary length. And since marriage of the two parties desiring each other past reason does not seem morally questionable to him, the ethical question of cure by "letting them have their desire," does not present itself.

To the physician Jacques Ferrand this type of cure is more problematical for two reasons: (1) he questions whether sexual intercourse within or outside marriage will in fact "cure" love madness, for acted out desire may beget more desire, and (2) he knows of a medical tradition of prescribing otherwise illicit sex for the cure of love madness.

Ferrand takes note of this tradition and rejects it as "impious":

> I dare not bee so impious as to prescribe for the cure of our Patient, as *Avicen*, and *Haly Abbas* doe, *Emptionem puellarum, et plurimum concubitum ipsarum: et earum renovationum, et delectationem cum ipsis.*[9]

Such wicked opinions (namely the cure by bought sex) are not surprising with these Mahometans, he says, considering that their Koran allows them to have many wives and concubines, nor should one be amazed to find them with poets who make luxury a virtue as for instance Ovid and Lucretius. He reserves his moral indignation for the Christian physicians like Arnaldus de Villeneuve, Valescus de Tarenta and Marsilio Ficino who subscribe to the same manner of cure. For him ultimately to leave it to theologians to dispute the question whether in an extreme case illicit intercourse may be allowed in the interest of cure is not truly a concession, for he clearly rejects this casuistic reasoning, saying that he believes, "as the Morall Philosophers teach us, that Vice is never cured by Vice, but by Virtue" (278).

While Ferrand thus has no interest in exploring the borderline between licit and illicit intercourse in therapy, he refers to a case (in the context of the cure of selective impotence) that is at least marginally relevant. He reports, with apparent approval, how in the twelfth century, Peter II of Aragon was cured of his inability to sleep with his wife by a bedtrick: the queen substituted for one of his concubines. The ruse worked so well that he abandoned his concubines and she bore him a successor.

That Ferrand, who so often wears his moral concerns on the tip of his tongue, does not show any awareness of the moral ambivalence of this "cure," indicates his narrow limits as a moral casuist. When Shakespeare had used the bedtrick in the intricate plots of *Measure for Measure* and *All's Well That Ends Well*, he, by contrast, held his moral flashlight into the murkiness and even the darkness of the trick. Nevertheless a medical writer like Ferrand is useful in approaching Renaissance imaginative literature in spite of and perhaps precisely because of that limited moral penetration, for he shows exactly how much clever subterfuge could go unquestioned if, as in the case of the medieval example of Peter II of Aragon, the end (in this case feudal succession) was felt compelling.

In spite of Ferrand's disagreement with it, the tradition of medical thought from Avicenna to Ficino referred to by Ferrand is also instructive background for the Doctor in *Two Noble Kinsmen*, who, for his ingenuity in healing a love melancholic by morally questionable trickery (that ultimately includes sexual intercourse), has been called a "despicable pandar" by editors possibly unfamiliar with that tradition. In fact, as Paul Bertram reports, the alleged difference between the Doctor's role as a "kindly" therapist in Act IV (scene iii) and as "a despicable pandar" in the final act has been used by some critics to argue for a dual authorship of these scenes and of the play (by Shakespeare and Fletcher).[10] Although Hallet Smith does not cut matters that fine, he says in the influential Riverside edition that these scenes are Fletcher's because, in addition to the extended sentimentality of the daughter's situation, "the coarseness of the doctor's suggested cure by seduction" is "far more characteristic of Fletcher than of Shakespeare."[11] My interest is not at all to determine authorship, but to highlight the ethical sophistication with which the author, whoever he may have been, presents the daughter's cure. It is well known that while much of the plot of *Two Noble Kinsmen* is based on Chaucer, the subplot involving the Jailor's Daughter, who falls in love with noble Palamon, frees him, goes mad because of unrequited love, and finally is cured by a clever stratagem, is the Renaissance playwright's invention.

Of course the Daughter's illness is love melancholy: her "distemper" is characterized by thirst (IV.iii.4; melancholy is a dry and cold humor), and her imagination is troubled by painful visions. This is not the pleasant delusion in the Athenaean/Erasmian tradition that can be called pleasing both to the patient and to the beholder;[12] the tell-tale sign for the Athenaean case is that cured of his folly, the patient chides his physician for returning him from king to footman or from the owner of all the ships entering Piraeus to a poor bagman walking the harbor. By contrast the Daughter's visions are painful and disturbing: she projects her searing jealousy of Palamon to the other world where she imagines Dido pleasing him. Even more disturbingly for those watching her, the Daughter seems to have an awareness of her "madness" and is both attracted and repulsed by suicide, with which the Renaissance associated certain types of melancholics: "If one be mad, or hang or drown themselves," she says as she mulls about hell, "thither they go—Jupiter bless us!—and there shall be put a cauldron of lead and usurers' grease, amongst a whole million of cutpurses—" (IV.iii. 34–38).

"How her brain coins [i.e., counterfeits]!" the Doctor explains as he listens to her unobserved (IV.iii.40), and as he notices that she "continues this fancy" (1. 48), he shows his astuteness by confirming a diagnosis the audience knows to be correct: "'Tis not an engraff'd madness, but a most thick and profound melancholy" (48–49). Like other doctors in Shakespeare, for instance the doctor in Macbeth who replies negatively to the question "Canst thou not minister to a mind diseased?" (Macbeth, V.iii.40), this doctor is conscious of his limitations:[13] "I think she has a perturb'd mind, which I cannot minister to" (IV.iii.39–60). But when he hears that the girl may have cared for another young man before setting eye on Palamon, the doctor comes up with a stratagem that at its first articulation is wrongly associated by some critics with a version of the bedtrick. According to Paul Bertram, "his plan for curing the Daughter . . . is no different in the earlier scene . . . even if it is necessarily less explicitly expressed . . . than it is in the later; he tells the Wooer to disguise himself as Palamon, slip in the darkened room where the girl is to be confined,

> crave her, drink to her, and still among,
> intermingle your petition of grace and acceptance into her favor. . . .
>
> (IV.iii.88–89; Bertram 272)

That this should necessarily be an implied invitation to the wooer to sleep with the girl does not seem warranted by the text; in fact the sentence partially quoted begins: "Desire to eat with her. . . ." By the pretense that her Palamon cares for her, she is going to be tricked to accept life-sustaining food: "It is a falsehood she is in, which is with falsehood to be combated. This may bring her to eat, to sleep, and reduce what is now out of square in her into their former law and regimen" (IV.iii.93–96).

The sentence "It is a falsehood she is in which is with falsehood to be combated" expresses the principle on which Renaissance doctors based mere modification of behavior, but also cure. This cure takes a new turn in the following act—as some critics would have it, to explicitness, but as I understand it, to a morally explicitly ambiguous compromise between the cure by "letting them have their desire" and the cure by falsehood or imagination.

We may begin by calling attention to the obvious, namely that the one traditional cure of love madness, which Ferrand summarizes in order to reject, is not a cure by the imagination: in fact if the patient is cured from melancholy stemming from unrequited love through sexual intercourse bought for money, the "cure" is brought about more by physical than mental gratification—at best one could talk of a remedy in the Ovidian *remedium amoris* tradition. At the other end of the spectrum in Ferrand, that is, at the pole of imagination, is the lightly told story of the young Egyptian who dreamed that he had sex with a young courtisan he admired; by gratifying his desire in his dream he was so well "cured of his Malady" that the courtisan in fact demanded payment for her (only imagined) services (ch. 23: 275). The doctor in *Two Noble Kinsmen* steers right between these two poles.

In the second scene dealing with the girl's therapy, the doctor explicitly eggs on the Wooer to have intercourse with her, whom in a previous meeting the young man has already "half persuaded" (V.ii.3) that he is Palamon:

DOCTOR: . . . If she entreat again, do any thing, Lie with her, if she ask you.
JAILOR: Ho there, doctor!
DOCTOR: Yes, in the way of cure. (V.ii.17–19)

As the Doctor addresses his words to the self-interested and naturally receptive Wooer (who is already dressed "in habit of Palamon," according to the headnotes), the girl's father is given the role of voicing the ethical objection in the simplest and most believable form: "Ho, there doctor!" The ethical dimension of the doctor's therapy becomes strikingly apparent through the father's almost automatic response. This is not the considered response of a Greek chorus, but a gut-reaction that is ethical although potentially comical. The Jailor gains in moral stature as he rejects the Doctor's justification of premarital sex as "in the way of cure" (equivalent to the casuist's "in the interest of cure") requesting: "But first, by your leave, / I' th' way of honesty" (V.ii.19–20). While the word honesty also has some gender-specific connotations, his unequivocal primacy of "honesty" marks a rejection of casuistry. His intransigent position is equivalent to the famous Kantian rejection of all compromise of truth in the most compelling (and even life-threatening) circumstances.[14]

Ultimately the playwright does not choose for us a view to be adopted. Both opinions are dramatic perspectives and have elements that lend themselves to satire (the ethical gut-reaction on the one hand, the physician's professional excitement about the neatness of the case on the other). Even in productions that play up the satirical and even farcical elements to the hilt, the ethical dimension of the cure will be foregrounded. The spectators may laugh at both protagonists, but they can hardly stay neutral on the crucial issue.

The contrast between rejection of casuistry and the acceptance of weighing ends and means is further sharpened by the Doctor's rejecting the logical priority or primacy of the ethical dimension proposed by the Jailor and the Doctor's substitution of chronological primacy for it:

JAILOR: But first, by your leave, I' th' way of honesty.
DOCTOR: That's but niceness.
Nev'r cast your child away for honesty.
Cure her first this way; then if she will be honest,
She has the past before her. (V.ii.19–23)

By Renaissance and even by modern standards this view accords well with a common opinion of a pragmatic physician: if adhering to the Jailor's principle of "honesty" would mean the death of the young woman, then, certainly by modern standards, the Jailor's understanding of "honesty" could indeed be seen as mere fastidiousness ("niceness")—although Renaissance medical tradition does not seem to be uniform on this subject. What may speak against adopting this view too hastily is that at this point in the plot some modification of behavior is already supposed to have been effected through the Doctor's stage managing and that perhaps by implication some of the perils of death have been averted.

Renaissance medical books tell us nothing about the state of mind of the famous retentive of Pisa after he was tricked into emptying his bladder by a physician's ruse that averted his death; or how the person who had refused all food, believing he was dead lived on after he was persuaded to eat through an elaborate show demonstrating to him that even the dead consume food. They do not address the step from life-sustaining behavior modification to a more thorough "cure." The Doctor of *Two Noble Kinsmen* appears to believe that the sex act will accomplish the transition from partial to perfect cure. Therefore he addresses the Wooer with an explicitness that has shocked the critics.

DOCTOR: Please her appetite.
And do it home; it cures her *ipso facto*
The melancholy humor that infects her.
(V.ii.36–38)

To some readers and spectators, struck by the bluntness, if not crudeness of this discourse, he seems to assume that any act of cohabitation will do it, i.e., that this doctor has moved to the side of those (whom Ferrand will reject) who will prescribe bought pleasures for the cure of melancholy. But since the Doctor previously so clearly articulated the principle of combating falsehood with falsehoods, his prescription can only be for her to sleep with a false Palamon: only this act, which is both physical and imaginary, will cure her *ipso facto*. Of course this implied sense, which I am only making explicit, at best salvages the doctor's prescription from the charge of crudeness but not from that of immorality. The author or authors of these scenes made that charge a topic, as we have seen, even while deriving comical effects from it. In a comedy one probably cannot wish for or expect a more thorough treatment of the ethical dilemma of curing through falsehood, a dilemma that remains unresolved in this play, except that we a little later learn from the Jailor that the therapy has been successful, so successful indeed that his daughter is going to be reintegrated into society: "Sir, she's well restor'd, / And to be married shortly" (V.iv.27–28).

Although the texts discussed belong to different literary genres, a few tentative general observations may be in order.

None of them present systematic intellectual reflection on what is right and wrong in the practice of medicine. If by medical ethics we understand only such systematic thought, the cases from Montaigne and Wier and the scenes from *Two Noble Kinsmen* are irrelevant. But fairly recently medical ethics may have developed a new perspective from which texts such as these assume some significance. The authors of a reputable textbook on the subject write, "As a result of these public concerns and the private reflections and discussions of physicians, medical ethics as understood by the medical profession has taken a new fork in the road from which it has not yet turned back, if it ever will. Medical journals now publish increasing numbers of articles in which physicians openly explore their thinking and practices concerning their ethical relationship to individual practices and to the general public. . . ."[15] In different ways the three Renaissance texts brought together here stimulated such thinking during that period, and in fact they still do. They do not expressely present the physician-patient relationship as a fiduciary one, but both Wier and Montaigne express their unease as they compare their own comportment with the deontological principle to be truthful. The unease of these skeptical users of magic seems to stem from long range consequences of deception, and articulation of that unease bears striking resemblance to modern hesitancy about continued use of placebos. "It is we physicians," Richard C. Cabot writes in an important essay in 1903 that is still being anthologized, "who are responsible for perpetrating false ideas about disease and its cure . . . and with every placebo we do our part in perpetrating error, and harmful error at that."[16] Just as for Wier the use of magic even by the skeptic or non-believer is questionable because it fosters belief in magic in the patient, so for some modern physicians the use of placebos, although just as strikingly effective, is problematic because it promotes the belief that curing is merely a matter of dispensing some medication.

We saw that neither Montaigne nor Wier resolve the contradiction: their second thoughts about curing by deception, i.e., pretended magic, come at the end of reports of successful cure by precisely those means. At the same time the ethical principles animating these qualms are too pervasive in the rest of their works to make it seem likely that such palinodes represent mere fig leaves to protect the authors from the scrutiny of the Inquisition. In short the dilemmas seem so real as to stimulate any reader of these works to some ethical probing.

The doctor in *Two Noble Kinsmen* is deftly drawn: he articulates and practices a theory that is quite believable in the context of Renaissance ideas of the imagination. Although I have seen him portrayed so on the stage, it is questionable whether he is satirized from the start as a medical pragmatic with blinders to human and ethical problems. Undoubtedly the play eventually problematizes his therapy in his interaction with the patient's father. It is of course important that we can anchor such problematizing in the text. As a modern reader or spectator, I may have numerous medical and ethical questions about the therapy presented here: why is the Doctor able to proceed with his therapy in spite of the father's objections? Are there decisions that should be the doctor's alone, are there others which should be shared with relatives? Does not this therapy demonstrate that ruses or lies tend to accumulate, one fiction needing support by another? How good a hunch is it to gamble that the tricked young woman will in fact switch her attention to the wooer after the premarital sex act? Derrida's *Disseminations* has forcefully argued that any questions stimulated by texts of the past are legitimate. Yet their status is of a different kind from that of the issue the play explicitly problematizes. While the modern readers or spectators may ask such questions, or in fact might not even be able to help asking them, the authors certainly did not ask them or even did their darnest to prevent them from being asked (which is, of course, no reason for not asking them). The Jailor's report to Palamon as the knight puts his head on the block has considerable finality:

"Sir, she's well restor'd / And to be married shortly" (V.iii.27–28). As an expression of gratitude and as a final good deed before his expected execution, Palamon will then offer his purse as a contribution to her dowry. Any speculation about how the poor bride might take this gift should she still be in love with Palamon (would this gift stab her heart?) is meant to be out of order—the likelihood that at this crucial moment Palamon should have turned sadist is small. If as modern spectators we should call his gift insensitive, then his "insensitivity" is a function of his nobility of rank, programatically identified in the play's title. Be this as it may, we are to accept the fact that the Jailor's Daughter leaves the play "cured," for undeniably the playwrights at this moment are shifting their interest to resolving the Palamon-Arcite conflict. While some recent historians of philosophy and literary critics would dismiss this basic distinction as historicist or even trivial, it is of considerable moment not only for literary history, but also for a history of medical ethics. To accept it at least provisionally will help us to inspect our data more rigorously, which is all the more important if, as we should do, we include texts of imaginative literature within the parameters of our interest.

University of California

NOTES

1 See, e.g., Dwight Cathcart, *Doubting Conscience: Donne and the Poetry of Moral Argument* (Ann Arbor: The University of Michigan Press, 1975); George A. Starr, *Defoe and Casuistry* (Princeton, NJ: Princeton U.P., 1971); Camille W. Slights, *The Casuistical Tradition in Shakespeare, Donne, Herbert, and Milton* (Princeton U.P., 1981).

2 See Thomas S. Kuhn, *The Structure of Scientific Revolutions*, 2nd ed. (Chicago: University of Chicago Press., 1970).

3 Jacques Derrida, *Writing and Difference*, trans. Alan Bass (Chicago: University of Chicago Press, 1978), ch. 2: "Cogito and the History of Madness."

4 "Renaissance Exempla of Schizophrenia: The Cure by Charity in Luther and Cervantes," *Renaissance and Reformation* N.S. 9 (1985), 157–76; "Justifying the Unjustifiable: The Dover Cliff Scene in *King Lear*," *Shakespeare Quarterly* 36 (1985), 337–348; "Prospero as a Renaissance Therapist," *Literature and Medicine*, 6 (1987), 54–60.

5 Felix Platter, *Observationum libri tres* (Basel, 1614), 40–43.

6 Jan Wier [Wierus], *Histoires, disputes et discours* (Paris: Delahaye & Lecrosnier, 1885), II, 450.

7 *Essays*, trans. J. Florio (London, 1603), 42. On the context of this passage, see Lee R. Entin-Bates, "Montaigne's Remarks on Impotence," MLN, 91 (1976),

540–54.

8 Robert Burton, *The Anatomy of Melancholy*, Pt. 3, sec. 2, memb. 5, subs. 4 (Everyman ed., III, 226).

9 Jacques Ferrand, *Erotomania*, trans. E. Chilmead (Oxford, 1640), ch. 33, 277–278.

10 *Shakespeare and The Two Noble Kinsmen* (New Brunswick, NJ: Rutgers U.P., 1985), 271.

11 *The Riverside Shakespeare*, ed. G. Blakemore Evans (Boston: Houghton Mifflin, 1968), 1640.

12 See my "Renaissance Exempla of Schizophrenia," *Renaissance and Reformation* N.S. 9 (1985), 157–76.

13 Marjorie Garber has made this point—without referring to *Two Noble Kinsmen*, see "The Healer in Shakespeare" in *Medicine and Literature*, ed. Enid R. Peschel (New York: Neale Watson Acad. Publications, 1980), 109.

14 Kant, "Von der Lüge," ln *Metaphysik der Sitten, Werke*, ed. E. Cassirer (Berlin; Cassirer, 1922), VII, 240–43.

15 *Ethics in Medicine*, ed. Stanley J. Reiser, Arthur J. Dyck, and William J. Curran (Cambridge, Mass.: M.I.T. Press, 1977), 3.

16 "The Use of Truth and Falsehood in Medicine: An Experimental Study," *American Medicine* 5 (1903), 344–49.

Raymond B. Waddington

The Poetics of Eroticism: Shakespeare's "Master Mistress."

A Womans face with natures owne hand painted,
Haste thou the Master Mistris of my passion,
A womans gentle hart but not acqainted
With shifting change as is false womens fashion,
An eye more bright then theirs, lesse false in rowling:
Gilding the object where-vpon it gazeth,
A man in hew all *Hews* in his controwling,
Which steales mens eyes and womens soules amaseth.
And for a woman wert thou first created,
Till nature as she wrought thee fell a doting,
And by addition me of thee defeated,
By adding one thing to my purpose nothing.
  But since she prickt thee out for womens pleasure,
  Mine be thy loue and thy loues vse their treasure.

[A woman's face, with nature's own hand painted,
Hast thou, the master mistress of my passion—
A woman's gentle heart, but not acquainted
With shifting change, as is false women's fashion;
An eye more bright than theirs, less false in rolling,
Gilding the object whereupon it gazeth;
A man in hue all hues in his controlling,
Which steals men's eyes and women's souls amazeth.
And for a woman wert thou first created,
Till nature as she wrought thee fell a-doting,
And by addition me of thee defeated,
By adding one thing to my purpose nothing.
  But since she pricked thee out for women's pleasure,
  Mine be thy love, and thy love's use their treasure.]

"A woman's face with nature's own hand painted / Hast thou, the master mistress of my passion."[1] As Joseph Pequigney recently observed,

"The figure depicted in Sonnet 20 is, in its simplest outlines, that of a woman with a penis." What kind of thing is that to say about a friend, lover, nobleman, patron? Critical responses to Sonnet 20 too frequently allow their energy to be diverted into wholly unprofitable speculation on the nature of the poet's own sexuality or, more simply, short-circuited by the enormity of what the poem seems to be saying. George Steevens found it "impossible to read . . . without an equal mixture of disgust and indignation"; Hyder Rollins described it as "about the most indecent sonnet of the lot"; and Gerald Hammond has labelled it "a piece of grotesquery."[2] Perhaps our contemporary taste for confessional poetry leads us astray, despite what we have been taught about reading Renaissance poems as rhetorical addresses.[3] Yet the question of what the poet tells the young man, and the related one of how he says it, should take precedence over the question of what it reveals about himself.

The commentators who have managed to keep this in mind raise some basic issues. James Winney muses, "Only an oddly imperceptive reader could mistake this sonnet for a complimentary address. Few men, however good-looking, would enjoy being told that they were designed to be women; and one who had just reached manhood would be still less amused if his sex were called into question, however wittily." And E.B. Reed remarks, "This sonnet has hardly the tone in which Shakespeare, the actor, could address a nobleman of high rank."[4] These objections confess a concomitant bewilderment: the sonnet self-evidently does what common sense decrees it cannot do. To explain how the poem succeeds in doing just that requires a more extensive look at sixteenth-century sexual attitudes and their literary and cultural manifestations than is possible here. Instead, I shall touch on several relevant areas that, however briefly explored, should inform our responses to the sonnet. The first of these is medical attitudes toward sex transformation and bisexuality; the second, sixteenth-century interpretations of bisexual myths; the third, a philosophical commonplace that Shakespeare exploits in the sonnet; and, finally, some of the formal and generic strategies by which he projects the meaning of the poem.

In narrative content, Sonnet 20 is a creation myth, an invented fable of origins to explain the existence of a particular phenomenon, with a description of the latter comprising the octave and the fable the sestet. Nature first created this extraordinary young man as woman, but then "fell a-doting" and converted her to a man. Behind this deceptively artless piece of flattery resonate several pseudo-scientific controversies to which we should be responsive. In Book III of *Il Cortegiano* Gasparo Pallavicino recites some misogynist commonplaces:

very learned men have written that, since nature always intends and plans to make things most perfect, she would constantly bring forth men if she could; and that when a woman is born, it is a defect or mistake of nature, and contrary to what she would wish to do: as is seen too in the case of one who is born blind, or lame, or with some other defect; and, in trees, the many fruits that never ripen. Thus, a woman can be said to be a creature produced by chance and accident.[5]

Foremost amongst these learned men would be Galen and Aristotle, who regard a woman as an imperfectly developed version of man: "Because of lack of heat in generation, her sexual organs have remained internal, she is incomplete, colder and moister in dominant humours, and unable to 'concoct' perfect semen from blood."[6] In his *De generatione animalium*, Aristotle notoriously compares woman to a eunuch, an impotent male, and a deformed male. Of the difficult word he translates as "deformed," A.L. Peck comments, "Other attempts to bring out the meaning . . . would include 'imperfectly developed,' 'underdeveloped,' 'malformed,' 'mutilated,' 'congenitally disabled'."[7] Two presumptions underlie the "deformed male" theory: "that the hottest created thing is the most perfect, and that a direct comparison can be made between the genitalia of man and woman in function, number and form."[8]

Retrospectively, it is evident that Shakespeare's Mother Nature is an Aristotelian-Galenic creationist who has effected the sexual metamorphosis by remedying the deficiency of heat in female physiology. Lines 5 and 6, "An eye more bright than theirs, . . . / Gilding the object whereupon it gazeth," implicitly casts the young man's roving eye as the sun, eye of the world and natural alchemist, a comparison that also occupies a quatrain of Sonnet 33:

Full many a glorious morning have I seen
Flatter the mountain tops with sovereign eye,
Kissing with golden face the meadows green,
Gilding pale streams with heav'nly alchemy. . . .
(33:1–4)

Since the masculine sun is the source of heat as well as light, Nature has corrected the deficiency in humor that first arrested this creature's development. It would be wrong to imagine the sex change as a grafting operation, the simple supplying of a penis, however immediately the furiously-punning sestet tempts us to do so: "And by addition me of thee defeated, / By adding one thing to my purpose nothing" (11–12). Add and addition do have a mathematical sense here, since the poet is playing on the ancient symbolism of the first even and odd numbers, two and three, as symbols for the feminine and masculine principles: "By adding one thing," a penis, "to my purpose nothing," both *no thing* or vagina and no longer a feminine number, *so nothing*.[9] But the primary meaning of addition is "augmentation" rather than "attachment," as the next line makes clear: "prick'd thee out" (13) punningly means "selected you from a list"; but, literally and precisely, it means that the inverted and internal female genitalia have been drawn out to proper, external male form by the function of heat, a process that the physician Ambroise Paré describes in his case histories of women become men.[10]

If Shakespeare expects us to respond to staples of physiological and anatomical discourse, he yet alludes to them selectively, elusively, and perhaps not consistently. A perfect woman should be a logical impossibility in the views of Aristotle and Galen; but this woman is not "a defect or mistake of nature." Nature, instead, seems to have set out to create a superior woman, "more bright" and "less false" than others of the species, succeeding so well that, Pygmalion-like, she becomes infatuated with her own handiwork and falls "a-doting" over what "she wrought." Classical physiology, with its bias toward male superiority, should insist on a complete sexual conversion for perfection. Here, however, both external and internal qualities, face and heart, remain female; the dominant impression is of male genitalia on a female body, thus "addition" as "attachment" after all, even if effected naturally. This "master mistress" might steal "men's eyes and women's souls amazeth"; but the colder context of medical examination might remind us that in the sixteenth century such combinations almost invariably were categorized as monsters.[11]

Sonnet 20 is a blazon, an anatomy of the young man's beauty in terms that can only be described as "bisexual." Readers have responded by identifying the character of his beauty as "androgynous" or "hermaphroditic," the interchangeability of adjectives accurately reflecting dictionary definitions, which treat the words as synonyms. It is important to remember, however, that the myths underlying the adjectives have very different implications. Aristophanes' fable of the Androgyne, the double beings who—split in two by an angry Zeus—perpetually seek to reunite themselves, is wholly positive in thrust. It presents love as a quest for fulfillment, wholeness, harmony, reintegration, health. Ovid's story of how Salmacis and Hermaphroditus were fused into one body is, in contrast, a punishment for the avoidance of love. Both myths are pertinent to understanding Sonnet 20, but they need to be considered separately.

Tracing the Androgyne myth from Ficino through Pico della Mirandola, Leone Ebreo, Erasmus, Rabelais, and Etienne Pasquier, one finds a rich variety of commentaries and interpretations; but, as the myth progresses through philosophic discourse to love treatises and emblem books, a dominant interpretation is established.[12] Although the Androgyne could symbolize an Adamic state of spiritual perfection, the harmoniously tempered and virtuous mind, or the union of the individual soul with God, the most common meaning was simply marriage. The marital Androgyne was used variously to imply the amelioration of carnal lust to lawful propagation, a Platonic union of spirits, a Pauline apprehension of Christian charity, or a combination of these connotations; as myth and image evolved in general usage, however, the idea of marriage remained foremost. It has long been recognized that the first seventeen of Shakespeare's *Sonnets*, the "marriage" sonnets, are a closely-linked group, urging the young man to perpetuate himself by begetting a son.[13] The androgynous blazon of Sonnet 20 allusively reprises the theme of the first group, even while ambiguously recognizing the greater likelihood of a possibility acknowledged in the opening sonnet: "But thou, contracted to thine own bright eyes, / Feed'st thy light's flame with self-substantial fuel" (1. 5–6). If he is indeed already married to himself in narcissistic sterility, the symbol of an anticipated completion and fulfillment in heterosexual marriage dissolves and redefines in the negative image of the hermaphrodite. Not prodigy, but monster.

When Plato apparently invented the fable of the Androgyne, he transformed a concept into a myth, thus converting an adjective, *androgynos* into a proper name. Nonetheless, the reality, or at least the fear, of bisexual individuals in Greek culture preceded Plato's literary invention, which—even in Aristophanes' narration—has the effect of a quixotic rehabilitation, as he remarks: "For though [*androgynos*] is only used nowadays as a term of contempt, there really was a man-woman in those days, a being which was half male and half female." (*Symposium* 189E).[14] Conversely, *Hermaphroditos* was first a proper name and only later became a synonym of *androgynos* in popular usage. A cult of the minor god Hermaphroditus seems to have emerged in the fourth century B.C., although Hellenists are divided on whether the cult had native or foreign origins.

The earliest sculptural representations of Hermaphroditus project him as, like Eros and Dionysos, an adolescent god, a physical type realizing a synthesis of masculine and feminine beauty. Later the standing figure of the ephebe came to be supplanted by the purely feminine beauty of the reclining or sleeping Hermaphroditus whose identity is revealed only by the male genitalia.[15] Along with the shifting of physical types of representation, we can mark a concomitant shifting of attitudes toward the god as the ambivalence of response that, according to Marie Delcourt, is always present, hardens in the negative.[16] The threat of the abnormal may be exorcised by contempt and ridicule. This is the cultural situation reported by two first century B.C. writers. Diodorus Siculus, although looking back to an earlier time, reports pro and con:

> Hermaphroditus . . . was born of Hermes and Aphrodite and received a name which is a combination of those of both his parents. Some say that this Hermaphroditus is a god and appears at certain times among men, and that he is born with a physical body which is a combination of that of a man and that of a woman, in that he has a body which is beautiful and delicate like that of a woman, but has the masculine quality and vigour of a man. But there are some who declare that such creatures of two sexes are monstrosities, and coming rarely into the world as they do they have the quality of presaging the future, sometimes for evil and sometimes for good.[17]

Pliny puts it more succinctly, stating that "Formerly hermaphrodites were considered as terrifying apparitions, but today only as objects for jest."[18]

Ovid's *Metamorphoses*, IV.285–388, the canonical literary text, concentrates the evolution of the myth. An equation of bisexuality with asexuality underlies Ovid's narrative: "neutrumque et utrunque videntur."[19] The invented story of metamorphosis only retraces the historical transformation of Hermaphroditus. In unmanning Hermaphroditus, Ovid does present him as monstrosity, even while allowing him Diodorus' "quality of presaging the future . . . for evil" in cursing the fountain with his impotence; at the same time, the elements of literary parody in Ovid's story suggest that for him, as for Pliny, Hermaphroditus is simultaneously an object for jest.[20]

Renaissance artists, commencing at least with Giorgione, responded directly to surviving examples of the classical Hermaphroditus in sculpture and gem carvings and, consequently, invested their recreations with something of the mysterious power of bisexuality.[21] For poets, however, the locus classicus was the *Metamorphoses*; and the potent example of Ovid—reinforced by the tradition of moralized commentary, by the illustrated editions of Ovid, and by the emblem books—kept the literary depictions of Hermaphroditus impotent.[22] An emblem in Barthelemy Aneau's *Picta Poesis* (1552) shows an aggressive Salmacis wrestling a worried Hermaphroditus down into the fountain; in the left background, an hermaphroditic figure foretells the outcome; and the title bluntly interprets the action: "Fons Salmacidos, Libido Effoeminans."[23] During the 1590s, Ovid's Hermaphroditus achieved the status of an archetype in the fashionable erotic, mythological poetry, for most of which Aneau's moralistic comment remains an apt description. When Spenser and Donne attempt to accentuate the positive with a "faire" or "blest" Hermaphrodite, they are working against the grain of poetic convention.[24]

In the response to sexual abnormality, however, it is impossible to eliminate the negative, as we see when we examine the history of Hermaphroditus' mythic twin and opposite, Priapus. Emerging in the mythological pantheon slightly later than Hermaphroditus, Priapus evinces their kinship in two obvious ways, parentage and function. They are half-brothers—Priapus is reported to be the son of Dionysos and Aphrodite (leading to, or possibly stemming from, an easy moralization: wine and beauty create lust)—and, as Hermaphroditus originally was the god of sexual union, so Priapus is always the deity of fertility, abundance, potency.[25] Originally, according to Diodorus Siculus,[26] he was simply the phallus personified. The naked potency of Priapus, universal principle of generation, quickly extended his function from simple embodiment of sexual fertility to his full-fledged role as god and guardian of orchards, gardens, and harvests, scarecrow and protector against thieves. It is this greater range of influence over human activity, Delcourt speculates, that caused Priapus to assume many of the attributes and offices of Hermaphroditus, even some aspects of his bisexuality.[27] She traces the process, parallel to that in the sculptural representations of Hermaphroditus, by which the initially grotesque and monstrous images of Priapus are beautified and even feminized. But writers always remembered the deformity of Priapus.

The 1552 Prologue to Rabelais' *Quart Livre* is an exuberant celebration of the Priapus myth, presenting it through a descending sequence of types—Priapus himself, Mercury, Couillatris, Rabelais—as a parable of the inspired poet/writer's creative potency. Rabelais balances an inherently unstable combination. On the one hand, he uses Priapus as a symbol; and, on the other he makes his physical presence grotesquely human. The two do not lie easily in one bed. As Delcourt observes, "Priapus brings fertility to gardens and cowsheds, yet parents would be horrified at a new-born child who resembled him. An idea may be translated into symbols, so long as they do not become so exact that they coincide with concrete reality."[28] Poussin's drawing of *The Birth of Priapus*, one of a set intended for a new illustrated edition of Ovid, makes Delcourt's point exactly. A perverse epiphany, the scene centers on the revelation of the infant's physical deformity to a group of nymphs who turn away in pretended horror and revulsion, although their expressions disclose delight at the scandal. Anthony Blunt comments that "As far as possible, Poussin eliminates the supernatural . . . " and "introduces a sense of drama into the drawings."[29] His Priapus, therefore, is no god, but a deformed infant—a human baby with a monstrous *membrum virilis.*

The role of Priapus leads us, circuitously, to our philosophical topos, the Latin formula, "*Tota in toto, et tota in qualibet parte,*" that is, "All in all, and all in every part." It refers to the belief, first fully articulated by Plotinus, that the soul exists as an indivisible whole both in the entire body and in every individual part of the body. Accepted by such authorities as Augustine and Aquinas, the doctrine was a commonplace in both Christian and Neoplatonic circles by the beginning of the sixteenth century; and, by the end of the century it had become a literary commonplace as well.[30]

Some years ago, T.W. Baldwin discussed the *topos* in relation to ten of Shakespeare's sonnets, concluding that he "has used the phraseology of the doctrine of the soul . . . as a principal theme."[31] Some of Baldwin's claims are unconvincing; but, in other instances, it is clear that he has gotten hold of something. Two sonnets, 22 ("My glass shall not persuade me I am old / So long as youth and thou are of one date") and 62 ("Sin of self-love possesseth all mine eye"), revolve on the same conceit: given the exchange of souls between lovers, the poet cannot be old, having assumed the youthfulness of his beloved. The glass of sonnet 22.1 dramatizes Ficino's metaphor of reciprocal love in *De Amore* (2.8): "the lover engraves the figure of the beloved on his own soul. And so the soul of the lover becomes a mirror in which the image of the loved one is reflected. For that reason, when the beloved recognized himself in the lover, he is forced to love him."[32] Not coincidentally, I think, the following chapter explains the benefits of love between a younger and an older man. Sonnet 62 ("Sin of self-love") plays imaginatively with the second of the statements quoted from Ficino. As Ingram and Redpath summarize, "This 'self,' throughout the octave, is made to seem to be the poet; but the sestet refutes this, and reveals that the true 'self' the poet loves is the Friend":[33]

But when my glass shews me my self indeed
Beated and chopped with tanned antiquity,
Mine own self-love quite contrary I read;
Self so self-loving were iniquity
'Tis thee, myself, that for myself I praise,
Painting my age with beauty of thy days.
(62.9–14)

Unmistakably Baldwin is correct in glossing line 2, "And all my soul, and all my every part," with "tota in toto, et tota in qualibet parte."[34] The assertion that self-love is the poet's soul, the essence of his being, resolves into a graceful declaration that the young man is his soul, although not without recognition of the narcissism implicit in Ficino's metaphysics of love.

The most intriguing of Baldwin's annotations relates to Sonnet 20, the "master-mistress," wherein the central lines—"A man in hue all hues in his controlling, / Which steals men's eyes and women's souls amazeth"—are interpreted, with the help of Castiglione, as describing the Neoplatonic exchange of souls through the sight: "Since the master-mistress is for beauty *all in all, and all in every part*, he controls 'all hues in his,' for both men and women." Baldwin concludes "Shakespeare is fully conscious that he is here giving the doctrine of 'souls' a twist."[35] Moreso, I would argue, than Baldwin ever realized. A strong part of the appeal that the "all in all" *topos* had for imaginative writers lay in its comic potential. Michael Screech has observed that, whereas in our society the idea of souls is comic and bodies are regarded with religious seriousness, the opposite was true in the sixteenth century.[36] If his aphorism holds true, then and now the "all in all" *topos* has to provoke a mixed response. No matter how venerable the doctrine of the soul, no matter how many saints of the Church and humanist heroes have certified its validity, the notion that one's entire soul dwells in each and every part of the body, when particularized, becomes inescapably risible. That awareness would be forced upon anyone not tone-deaf to language since, in Latin and in English, *pars* and *part* are charged with the same ribald connotation. Just as Donne can say, "but we love the Centrique part," so when Ovid describes Priapus' assault on Lotis, he speaks of the aroused god's "parte paratus."[37]

The most striking illustration of such an awareness occurs with two personal medals of Pietro Aretino—satirist, dramatist, poet, man of letters—whose *Sonetti lussuriosi*, written to accompany the pornographic engravings made by Marcantonio Raimondi from Giulio Romano's drawings, earned him such notoriety that he became a Henry Miller to the Elizabethans.[38] The medals, by unknown artists, probably date from the 1540s. The portrait heads of Aretino differ, one deriving from an earlier medal executed by Leoni Leone and the other from a portrait type attributed to Titian; but the two reverses are identical, one copied from the other and altered only in size. Possibly because of a more reticent scholarly decorum in earlier times, they have been described and illustrated rarely and with considerable circumspection. They were first discussed in Count Giovanni Maria Mazzuchelli's eighteenth-century biography of Aretino. Of the reverses, Mazzuchelli writes, "Il quale, qual figura rappresenti, la modestia non ci permette di dire." Alfred Armand, writing a hundred years ago, is only somewhat more explicit: "Tête a gauche de satyre formée d'emblemes obscenes."[39]

At first glance, the satyr's head appears to be an entertaining adaptation of the Medusa myth with the hair composed not of snakes but of penes. Although this allusion must have been in the artist's mind, it is a partial response. On closer inspection, the method is an anticipation of Arcinboldo's; rather than fruits and vegetables, the entire head—neck, hair, facial features—is composed of penes and testes. The neck, for instance, consists largely of two phalli with the testes at the base simulating the collar bone. The eyebrow is a small, curved penis, as are the lips; the swell of the cheekbone is indicated by testes; likewise the chin; the nose and nostril are doubled by the penis and testes combination. The phalli, except those curved for anatomical verisimilitude, are depicted erect; a prominent ithyphallus in the hair configuration, extending forward from where the ear would be located and ending beneath the chin, is presented in the act of ejaculation. Surrounding the satyr head on the reverse of both Aretino medals is the motto, "TOTUS IN TOTO ET TOTUS IN QUALIBET PARTE." The meaning is clear enough: the satyr's soul, the essence of his being, is his sexuality, his satyriasis, if you will. Mazzuchelli assumed the medals were an attack on Aretino, commissioned by an enemy; I have argued elsewhere that they are a projection of his persona as a satirist.[40] In either case, the implication is the same—the satyr/satirist's soul is his penis, his penis is his soul.

The conception of the Aretino medal reverse is learned and sardonic, designed to shock and amuse with its frank crudity. In this it illuminates the more oblique strategy and tone of Shakespeare's Sonnet 20, a double-edged celebration of the young man's androgynous beauty and an analysis of its effects on others. The praise is cast in the structure of an anatomical blazon, with each odd line of the octave specifying a single feature—"A woman's face" (1), "A woman's gentle heart" (3), "An eye more bright than theirs" (5), "A man in hue all hues" (7). Hue carries the primary sense of form, shape, or appearance with secondary implications of complexion and color and, possibly, of an apparition.[41] Thus, a man in appearance, the "master-mistress" epitomizes all physical beauty, is an archetype of sexual attractiveness, as his hue "steals men's eyes and women's souls amazeth."[42] "All in all," the implied subtext, in this case means that his "soul" is the aura of sexual attractiveness which is completely and perfectly manifested in every part of his body.

The blazon is completed, however, with the part that stands for the whole in a manner reminiscent of the Aretino satyr medal:

And for a woman wert thou first created,—
Till nature as she wrought thee fell a-doting,
And by addition me of thee defeated,
By adding one thing to my purpose nothing.
But since she prick'd thee out for women's pleasure,
Mine be thy love and thy love's use their treasure.
(20:9-14)

The rhetorical exaggeration here—four lines as opposed to the two for each of the other anatomical features enumerated—assigns dominance to the phallus in the physical portrait. The effect is similar to the anatomical exaggeration employed by Renaissance artists in the representations of ithyphallic satyrs and gods—for instance the "Garden of Vertumuus" engraving from Fontainebleau or the ithyphallic herm of the "Sacrifice to Priapus" woodcut from the *Hypnerotomachia Poliphii.* As in the scene of the Priapic worshippers, Shakespeare's young man has "all hues in his controlling, / Which steals men's eyes and women's souls amazeth" (20.7–8). Himself an "unmoved mover" (94), the young man becomes, in Northrop Frye's apt phrase, "an erotic messiah."[43] Because he is a human and not a god, however, here the exaggeration differs from the woodcut in its flirtation with the ridiculous. One might note in passing the sonnet's exploitation of conventions from Latin Priapic verse. These include: plays upon obscene words ("prick" and "nothing"); the personification of the phallus (here, by synecdoche, the part becomes the whole); and the fiction of the poem as both an offering to the god and a threat by the god.[44] The sonnet pays tribute to the young man's unequalled beauty and sexuality, while hinting that too much sexuality is as unnatural as too little. Priapus and Hermaphrodite are true brothers in this essential respect.

With dazzling technical facility, Shakespeare uses formal, prosodic, and generic cross-blendings to symbolize the ambivalent sexuality that is the essence of this beautiful young man's character. The poet's handling of the blazon evokes both English and French generic strategies. The progressive anatomical catalogue is more usual in the English blazon, whereas the *Blasons anatomiques du corps feminin* more frequently celebrate a single part of the body. The rhetorical manipulation of the catalogue in 20 results in a poem that nicely conforms to Schmidt's definition of the French blason as "a series of repetitive verbal convergings on the given central object."[45] Further, the tonal and attitudinal ambivalence of Sonnet 20 suggests an internal co-optation of the contre blason, a dispraise designed to disgust or to provoke a moralistic attitude toward the body. The undercurrent of mockery set against the effusive, exaggerated praise gives Sonnet 20 a tonality not unlike that in Niccolo Bellin da Modena's celebrated bisexual portrait of Francis I. Despite the verses extolling the monarch as a god, the artist has grafted Francis' head on a woman's body. This is not the transcendent Androgyne, but the effeminate Hermaphroditus.[46] A comic monstrosity.

Georgio Melchiori has analyzed the formal structure of Sonnet 20 in which the central lines 7 and 8 make the only references to *man* while the surrounding lines describe *woman*: feminine without, masculine within.[47] Similarly, the English "masculine lines" of the sonnet are feminized by the use of feminine rime throughout, the only such occurrence in the entire sequence. A fusion of identities occurs with the hybridization of the sonnet itself. Because the sequence of argument so emphatically follows an octave-sestet pattern, the poem requires us at once to apprehend English and Italian sonnet modes. Rosalie Colie's accounts of generic encoding might allow us to perceive that the Italian sonnet itself had come to symbolize the unattainable ideal beauty to whom it was so frequently addressed. That is, the body of the sonnet represents the body of the beloved. The metaphor of text as human body, pervasive in the language of rhetorical theory, extends easily from the notion of literary creativity as procreation and perpetuation: "Nor shall Death brag thou wandr'st in his shade, / When in eternal lines to time thou grow'st" (Shakespeare 18.11–12). More particularly, sixteenth-century critics were given to contrasting the "masculine" and "feminine" genres of epic and lyric.[48] For Petrarchists the identification between the body of the poem and the body of the beloved would be something more than a psychologically necessary substitution for the distant and disdainful beauty. Since in a very direct sense she is the poet's creation, the sonnet has a greater reality and apprehensibility than its subject.[49]

Sonnet 20's disturbing juxtaposition of English and Italian, Latin and French, masculine and feminine codes culminates with the closing couplet that delivers the "prick" of the epigram from which it derives formally.[50] At the same time, however, it is figuratively both the anatomical "prick" that it describes and the "tail" of the sonetto caudato.[51] Shakespeare's formal joke is similar to Ben Jonson's prosodic one in the epigram "To Pertinax Cob" (LXIX): "Cob, thou nor soldier, thief, nor fencer art, / Yet by thy weapon liv'st! Thou hast one good part."[52] The extra-metrical syllable of line 2 stands for the part by which Cob lives. In sixteenth-century usage, *coda*, *cauda*, and *tail* all had possible sexual meanings as either the male or female genitals; and in poetic usage of the "tailed" sonnet there was an obvious and frequent play on this correspondence among others, by Aretino in his *Sonetti lussuriosi*—referring to the anatomical "tail" in the tail of the sonnet. The form of Sonnet 20 itself, thus, inscribes the figure of a woman with a penis.

In his magisterial study of *Cellini*, John Pope-Hennessy reflects on the difficulty of reconstructing sexual attitudes in a distant culture, but risks a formulation: "Cinquecento life seems generally to have conformed to a bisexual norm."[53] This obviously needs considerable qualification. But it does seem true that gender attitudes in sixteenth-century humanist, literary, and courtly circles largely were an adaptation of the Roman values projected to them through Latin literature, of which Paul Veyne offers this summary: "To be active was to be male, whatever the sex of the compliant partner. To take one's pleasure was virile, to accept it servile—that was the whole story."[54] Looking at the couplet from the perspective of this active-passive/masculine-feminine paradigm, we find a passive young man "used," sexually exploited, by aggressively un-feminine women, yet himself potentially exploiting, actively "using" the love of the poet, who—like the creator, Mother Nature—"wrought thee" and "fell a-doting," the poet thus switching from an active to a passive role, inverting the young man's pattern. "Mine by thy love and thy love's use their treasure." Charged with profoundly ambivalent eroticism to the end, the sonnet makes its provocative statement through the encoded sexual myths and amatory poetic genres, both high and low, of the culture from whence it comes.

University of California at Davies

NOTES

1 The Sonnets are quoted from Stephen Booth, ed., *Shakespeare's Sonnets* (New Haven and London: Yale UP, 1977).
The present essay is an abstract and brief chronicle of a monograph-in-progress that seeks to understand Sonnet 20 in its sixteenth-century contexts. For full development of those contexts, I must refer the reader to the longer study. I also draw some paragraphs from a related essay, " 'All in All': Shakespeare, Milton, Donne, and the Soul-in-Body *Topos*," *English Literary Renaissance* (forthcoming).

2 In sequence, the quotations are from: Joseph Pequigney, *Such Is My Love: A Study of Shakespeare's Sonnets* (Chicago and London: University of Chicago Press, 1985), p. 37; *The Sonnets of Shakespeare*, ed. Raymond Macdonald Alden (Boston: Houghton Mifflin, 1916), p. 56, for Steevens; and *A New Variorum Edition of Shakespeare, The Sonnets*, ed. Hyder E. Rollins (Philadelphia, 1944), vol. 2, p. 239; G. Hammond, *The Reader and Shakespeare's Young Sonnets* (London: McMillan, 1981), p. 109.

3 To cite just one example, see Marion Trousdale, "A Possible Renaissance View of Form," *ELH* 40 (1973), pp. 179–204. Kenneth Muir, *Shakespeare's Sonnets* (London: George Allen & Unwin, 1979), sensibly reiterates warnings against reading the Sonnets as confessional.

4 James Winney, *The Master-Mistress: A Study of Shakespeare's Sonnets* (New York: Barnes & Noble, 1968), pp. 152–53; and E.B. Reed, ed., *Shakespeare's Sonnets* (New Haven: Yale UP, 1948), p. 81. Winney attempts to resolve the impasse by eliminating the young nobleman: "Shakespeare is not analyzing the character of an actual person but exploring a complex of ideas which his creative consciousness holds together" (p. 154).

5 Baldesar Castiglione, *The Book of the Courtier*, trans. Charles S. Singleton (Garden City, N.Y.: Doubleday & Company, 1959), 3:11, 213.

6 Ian Maclean, *The Renaissance Notion of Woman* (Cambridge: Cambridge UP, 1980), p. 31.

7 Aristotle, *Generation of Animals*, trans. A.L. Peck, Loeb Classical Library (Cambridge, Mass.: Harvard UP, 1963), 2.3.737a pp. 26, 28. On the gender implications of Aristotle's theory, see the ground-breaking essay by Maryanne Cline Horowitz, "Aristotle and Woman," *Journal of the History of Biology* 9 (1976), pp. 183–213; and G.E.R. Lloyd, *Science, Folklore and Ideology: Studies in the Life Sciences in Ancient Greece* (Cambridge: Cambridge UP, 1983), pp. 94–111. Johannes Morsink, "Was Aristotle's Biology Sexist?" *Journal of the History of Biology* 12 (1979), pp. 83–112, defends Aristotle's biological theory, while conceding to Horowitz that its author was anti-feminist and that the theory had sexist consequences.

8 Maclean, *Renaissance Notion*, p. 31.

9 On the number symbolism, see Plutarch, *Moralia* 263f–264a; and R.B. Waddington, *The Mind's Empire: Myth and Form in George Chapman's Narrative Poems* (Baltimore and London: Johns Hopkins UP, 1974), pp. 162–64. For the sexual implications of thing and nothing, see Booth's note on line 12.

10 See Ambroise Paré, *Des Monstres et Prodiges*, ed. Jean Céard, Travaux d'Humanisme et Renaissance, 115 (Genève: Librairie Droz, 1971), ch. 7, "Histoires Memorables de Certaines Femmes qui sont Dégénerées en Hommes," pp. 29–30. See also Maclean, *Renaissance Notion*, pp. 33, 38–39.

11 Maclean comments, "It is generally agreed that hermaphrodites belong not at a mid point on the sexual spectrum between (normal) female and (normal) male births, but rather to the category of monster" (*Renaissance Notion*, p. 39). The medical attitude is exemplified by Paré's dichotomous title.

12 For full discussion with documentation of the Androgyne in the sixteenth-century, see my forthcoming monograph on Sonnet 20.

13 On the "marriage group," see, e.g., Muir, *Shakespeare's Sonnets*, pp. 35–41, 45–52.

14 Translation by Michael Joyce, in *The Collected Dialogues of Plato*, ed. Edith Hamilton and Huntington Cairns, Bollingen Series 81 (Princeton: Princeton

UP, 1961), p. 542.

15 See Marie Delcourt, *Hermaphrodite: Myths and Rites of the Bisexual Figure in Classical Antiquity*, trans. Jennifer Nicholson (London: Studio Books, 1961), p. 48.

16 See Delcourt, pp. 43–67; and, for a fuller consideration of the typology of hermaphroditic presentation, see her later study, *Hermaphroditea: Recherches sur l'être double promoteur de la fertilité dans le monde classique*, Collection Latomus 86 (Brussels, 1966).

17 Diodorus Siculus, *Historical Library*, trans. C.H. Oldfather, Loeb Classical Library, (London: Heinemann, 1967), Bk. VI, sec. 5, vol. II, p. 361.

18 Pliny, *Natural History*, Bk. VII, xxxiv, quoted by Delcourt, *Hermaphrodite*, p. 45.

19 *Metamorphoses* 4.379; and see Delcourt, *Hermaphrodite*, pp. 53–5.

20 On the parodic elements, see G.K. Galinsky, *Ovid's Metamorphoses: An Introduction to the Basic Aspects* (Berkeley: University of California Press, 1975), pp. 186–90.

21 See, particularly, Seymour Howard, "The Dresden Venus and its Kin: Mutation and Retrieval of Types," *Art Quarterly* 2 (1979), pp. 90–111, who relates Giorgione's *Sleeping Venus* to the Sleeping Hermaphrodite type. See also André Chastel, *Fables, Formes, Figures* 1 (Paris: Flammarion, 1978), pp. 290–1 and plates 126–7, for an analogous suggestion regarding Michaelangelo's Conversion of Saint Paul.

22 On the allegorized Ovid, see Don Cameron Allen, *Mysteriously Meant: The Rediscovery of Pagan Symbolism and Allegorical Interpretation in the Renaissance* (Baltimore and London: Johns Hopkins UP, 1970), pp. 163–99; also Ann Moss, *Ovid in Renaissance France: a survey of the Latin editions of Ovid and commentaries printed in France before 1600*, Warburg Institute Surveys 8 (London: Warburg Institute, 1982); and, for illustrated editions, M.D. Henkel, "Illustrierte Ausgaben von Ovids Metamorphosen in XV., XVI. und XVII. Jahrhunderts," *Vorträge der Bibliothek Warburg, 1926–27*, 6 (1960), pp. 58–144.

23 The emblem is reproduced in Arthur Henkel and Albrecht Schone, *Emblemata: Handbuch zur Sinnbildkunst des XVI. und XVII. Jahrhunderts* (Stuttgart: J.B. Metzler 1967), p. 1628.

24 See the 1590 ending to Book III of *The Faerie Queene*; and Donne, "To Mr *Tilman* after he had taken orders," 54.

25 See Delcourt, *Hermaphrodite*, pp. 50–2; also Hans Herter, *De Priapo*, Religionsgeschichtliche Versuche und Vorarbeiten 32 (Giessen: Verlag von Alfred Topelmann 1932), especially pp. 138-70 for the confusion of Priapus and Hermaphrodite. H.J. Rose, *A Handbook of Greek Mythology* (New York: Dutton, 1959), p. 149, notes that "According to some genealogies, Priapos also was a child of Hermes and Aphrodite," which draws the twinning with Hermaphroditus even closer.

26 Diodorus Siculus, Vol. II, Bk. IV, sec. 6.

27 See Delcourt, *Hermaphrodite*, p. 52; and Herter, *De Priapo*, pp. 138–70.
28 Delcourt, *Hermaphrodite*, p. 51.
29 Anthony Blunt, *Nicolas Poussin*, Bollingen Series 35.7 (New York: Pantheon, 1967), p. 45.
30 On this tradition, see Waddington, " 'All in All'."
31 T.W. Baldwin. *On the Literary Genetics of Shakespeare's Poems and Sonnets* (Urbana: University of Illinois Press, 1950), pp. 157–80; quotation, p. 177.
32 Marsilio Ficino, *Commentary on Plato's Symposium on Love*, trans. Sears Jayne (Dallas: Spring Publications, 1985), p. 57.
33 *Shakespeare's Sonnets*, ed. W.G. Ingram and Theodore Redpath (London: Hodder and Stoughton, 1978), p. 144.
34 Baldwin, *Literary Genetics*, pp. 169–70.
35 Baldwin, *Literary Genetics*, p. 166.
36 In a public lecture, University of Wisconsin-Madison, 1979. A similar point is made in his *Rabelais* (Ithaca: Cornell UP, 1979), pp. 53–6.
37 *Fasti* 1.437; see also *Artis amatoriae* 2.584, "partibus obscenis."
38 See, e.g., Saad El-Gabalawy, "Aretino's Pornography in the later Renaissance," *English Miscellany* 25 (1976), pp. 97–118; and David O. Frantz, " 'Leud Priapians' and Renaissance Pornography," *Studies in English Literature* 12 (1972), pp. 157–72.
39 I have quoted Mazzuchelli's *Vita di Pietro Aretino* from Fidenzio Pertile and Ettore Camesasca, eds., *Lettere sull'arte di Pietro Aretino*, 3 vols. (Milano: Edizioni del milione, 1960), vol. 3, p. 76; Armand, *Les Medailleurs Italiens* (Paris, 1883–7), vol. 2, p. 153, no. 12. The medals are also illustrated by P.A. Gaetani, *Museum Mazzuchellianum, seu numismata virorum doctrina praestantium*, 2 vols. (Venice, 1761–3), vol. 1, p. 292 and Table 63, figures 5 and 8; and by Aloiss Heiss, *Les Medailleurs de la Renaissance*, 8 vols. (Paris, 1881–92), vol. 7, pp. 141–2.
40 R.B. Waddington, "A Satirist's Impresa: The Medals of Pietro Aretino," *Renaissance Quarterly*, Vol. XLII, No. 4 (Winter, 1989), pp. 655–81.
41 See Baldwin, *Literary Genetics*, pp. 165–6, and the notes to line 7 by Booth and by Ingram and Redpath.
42 A particularly convoluted sexual innuendo is perceived in line 8 by Martin Green, *The Labyrinth of Shakespeare's Sonnets* (London: Charles Skilton Ltd., 1974), pp. 59–81.
43 Northrop Frye, "How True a Twain," in *The Riddle of Shakespeare's Sonnets* (New York: Basic Books, 1962), p. 42.
44 On these conventions, see Amy Richlin, *The Garden of Priapus: Sexuality and Agression in Roman Humor* (New Haven and London: Yale UP, 1983), pp. 116–27.
45 Quoted from D.B. Wilson, *Descriptive Poetry in France from Blason to Baroque* (Manchester: Manchester UP, 1967), p. 8.
46 As I argue in "The Bisexual Portrait of Francis I: Fontainebleau, Castiglione,

and the Tone of Courtly Mythology" (forthcoming).

47 See Melchiori, *Shakespeare's Dramatic Meditations* (Oxford: Clarendon, 1976), pp. 111–12.

48 The metaphor of text as body especially is pervasive in Montaigne. See Robert D. Cottrell, *Sexuality/Textuality: A Study of the Fabric of Montaigne's Essais* (Columbus: Ohio State UP, 1981), especially pp. 109, 127–28; also Michel Jeanneret, "Rabelais et Montaigne: l'ecriture comme parole," *L'Esprit Createur* 16 (1976), pp. 78–94. In arguing that censorship constitutes genocide, Milton crystallizes an attitude of textual veneration fostered by Renaissance humanism: "a good book is the precious lifeblood of a master spirit, embalmed and treasured up on purpose to a life beyond life" (p. 720).

49 See Paul Julian Smith, "Barthes, Gongora, and Non-Sense," *PMLA*, 101 (1986), pp. 84–86, for citations from Quintilian, Scaliger, Tasso, and others. Smith also quotes Fernando de Herrera (1580), contrasting the feminine vices of Italian style with the masculine virtues of Spanish style (pp. 85–85).

50 For a late, and therefore particularly clear, example, see Giambattisita Marino's sonnet, "Seno," in *Amori*, introduction and notes by Alessandro Merlini, Biblioteca Universale Rizzoli (Milan: Rizzoli, 1982), p. 71; and Merlini's instructive commentary, pp. 135–9. I owe this reference to Paolo Cherchi.

51 For discussions of the interplay of sonnet and epigram, see Rosalie Colie, *The Resources of Kind*, pp. 67–75: and *Shakespeare's Living Art* (Princeton: Princeton UP, 1974), pp. 68–134. She is concerned with tones, however, rather than forms.

52 On the *sonetto caudato*, see Leandro Biadene, *Morfologia del sonetto nei secoli XIII–XIV* (Firenze: Casa editrice le lettere, 1977), pp. 65–78.

53 Quoted from *Poems*, ed. Ian Donaldson (London: Oxford, 1975).

54 John Pope-Hennessey, *Cellini* (New York: Abbeville Press, 1985), p. 254.

55 Veyne, "Homosexuality in Ancient Rome," in Philippe Aries and André Bégin, eds., *Western Sexuality: Practice and Precept in Past and Present Times*, trans. Anthony Forster (Oxford: Basil Blackwell, 1985), pp. 26–35; quotation, pp. 29–30.

Charlotte F. Otten

Eros Vulgarized: The English Vocabulary of Medical Writing on Sexuality in the 16th and 17th Centuries

Mr. Samuel Herring, in an impassioned speech before Parliament on August 4, 1653, urged linguistic reform on a nation that was accustomed to using Latin in its professional writing: "All law bookes, physick or whatsoever . . . should be translated into English."[1] There was already a rise, however, in the publication of medical books In the vernacular between 1649 and 1660, as Charles Webster points out in *The Great Instauration*: "Of the 238 medical works published in England between 1640 and 1660 which have so far been recorded, only twelve per cent are in Latin, which was still the dominant vehicle of communication among European academic physicians."[2] The highest number of medical books published in English during this period was in 1652, with 21 in English and 2 in Latin; in 1660, however, there was a return to Latin, with 8 in Latin and 13 in English.[3]

There were obstacles to translating medical works into English, not the least being the rivalries between the College of Physicians, the Barber-Surgeons' Company, and the Society of Apothecaries. Latin, argued the advocates of writing in the vernacular, was the language of monopoly and tyranny, designed to keep medical knowledge out of the hands of the people and in the control of a tightly guarded medical elite; if medical knowledge was to be advanced and health care improved in England, medical literature had to be made available to all who could read English.

The configurations of the argument for writing medicine in English are apparent in the writings of Helkiah Crooke, physician to King James I and Professor in Anatomy and Surgery to His Majesty; Nicholas Culpeper, physician and astrologer; and Peter Cole, London printer to Culpeper and his team of translators.

Crooke, in his *Microcosmographia*, published in 1616 and again in 1631 (which was "collected and translated out of all the best authors of Anatomy, especially Gaspar Bauhinus and Andreas Laurentius"), argued that knowledge is essential for diagnosis and cure: this knowledge must be vulgarized and widely disseminated. Not a rabid patriot, he observed that since physicians, both ancient and contemporary, had written in their native tongues with no loss of scientific accuracy, it would be equally appropriate for him to put scientific medical material into English: "the examples of all men who have undertaken this taske even in their mother tongues did sway much with me whose writings have received allowance in all ages and Commonwealths."[4] English, he asserted, was a fit vehicle for medical writing.

The most aggressive writer in the vernacular was Nicholas Culpeper, who, with his collaborators, was responsible for forty-one issues of thirty different works between 1649 and 1660. Professional rivalry and patriotism strongly motivated Culpeper. He believed that by giving the nation the "whol Moddel of Physick" in English, he could free England from the linguistic tyranny of the College of Physicians, a linguistic tyranny dating as far back as the Norman Conquest: "William the Bastard having conquered this Nation, and brought it *sub jugo*, brought in the Norman Laws written in an unknown tongue, and this laid the foundation to their future, and our present slavery . . . my pen (if God permit me life and health) shall never lie still till I have given them the whol Moddel of Physick in their Native Language . . . ."[5]

In the 1644 English edition of Riverius's *The Practice of Physick*, Peter Cole, Culpeper's printer, joined the argument, supplying the credentials of his translators:

The Printer to the Reader

And that thou maist know to whose great Industry and pains thou art obliged for the Englishing this most excellent piece of Art, know that (by reason of eight several Editions in Latin, of which there hath been fifteen thousand Books sold) it hath been three times translated at my charge, By *Nicholas Cullpeper*, Physitian and Astrologer; *Abdiah Cole*, Doctor in Physick twenty nine Yeers in the Service of three of the greatest Princes in Europe: and William Rowland, a Knowing Physitian: and also by an eminently learned and pious Physitian, who desires not to be named, being (as he saies) content with the applause of his own Conscience, which tel him that while he was imployed about this Work, he was doing that which would weigh down in profit to his Country, all the good that all the Physitians in *London* did or could do in the same time; a work that tends to profit many millions, not only of this Generation, but of all that shall follow, till the world become one great Bone-fire; or this Nation and Language perish together. . . .[6]

Cole's belief in the profitability of Englishing medical writing—to the country and to "Many millions" until the world ends in conflagration—culminates in the apocalyptic vision found also in the vernacular writing of the botanists and agriculturalists of his day.[7]

What troubled the English vernacular writers in medicine—and what is the focus of this paper—is the anglicizing of the vocabulary used to describe the genitals and the process of reproduction. Crooke, for example, in 1616 had so many doubts about using the vulgar tongue for the genitals that he consulted clergymen before going to print. Their endorsement prevented him from being brought to court for bawdiness; and their reassurance that chastity resides in the eye and ear of the "beholder" made his linguistic venture of 180 pages on male and female genitalia possible:

there was onely one obstacle, to reveyle the veile of Nature, to prophane her mysteries for a litle curious skilpride, to ensnare mens minds by sensual demonstrations, seemeth a thing liable to heavy construction. . . . God that created them, did he not intend their preservation, or can they bee preserved and not knowne? or knowne and not discovered? Indeed it were to be wished that all men would come to the knowledge of these secrets with pure eyes and eares, such as they were matched with in their Creation: but shall we therefore forfet our knowledge because some men cannot conteine their lewd and inordinate affections? . . . As much as was possible we have endevoured . . . by honest words and circumlocutions to molifie the harshnesse of the Argument. . . . I have not herein relyed uppon my owne judgement, but have had the opinion of grave and reverent Divines, by whome I have bin perswaded not to intermit this part of my labour. . . .[8]

Another type of concern was expressed by physicians who wrote on the birth process. John Banister in *The Historie of Man* could not bring himself to describe female genitals for fear of committing "more indecencie agaynst the office of *Decorum*, then yeld needefull instruction to the profite of the common sort . . . ";[9] Richard Jones and Thomas Raynalde thought that vulgar descriptions of the organs involved in birth might be used to "the discredit of women, that men might hereby conceive a certain . . . abhorrance toward a woman" and that women readers might be offended by what "is spoken of the body."[10] Jane Sharp, however, "practitioner in the art of midwifry above thirty years," defended her use of plain English in *The Midwives Book* in 1671: "Thus I have as briefly and as plainly as I could, laid down a description of the parts of generation of both sexes, purposely omitting hard names, that I might have no cause to enlarge my work, by giving you the meaning of them where there is no need, unless it be for such persons who desire rather to know Words than Things."[11]

Defenses for vulgarizing the sexual organs ranged from nuanced statements about the necessity for using "grosse" terms to open attacks on the integrity of physicians. Jacques Ferrand (a French physician writing in the French vernacular and translated into English by Edmund Chilmead of Christ Church, Oxford, in 1640), said that he desired "to speake as modestly as possibly I can: yet must I withall observe the Precepts and Tearmes of Physicke, which cannot so well stand oftentimes with the Civility and modesty of Language. *Amo Verecundia* (saith Tully,) *sed magis amo libertatem loquendi.* I love Modesty: but yet I love the Liberty of Speech more."[12] Culpeper, however, who had no such reservations about linguistic modesty, used words such as water-gate, dung-gate, fart-forcing medicaments, piss-drivers, even neologisms, and in a vitriolic attack on physicians, denounced all those who opposed the Englishing of the sexual organs:

> These are the parts common both to the Yard, and also to the rest of the Body, which although I have been somewhat large about, yet I cannot account it tedious, because it conduceth to the teaching of Knowledg to my Country Men and Women, who have been two [*sic*] long reind in with the bridle of Ignorance by Physicians . . . for just for al the world as the Popish Priests serve those they cal the Laity, (which is but a word derived from the Greek word laos, which is, People in plain English, as though the Priests were no People, but either Angels, or (which is more probably Monsters) as I say, the Popish Priests serve their Laity, so do our Physitians serve the commonalty of this Nation; viz. Hide all from them they can . . . should the vulgar but be a little acquainted with their Mysteries, all their jugling and knavery would be seen, and their wealth and esteem, which is the *Diana* which they adore, would be put to a *non plus*; and that's the reason when you hear any of them cry out against Me for writing Physic in my mother Tongue. . . .[13]

As most of the writers suggested, there were hazards in translating the names and functions of the genitals into the vernacular. Since by definition the vulgar language is the common language, the language accessible to native speakers, and hence the language that can easily descend into the coarse or gross, they risked being discredited as unprofessional and unscientific by the medical community; and they dreaded being charged with sexual irresponsibility by the community at large in substituting prick and yard for penis; stones for testicles; lips or doors of the water-gate for vulva; pisspipe for urethra; great chink for Rima Magna; rubsters for Tribades. In comparing the parts of the genitals (which, if I were following their example I would call the "begetters," not the genitals), to bats' wings, a plow, letters of the Greek alphabet, woodworm, earthworm, silkworm, sponge, mushroom, pomegranate, head of a tench or young kitten, half-blown rose or gilliflower, leather purse, knots of a Franciscan friar's girdle, and in using analogies from common experience, comparing male impotence and infertility to engines that are broken, to gunpowder that is adulterated and which hisses instead of roars, with thunder that produces no rain or water in the "inward ground of the matrix,"[14] they knew that they were skirting the borders of professional propriety and communal morality, and that they might even be encouraging flippancy, bawdiness, salaciousness.

Beneath these surface issues, then, lurked three basic issues: the nature of the language of sexuality; the nature of the reproductive system; and the nature of the audience. I shall discuss these issues in this order.

In considering first the nature of the language of sexuality, I shall limit my discussion to three aspects of it: the role of the senses and imagination in the use of vulgar words for the reproductive process; the possible psychological and moral effects of English words used hitherto in contexts of sexual titillation and arousal; and the absence in English of a strictly denotative, scientific language for the genitals and reproduction. First, then, the role of the senses and imagination.

One of the three internal senses, the imagination was defined as the faculty which "doth represent and set before the intellectuall, all the objects which she hath received from the spies [senses] abroad . . . upon which reports the intellectuall or understanding part of the minde, frameth her conclusions, which are very often false, the imagination making untrue reports"; Reason then can be "misse-informed by a fayned fantasie."[15] The questions implicit in their discussions of the imagination were these: Does word, through reading or hearing, meet image already lodged in the imagination? Can explicit English words for the genitals imprint "images or shaddowes of venerious delights in the fantasies of men?"[16] Can English words and phrases (a list follows) stimulate "the appetite and desire of copulation . . . excited by Imagination?"[17] What happens in the imagination when, in the vivid language of the native tongue, the *glans* is called the *nut* and is described as "somewhat round compassed with a circle as with a garland . . . about the root of it . . . there is a little pit";[18] when the *nut* is described as "not unlike to a mushrum upon the heads of the two bodies of the yard";[19] when a coat of the testicles is compared to "corne in the huskes";[20] when the testicles "resemble a small pullets Egge somewhat flatted";[21] when the passage through which the semen passes is described as "a seed trough";[22] when the ties of the womb are compared to bats' wings;[23] when the position of the womb is compared to "a moored Ship in a Tempest betweene her Anchors";[24] when the mouth of the womb is "transverse or outward like a Plaice [fish] mouth . . . the whole orifice with the transverse slitte, is like the letter, Z, small and wondrous narrow";[25] when the cervix is called "The Bason or Laver . . . it receiveth the yard fitly like a sheath";[26] when the vulva is "a valley, or Valva a Flood-gate, because it is divided into two parts by a cleft, which like Floodgates or leafe-doores are easily opened or shut as need is. We will call it the lappe";[27] when the Nymphae "are very like colour and shape to that part of a Cockes combe which hangs under his throate";[28] when they are called *Nymphae* because "the Nymphes are sayed to bee presidents or Deities of the Fountaines . . . for the Poets say that the *Nymphes* laciviously seeke out the Satyrs among the Woods and Forrests";[29] when the Carunculae are called "fleshy knobs" resembling "the form of a Rosehalf blown";[30] when an imperforated womb is compared to a "Barrel of Beer that hath no hole to put in a Spigot";[31] when the yard is "the Plow wherewith the ground is tilled and made fit for the production of Fruit: we see that some fruitful persons have a Crop by it almost every year, only plowing up their own ground";[32] when the vessels carrying the seed are called *erectors*, *accelerators*, *hasteners*;[33] when the neck of the womb is described as "wrinckled with many crests, like the upper part of a dogges mouth";[34] when a woman's womb "skipping as it were for joy, may meet her Husbands Sperm, graciously and freely receive the same, and draw it into its innermost Cavity or Closet, and withal bedew and sprinkle it with her own Sperm, powred forth in that pang of Pleasure."[35]

This list, although partial, shows immediately that the use of English words for the genitals and the process of reproduction raised issues beyond the linguistic for these writers. Although they borrowed many of the names and metaphors from their originals (whether in Latin or one of the continental languages), they voiced concern for the way sexual language is received and the way sexual language operates on experience or fantasized experience. Since the imagination never stops working and continues to operate even in dreams, the imagination has the power to command the "moving faculty"; that is, motions, affections, passions, and perturbations can be activated by the English words, and the genitals may respond by being "puffed up."[36] Once the senses and imagination have been stimulated by the vocabulary of sexuality, passion can take over from Reason—passion in this context being defined as "a Motion of the blood . . . through the hope of pleasure."[37] The possible psychological and moral effects of English used in contexts of sexual titillation and arousal, and the contextuality of this diction and of these metaphors, were important considerations for the English vernacular writers. (We recall in passing, that Samuel Pepys had both erection and ejaculation while reading a sexually explicit book.)[38]

The word *lap*, for example, which today has shed its sexual anatomical designation and means the region stretching from the waist to the knees of a seated person, and which the English medical writers used to designate the outwardly visible female privities, comes in a famous Shakespearean context of double entendre. Hamlet, lying down at Ophelia's feet for the play-within-a-play, says, "Lady, shall I lie in your lap?" Ophella responds, "No, my lord." Hamlet replies, "I mean, my head upon your lap. . . . Do you think I meant country matters?"[39] Hamlet here is projecting his own intended bawdiness into what he likes (or pretends) to think are Ophelia's linguistically astute sexual perceptions. Decoding the word *lap* for Ophelia, he imputes the bawdy, obscene sense to her.

Perhaps the most notorious example is the word *prick*, which today has not shed its sexual anatomical designation. The context here is *Romeo and Juliet.* Mercutio is speaking: "the bawdy hand of the dial is now upon the prick of noon," which Peter De Vries, no less bawdy than Mercutio, used as the title of his book, *The Prick of Noon.*[40]

English words for sexuality cannot escape the dual nature of the pun. Again Shakespeare. Boyet in *Love's Labor's Lost*, using the word *foot* as a unit of measurement but also as a part of the anatomy of the leg, says, "Loves her by the foot." Dumaine, using the word *yard* as both a unit of measurement and as a term for a part of the male sexual anatomy, replies, "He may not by the yard."[41] Contextuality makes the psychological difference; shedding contextuality is psychologically impossible. We understand the hesitancy of the medical writers in employing words whose presence in sexual contexts can make them provocatively sensual in medical contexts.

This leads to the observation that to English eyes and ears the strictly denotative nature of Latin and Greek prevented sexual language from becoming bawdy, obscene, distorted through equivocation or punning. Using the previous examples from Shakespeare, we recognize what happens when a language rich in connotation is substituted for a vocabulary of strict denotation. It would have been unspeakably indecent for Hamlet to say to Ophelia, "Lady, shall I put my penis in your vulva?"; meaningless for Mercutio to describe the bawdy hand of the dial on the penis of noon; inane for Dumaine to use the word penis in a measurement pun. Those who used English sexual terms for Latin and Greek terms had to cope with the fact that the English words for the genitals had overtones, connotations, contexts. Although eager to promote knowledge and health, they knew that the sexual territory they were entering was booby-trapped with language that could be risqué, bawdy, risible, improper, disgusting, obscene, even pornographic; and they had to exonerate themselves from being regarded as promoters of voyeurism, lust, or even metaphorical coition. It should be noted that Culpeper's *Midwife*, *The Compleat Midwife*, and *The Birth of Mankind* were linked with filthy books in *The Practical Part of Love*;[42] and that the son of John Henry Meibomius was initially unwilling to translate his father's medical *Treatise on the Use of Flogging in Venereal Affair*, fearing he might "incur the censure of such to whom these papes tinctured with a tickling Salt might seem too ludicrous and libertine."[43]

Since the language of sexuality is no more autonomous than any other language, the language of sexuality reflected attitudes toward the reproductive system prevalent in 16th and 17th century England—attitudes not new or unique to England but stretching across centuries of belief and experience. Rooted in theology, these beliefs included two apparently contradictory positions: that God the Creator in His benevolence had created the genitals for coition, and hence the sexual parts and sexual act are good, and the language used to describe them is clean; that through the fall of Adam and Eve the genitals and coition are stained by passion, lust, concupiscence, and hence the sexual parts and the sexual act are to be covered with clothing and with language. These emerge not so much as contradictory beliefs but as complementary beliefs in perpetual conflict.

This tension is reflected in the ancient word *pudenda*, defined as "those parts of which one ought to be ashamed." This word, incidentally, is footnoted and glossed by John Updike in his novel *Roger's Version*: Roger, drawing on Tertullian for a definition of *pudenda*, goes on to make the observation that *pudenda* has in the twentieth century become *pudendum*, "a grammatically neutral form whose onus has been patriarchally shifted onto the female genitals alone."[44]

The beauty and constructiveness of the reproductive process compelled the English writers to describe it in the vernacular; the potential ugliness and destructiveness of it after the Fall gave them pause. Not one of the writers is free of this tension: the personal, narrative voice vibrates with it.

Ambroise Paré, for example, whose works were translated by Thomas Johnson (the London apothecary and botanist who enlarged and amended John Gerard's *Herball* in 1633), is known as one who made significant contributions to obstetrics. He provided elaborate and detailed instructions to husbands on how to "entertain" their wives "with all kinde of dalliance, wanton behaviour, and allurements to venery . . . handling her secret parts and dugs, that she may take fire";[45] three pages earlier, however, he reveals the tension:

> But man, that is endued with reason, being a divine and most noble creature, would never yeeld nor make his minde subject to a thing so abject and filthy as is carnall copulation, but that the venerous ticklings, raised in those parts, relaxe the severity of his mind, or reason admonish him that the memory of his name ought not to end with his life. . . . Therefore by reason of this profit or commodity, nature hath endued the genitall parts with a far more exact or exquisite sense than the other parts . . . unlesse nature had prepared so many allurements, baits, and provocations of pleasure, there is scarce any man so hot or delighted in venereous acts, which considering and marking the place appointed for humane conception, the loathsomnesse of the filth which daily falleth downe unto it, and wherewitthall it is humected and moistened, and the vicinity and neerenesse of the great gut under it, and of the bladder above it, but would shun the embraces of women. . . .[46]

The tension existed even in the word *obscene*, with Crooke using it to mean simply "the organs of generation," without pejorative connotations, but also to mean "shameful, indecent, impure": in his section on the organs of generation he speaks of "The nature of the obscene parts";[47] in his specific discussion of "the female fissure that admitteth the yard," he writes that it is "thought too obscoene to look upon; which is the reason sayth *Pliny* that the carcasses of women doe floate in the water with their faces downward, contrary to mens which swimme upward, even Nature it selfe yeelding to modesty."[48]

It is a "disputable businesse," said Ferrand, "whether or no the names are obscene and dishonest, when as the Parts themselves that are signified by them, are not so, but are Naturall, usefull, and necessary."[49] Juxtaposed in the medical writing are two aspects of carnal copulation: Lemnius's rhapsodic view of man's creation with resonances of Psalm 8 rests comfortably next to Crooke's acknowledgment of the "poyson of mans sin." The point is that the statements are authorially interchangeable. Lemnius says:

> For nothing in the world though it be comely and excellently made, can be compared with the excellency of Man; so that from Man God would have the valuation of his own Excellence to be made, and that mortals should thus have a character of his Divinity. . . . Whereby man was made like unto Gods Image and similitude. For Man is the most expresse representation of God . . . and that he might not lead a disconsolate life, he gave a woman for an helper and companion, and he put

> into them both force to love, and a greedy desire of procreating their like, having prepared for that purpose a swelling humour and spirit, and organical parts: and that the one should not be afraid or decline the society of the other: he added allurements and a desire of mutual Embracing, that when they did use procreation, they should be sweetly affected, and pacified wonderfull wayes.[50]

And Crooke says, it is "so obscoene a piece of business"[51] that had Providence not ordained copulation for procreation, males would have scorned and detested "so brutish and base a worke," and women would have abhorred it for its consequent pain.[52]

Recognizing the perils of describing sexuality in the vernacular, and admitting the ambiguities of sexuality, they candidly spoke of the necessity for the sting of sensual pleasure to preserve the human race. We remember, however, that Dr. Thomas Browne never quite made his peace with the genitals and carnal copulation and that he openly expressed the wish that humans could procreate like trees. Sensual pleasure was integrated into their spiritual vision, for they believed that Nature had given the sexual organs the appetite for eternity. By returning to the creative act of the Divine Wisdom, who, they said had "perpetrated below" the species so that it could be "eternized above, after an ineffable manner of recreation,"[53] they averted even self-charges of possible indecency and obscenity. Since the natural and the supernatural coexisted in the genitals, the English words to describe them and their function were neither coarse nor base; the language was capable of sharing in and conveying the vision of eternity.

The nature of language and the nature of reproduction lead inevitably to my third section—the nature of reception. And here the writers realized (and now I am quoting John Donne) that the paths of sexual language are "dark and dangerous" and "ambush'd round with household spies."[54]

Obviously, vernacular medical books were not written for strictly academic physicians in the College of Physicians who made their way in Latin and who guarded the technical vocabulary of medicine. On the other hand, the surgeon Alexander Read, a popular lecturer at the Barber-Surgeons' Hall, was, according to Webster, "one of the most widely-read of medical writers during the Puritan Revolution"[55] —and, we assume, read by those who attended his lectures and who were in the medical profession. The readership was, then, a part of the medical community.

Haunting their writing on sexuality, however, is the fear that those who read these candid vernacular discussions might be "lewd and inordinate" in their affections and that they would turn these sexual secrets into material for sexual gratification. These writers frequently expressed the hope that their auditors would be fit for "such kind of Philosophy."[56] Knowing that "the heart is very easily surprised, and impoysoned" by sexually explicit discourse,[57] they defended their books by saying that they were providing reputable medical books, not for students of the obscene, bawdy, erotic, or pornographic, but for serious students of anatomy, for those concerned with the health care of the community, and even for those non-Latin readers who might be involved in protecting the health of themselves and their families.

It is difficult, however, to prevent books on the anatomy of the genitals and on the physiology of the reproductive system from being used as sex manuals. What was to keep these books from being regarded as pseudo-medical writing, from being placed in the same category as a work variously called *Aristotle's Legacy*, *Aristotle's Problems*, *Aristotle's Master-piece*, *Compleat Midwife*; or from being placed side by side with the English translation of Sinibaldi's *Geneanthropeia* (titled *Rare Verities* in English) and whose English adaptation was designed for titillation, with chapter headings running like this: "Examples of such men and women that have been very lustful and lecherous"; "Concerning some men that have had wonderful great Genitals"; "How to contract the vulva being too large and wide"; "Concerning pendulous venery, as also many other fantastical venereal postures."[58]

I cannot provide detailed information on the readership of vernacular medical books nor precise data on their reception; it is also impossible to chart "the eye and ear of the beholder." As Roger Thompson shows in his *Unfit for Modest Ears: A study of pornographic, obscene and bawdy works written or published in the second half of the seventeenth century*, readership statistics are hard to come by.[59] Although the readership lies in a murky area, the voice of the writer is clear and the values expressed are explicit: to alleviate anxieties and fears about sexuality and to promote physical and mental health through accurate information on the anatomy and physiology of the genitals.

What the reader brought to the text is unknown, except in one mid-18th century case in New England. This one case, however, does not prove that the "household spies" had won. The book in question was a volume on midwifery, which, if Thomas H. Johnson is right, was known as *Secret of Secrets, Compleat Midwife, Aristotle's Master-piece.*[60] It was read by young men in Jonathan Edwards's parish and called by one of the offenders the "young folks Bible."[61] These young men were brought to trial for using their new-found knowledge to shock young women by talking exceeding "uncleanly and Lasciviously."[62]

The conflicts which were built into this enterprise were never quite resolved, although they were tackled with candor, spirit, patriotic fervor, and personal and professional courage. The linguistic ambiguities springing from the perceived nature of carnal copulation remained, although theological arguments were adduced and visions of spiritual joy invoked. The anxieties about violating semantic codes by presenting the reproductive system in the vernacular to anyone who could read did not disappear, although the dissemination and advancement of knowledge and the improvement of health care remained their goal. Their faith in the English language, their unabashedly realistic approach to the genitals, their medical commitment to the reading public and to human need was strong. Not resorting to euphemism, which is the language of prurience, they did not do what the United States group promoting safe sex today is doing on television: telling males how to put a condom on a banana. These linguistic reforms in the use of English for the genitals proved to be ephemeral, a momentary ruffling of the placid surface of respectable, professional diction.[63] What they did establish, however, was the fact that the language of sexuality could be read and spoken without shame or contempt; without descending into bawdiness or obscenity; that the sexual organs ought to be placed where they began, in the Grand Design of the benevolent Creator; and that the reproductive system could produce eternal as well as temporal bliss. Optimistic about the uses of language, they had faith in the metaphors of common experience. And if mysteries remained about how physical generation contributed to the mystical experience of love, they lived with John Donne's paradox

> Loves mysteries in soules doe grow,
> But yet the body is his booke.
> ("The Extasie")

Calvin College

NOTES

1 Charles Webster, *The Great Instauration* (London: Duckworth, 1975), p. 262; J. Nickolls, ed., *Original Letters and Papers of State Addressed to Oliver Cromwell* (London, 1743), pp. 99–102. Webster observes in his chapter on "The Prolongation of Life": "Generally, the pressure for vernacular medicine came from the medical reformers and amateurs; the academic physicians continued to publish predominantly in Latin for the benefit of audiences on the continent."(p 272). Christopher Hill in "The Medical Profession and Its Radical Critics" provides the context for the democratization and dissemination of theological, legal, and medical knowledge through the vernacular. *Change and*

Continuity in Seventeenth-Century England (Cambridge: Harvard UP, 1975), pp. 157–78. C. Donald O'Malley in "English Medical Literature in the Sixteenth Century" reviews conflicting attitudes toward writing in the vernacular: John Hatchett (1566) argued that making medical writing available to all who could read would open medical practice to "syr John lack latin a pedler, a weaver, and often tymes a presumptuous woman"; John Caius (1552) believed that the use of English would "diminishe the grace of thynges learned"; but Edward Jorden (1603) by writing in English made available diagnoses and cures of hysteria to combat popular and professional attributions of hysterical symptoms to demonical possession *William Andrews Clark Memorial Library Seminar Papers*, 1961, pp. 7, 9, 18–20).

2 Webster, *The Great Instauration*, p. 266.

3 Webster, p. 267.

4 Helkiah Crooke, *Microcosmographia* (London, 1616, 1631, the latter edition cited here), p. 197.

5 Nicholas Culpeper, *A Physicall Directory or A Translation of the London Dispensatory Made by the Colledge of Physicians in London* (London, 1649, 1650, 1651),"To the Reader."

6 Culpeper, "To the Reader."

7 See Charlotte F. Otten, *Environ'd With Eternity: God, Poems, and Plants in Sixteenth and Seventeenth Century England*, ch. 2, "The Values of Terra culture," for the political theology of terraculture (Lawrence, KS: Coronado, 1985). "Love of country" motivated a distinguished group of vernacular botanico-agricultural writers such as Ralph Austen, Sir Richard Weston, Walter Blith, John Beale, and Robert Sharrock, who emphasized the eternal values of their enterprise as well as the temporal (pp. 23–51).

8 Crooke, p. 197.

9 John Banister, *The Historie of Man* (London: 1578), Bbiiii^{v}.

10 Richard Jones and Thomas Raynalde, *The Byrth of Mankynde* (London, 1552), "Prologue."

11 Jane Sharp, *The Midwives Book* (London, 1671), p. 80.

12 Jacques Ferrand, *Erotomania . . .* , trans. Edmund Chilmead (Oxford, 1640), p. 271.

13 Nicholas Culpeper, *A Directory for Midwives* (London, 1656), pp. 17–18.

14 Levinus Lemnius, *The Secret Miracles of Nature* (London, 1658), pp. 26–7.

15 André DuLaurens, *A Discourse of the Preservation of the Sight. . .* , trans. Richard Surphlet (London, 1599), p. 74.

16 Crooke, p. 248.

17 Lemnius, p. 26.

18 Alexander Read, *The Manuall of the Anatomy or Dissection of the Body of Man* (London, 1638, 1642), pp. 226–27.

19 Ambroise Paré, *Workes*, trans. T. Johnson (London, 1634), p. 215.

20 Crooke, p. 205.

21 Paré, p. 119.
22 Crooke, p. 206.
23 Crooke, p. 223.
24 Crooke, p. 223
25 Crooke, p. 233.
26 Crooke, p. 234.
27 Crooke, p. 237.
28 Crooke, p. 237.
29 Crooke, p. 238.
30 Culpeper, *Midwives*, p. 25.
31 Culpeper, *The Practice of Physick* (London, 1655), p. 501.
32 Sharp, p. 19.
33 Read, p. 117.
34 Paré, p. 130.
35 Culpeper, *Practice*, p. 503. For an example of the vernacular turned racy, see the jocose epistolary exchange between two medical doctors, Edward Baynard and Sir John Floyer, who speak of a male's "Whore-tackle," "the whole Cod-Piece Oeconomy," "broke and bankrupt in his *Bed-Tackle*," and who recommend an "Office of *Inspection* to measure *Man* and his *Manners*" (*Essay to Prove Cold Bathing* [London, 1702]), pp. 238–310.
36 Crooke, p. 248.
37 Ferrand, p. 6.
38 Pepys's entries in his *Diary* for 13 January, 8 February, and 9 February 1668, reveal the effect on the genitals of reading a lewd book purportedly "for information sake": "I did read through *L'escholle des Filles*; a lewd book, but what doth me no wrong to read for information sake (but it did hazer my prick para stand all the while, and una vez to decharger); and after I had done it, I burned it, that it might not be among my books to my shame." *The Diary of Samuel Pepys*, ed. R.C. Latham and W. Matthews, 9 vols. (Berkeley and Los Angeles: University of California Press, 1970–76), Vol. IX, ch. 21, pp. 57–59). The editors of the *Diary* note that the book, which was a fictional dialogue between a sexually-experienced woman and a virgin, was burned in Paris in 1655, and English translations were prosecuted in 1677, 1688, and 1744–45.
39 William Shakespeare, *The Riverside Shakespeare*, ed. Evans, G. Blakemore, et al. (Boston: Houghton Mifflin, 1974), *Hamlet*, III.ii.112–16.
40 Shakespeare, *Romeo and Juliet*, II.iv.113. Peter De Vries, *The Prick of Noon* (Boston: Little-Brown, 1985).
41 Shakespeare, *Love's Labor's Lost*, V.ii.669.
42 *The Practical Part of Love* (London, 1660, p. 40; retitled *Venus Undrest*, 1662.
43 Roger Thompson, *Unfit for Modest Ears* (Totowa, NJ: Rowman and Littlefield, 1979), p. 161.
44 John Updike, *Roger's Version*. (New York: Fawcett, 1987), p. 168.
45 Paré, p. 889.

46 Paré, pp. 886–87.
47 Crooke, pp. 199–272.
48 Crooke, p. 239.
49 Ferrand, p. 272.
50 Lemnius, pp. 6–8.
51 Crooke, p. 211.
52 Crooke, p. 287.
53 Crooke, p. 216.
54 John Donne, *The Elegies and the Songs and Sonnets of John Donne*, ed. Helen Gardner (Oxford: Clarendon Press, 1965).
55 Webster, p. 252.
56 Crooke, p. 216.
57 Ferrand, p. 251.
58 J.B. Sinibaldi, *Geneanthropeia* (*Rare Verities*), anon. trans. (London, 1658).
59 See note 43 above.
60 *Aristotles Master-piece* (London, 1684).
61 Thomas H. Johnson in John Gerard, *The Herball or Generall Historie of Plantes* (London, 1597). Enlarged and Amended by Thomas Johnson (London, 1633, 1636).
62 In "Jonathan Edwards and the 'Young Folks' Bible," Johnson gives the list of conjectured titles and concludes: "Quite evidently the book was the 'Works' of the pseudonymous Aristotle variously known as 'Secret of Secrets,' 'Last Legacy,' 'Master-piece,' 'Compleat Midwife,' or 'Problems of Aristotle'." The 1684 edition of *Aristotles Master-piece* is subtitled *The Secrets of Generation displayed in all the parts thereof*; it makes frequent disclaimers for inciting lewdness, e.g., "I am not desiring this Book should fall into the hands of any obscene Person, whose Folly or Malice may turn that into Ridicule that loudly proclaims the infinite Wisdom of an omnipotent Creator . . . " (p. 4); "for the publick good, and in no wise convert them to obscenity" (p. 99). Although several sections resemble Johnson's Paré, ch. XXXVII, "A Word of Advice to both Sexes in the time of Copulation," is identical to Paré. Its blend of Latin and English for the genitals and copulation, designed to give this book a scientific aura, may actually titillate; e.g. ch. X, on virginity: "In the Secret place about the *Sinus Pudoris*, or rather by some called the Neck of the Womb, is that pendulous production by some called the Hymen, but more rightly the *Claustrum Virginale*, and in *French* it is termed the . . . Roses Bud, for that it much resembles the Bud of a Rose, expended, or a Clove Gilliflower . . . " (pp . 92–93).
63 Two prominent physicians after the Restoration resumed Latin terminology. Thomas Sydenham, who wrote his major works in English, had them translated into Latin for publication: *Methodus Curandi Febres* (1666) and *Observationes Medicae* (1676); they were then translated back into English, *The Whole Works*, trans. John Pechy (London, 1696) . Thomas Willis wrote in Latin, *Opera omnia*

cum . . . multis figures aeneis (1680); an English translation titled *The Remaining Medical Works* trans. S. Pordage appeared in 1684 in London. In both cases, when the genitals and the reproductive system were discussed, the language of Eros remained essentially latinate.

Jackie Pigeaud

Reflections on Love-Melancholy in Robert Burton

From the moment one sets out to expound Burton, it is as if one is trapped. Is one supposed to summarize the book, or exhibit the logic of its structure? It seems that the synoptic table proposed by Burton is sufficient for those purposes. Any exposition will always be inadequate because it can only reduce the number of examples, while Burton's project is to exhaust them. Nor should it cling to a line of reasoning, because none exists. There is nothing of the philosopher about Burton.[1]

At first sight, the book devoted to love-melancholy is nothing but a prolific digression on a single passion amongst many, and a justifiable one, for as literature and history show, love is a terrible passion. But as we shall see, the construction of the book proves that it is something else besides.

The preface is written in a light-hearted tone. Yet Burton feels the need to justify himself. No, this is not a frivolous subject unworthy of the dignity of a thinker and a theologian. Many weighty men have written upon this theme (p. 4). On the other hand, one cannot set aside the playful aspect of love. "Give me leave then to refresh my Muse a little, and my weary readers . . . " (p. 6). Besides, who has not had his moment of madness? (p. 8).

Butafter the beginning of the book, the tone reverts to the sententious. Burton proposes to examine "the kinds of love, his nature, beginning, difference, objects, how it is honest or dishonest, a virtue or a vice, a natural passion or a disease, his power and effects, how far it extends . . . " (p. 10). But as usual with Burton, one must not expect a very rigorous method. He presents some definitions from Leon Hebraeus, Plato, Plotinus and others in order to demonstrate briefly that love varies with its objects, and to express agreement with Aristotle in his *Ethics* that " 'All things desire that which is good' . . . or at least that which to them seems to be good" (p. 11). To that which the individual deems good, beauty is joined; to beauty are added grace and desire. Thus the question of beauty arises, and with it the commonplaces of philosophy, leading to this banal conclusion: "every fair thing is amiable, and what we love is fair and gracious" (p. 12).

Hence there is a kind of vicious circle: every beautiful thing is amiable, and that which we love is beautiful and gracious. We are in a world of contradiction, of scintillation and variety. All definitions of love are good because love is precisely what ascribes beauty to things. This manner of conducting a discourse bears a strong resemblance to that of the Sophist Hippias in the dialogue of Plato which Burton cites in this passage. The names of love are as numerous as its objects: love of money, of beauty, of riches and so forth (p. 13).

More interesting is the idea of the universality of love, manifest even in inanimate creatures (p. 15). From this derive the behaviour of the stars, the elements, the magnet. "No creature, St. Hierome concludes, is to be found, *quod non aliquid amat*" (p. 15). Love emits a cosmic, universal power. This will afford us later on some beautiful passages on the love of plants and the passion of palm trees (pp. 43–4). Of all the objects of love, the most attractive is profit. No love is as attractive as gold (p. 19). This occasions a moralizing digression in which Burton's fundamental pessimism rears its head (pp. 19–21). "They were tied to thee by the teeth, and would follow thee as crows do a carcass: but when thy goods are gone and spent, the lamp of their love is out, and thou shalt be contemned, scorned, hated, injured" (p. 20).

The objects of love are infinite. Burton briefly attempts to classify them, beginning with inanimate objects, and rapidly draws the conclusion that when we fix an inordinate eye upon an object and rave about it, "this pleasure may turn to pain . . . and cause melancholy in the end" (p. 22). Here, at last, melancholy makes its appearance. Melancholy is due, therefore, to an excess of love. In itself, love is not *a priori* damnable. There are objects worthy of love. There is even a specific and glorious love, which is none other than charity. And in the end, might not our torments, our melancholy, be due to a lack of charity? "Angelical souls, how blessed, how happy should we be. . . . But this we cannot do; and which is the cause of all our woes, miseries, discontent, melancholy, want of this charity" (p. 34). "Monsters of men as we are," to others and to ourselves, "dogs, wolves, tigers, fiends, incarnate devils, we do not only contend, oppress, and tyrannize ourselves, but as so many firebrands we set on and animate others: our whole life is a perpetual combat . . . " (p. 35). This is an example of Burton's style, a subject to which we shall return later.

This theme leads us to the definition of specifically human love—which is the cause of heroical or love-melancholy—and of heroical love. "That causeth heroical, or love-melancholy, is more eminent above the rest, and properly called love. The part affected in men is the liver, and therefore called heroical, because commonly gallants, noblemen, and the most generous spirits are possessed with it" (p. 40). Therefore heroical love, at least in the beginning, is a hero's love, a noble love.[2] The affected part is the liver, which of course houses the physiological cause of melancholy. The range of this love is almost infinite, and one may divide it, as does Plato, into two branches, φιλεῖν and ἐρᾶν. If this love bears the name of human, and is found most notably amongst human beings, it is nevertheless not confined to them, but extends to all sentient creatures and even to plants. This is demonstrated by the account of the passionate love of palm trees (p. 43), and permits Burton to reason *a fortiori* that "If such fury be in vegetals, what shall we think of sensible creatures? how much more violent and apparent shall it be in them!" (p. 44). After plants, animals suffer from this folly, as is shown by the classic example of mares—"*furor est insignis equarum*" (p. 44). But animals can also love humans (p. 45). And what of the spirits of the air, the demons of the sky, the incubi and succubi? (p. 46). "That the devil hath any carnal copulation with women" (p. 46) sets off a whole train of extraordinary stories.

Thus this tyranny of love holds sway over the entire universe. But what about human beings in particular? To be sure, there is a power of love which unites provinces, constructs cities, and by perpetual generation makes and preserves humanity, and propagates the Church; "but if it rage, it is no more love, but burning lust, a disease, frenzy, madness, hell" (p. 49). Love, therefore, can be the best of things and the worst of things. But Burton's zest finds its best exercise in the worst: "Besides those daily monomachies, murders, effusion of blood, rapes, riot, and immoderate expense, to satisfy their lusts, beggary, shame, loss, torture, punishment, disgrace, loathsome diseases that proceed from thence, worse than calentures and pestilent fevers, those often gouts, pox, arthritis, palsies, cramps, sciatica, convulsions, aches, combustions, etc., which torment the body, that feral melancholy which crucifies the soul in this life, and everlastingly torments in the world to come" (pp. 49–50). And the hell of love is made plain in zoophilia, exemplified in Semiramis' love for a horse, and Pasiphae's for a bull (p. 50).

Apparently we return to the subject: "I come at last to that heroical love, which is proper to men and women, is a frequent cause of melancholy . . . " (p. 52). One would think one has finally arrived. But the dichotomy begins anew: "There is an honest love, I confess, which is natural" (p. 52), and which introduces an apology for marriage (pp. 52–3). But that being stated and acknowledged, there is the threat of excessive love, frenetic love, for which women are especially to blame: "Of women's unnatural, unsatiable lust, what country, what village doth not complain"? (p. 55) At any rate, to unfold or illustrate the powers of love "is to set a candle in the sun" (p. 56).

Returning to the term *heroical love*: "it rageth with all sorts and conditions of men, yet is most evident among such as are young and lusty, in the flower of their years, nobly descended, high fed, such as live idly and at ease; and for that cause (which our divines call burning lust) this *ferinus insanus amor*, this mad and beastly passion, as I have said, is named by our physicians heroical love . . . " (p. 56). This passage is interesting because it sketches out a causality. It is the love of noblemen, because noblemen are idle, and the result is that this savage and insane love has earned from the physicians the fair name of "heroical love"; in fact, as Avicenna and others declare, it is nothing but a disease, a melancholy, an anguish of the mind (pp. 57–8).

But apart from this, is it a disease of the body or of the soul? (p. 57) On the one hand, Cicero and Plato call it a furious disease of the soul, madness itself (p. 57), and on the other, Rhazes calls it a melancholic disease. The majority of physicians make it a species of melancholy and treat it separately: "whom I mean to imitate, and to discuss it in all his kinds, to examine his several causes, to show his symptoms, indications, prognostics, effects, so that it may be with more facility cured" (p. 57).

It is, of course, with great pleasure that I find here the ancient problem which I have described at length, and which was the fundamental element of the question of insanity for men of Antiquity: is it a disease of the soul, and the concern of the philosopher, or a disease of the body, and the concern of the physician? Burton's methodology orients him towards the medical expository procedure, but as we shall see, he does not separate the two causal sequences; rather, he reunites them. The seat of love is, according to some, the front part of the head by reason of its dryness, and, according to others, the liver or the heart, but "properly it is a passion of the brain, as all other melancholy, by reason of corrupt imagination" (p. 58).

Burton undertakes to present a hierarchy of causes. It begins with the stars: astrology. There follow the physicians who attribute its origin to temperament: phlegmatics are the least exposed, but that is open to debate. The discussion of the sexual organs themselves is mediated through references to Guainerius ("hot temperature of the testicules") and Ferrand (one learns here that Burton only became acquainted with his book after the third edition of the *Anatomy*: p. 60), who ascribes the origin of the evil to certain atoms in the semen; to these one must add the Aristotle of the *Problemata*. But the principle cause, Burton reiterates, is the idleness of youths, who, like a flock in a meadow, idle and solitary, feel the need to *hirquitallire* (play the goat) (p. 60).

The series of causes comprises, first, place (there was much adultery at Rome, none at Pergamum; if a favorable location coincides with permissiveness in the city, then the conditions for madness are ripe); then, once again, idleness (*vacuo pectore regnat amor*: pp. 62–3); diet, and Burton provides a list of foods (*Aestuans venter cito despuit in libidinem*: p. 64); and the senses, of which the chief is sight. This occasions a long digression on beauty and its importance, on its epithets, its triumph (pp. 64–8), its definition (p. 80), with a sort of heraldry of the body: face, forehead, cheeks, lips, breath, neck, teeth, breasts and hair (pp. 80–1). Here one may amuse oneself in forming a mental picture of Burton's ideal woman: high alabaster forehead, lofty brows, cheeks of vermilion, lips of coral, breath like honey, a neck round and white, white teeth, a bosom softly rounded with a valley of charms between two hills of chalk, flaxen hair, etc. (pp. 80–1).

Paradoxically, ugliness is sometimes seductive, as witness Cyclops and Vulcan. But much space is devoted to the praise of the eyes (pp. 84–5). They emit rays which transport certain spirits by which they are infected in their passage. Here one recognizes the ancient theory of contagion by sight.[3]

In truth, beauty is a "loadstone of itself" (p. 88). But what are we to make of the question posed by the sages as to whether it owes more to art or to nature? Surprisingly, Burton confesses that while natural beauty is very potent, artificial beauty is even more so, and ought to be preferred.[4] When artifice is joined to nature, then the power of beauty is terrible.[5] This affords us a splendid portrait, worthy of an ethnologist:

> Why do they adorn themselves with so many colours of herbs, fictitious flowers, curious needleworks, quaint devices, sweet-smelling odours, with those inestimable riches of precious stones, pearls, rubies, diamond, emeralds, etc.? Why do they crown themselves with gold and silver, use coronets and tires of several fashions, deck themselves with pendants, bracelets, earrings, chains, girdles, rings, pins, spangles, embroideries, shadows, rabatoes, versicolour ribands? Why do they make such glorious shows with their scarfs, feathers, fans, masks, furs, laces, tiffanies, ruffs, falls, cauls, cuffs, damasks, velvets, tinsels, cloth of gold, silver, tissue? . . . " (pp. 93–4).

But the essential ornament is wealth—*veniunt a dote sagittae* (p. 100).

Beauty, therefore, is reinforced by seduction, and the origins of seduction are cultural and social. Hence the role of the word, of song and dance, and of learned speech, as one sees in the case of Abelard, that great seducer. Of course one must add kisses (p. 110), stories (p. 113), and the role of go-betweens.[6] Thus is the list of the causes of heroical love to all intents and purposes brought to an end.

Burton then launches into a chapter on symptoms, maintaining all the while the division between body and soul. He distinguishes the physical symptoms, such as palor, thinness, dryness, groaning, sadness, and lack of appetite, basing himself on an author he is especially fond of citing, Jason Pratensis,[7] who explains it as a dysfunction of the liver (p. 133) which results in the "green-sickness" in young women and cachexia in men. There are other symptoms, such as tears "as drops from a still" (p. 133). It is possible to disguise the disease, and so there follows the inevitable example of Antiochus, Stratonice and Erasistratus (p. 135), and the prodigies of Galen. On the basis of these examples it has even been held that there is a *pulsus amoris*. Trembling is also a clue. Insensibly we make the transition to mental symptoms: the desire to see the beloved, impatience, etc. (p. 140). But these, says Burton, are almost infinite, and so various that no art can encompass them. Even if sometimes lovers are happy, nevertheless most of the time "love is a plague, a torture, an hell, a bitter-sweet passion at last" (p. 141). Here we find a theme dear to love-poetry, even to tragic love-poetry: that of the γλυκύ–πικρόν, the *suavis amarities*, the bitter-sweet (p. 141). Burton concludes that if there is any sweetness in love, it is nothing in comparison with the bitterness. Beauty's impression remains fixed in the mind, "as he that is bitten with a mad dog thinks all he sees dogs, dogs in his meat, dogs in his dish, dogs in his drink, his mistress is in his eyes, ears, heart, in all his senses" (p. 148)—a beautiful image of obsession.

That is how things are when love presents its positive side. What torments far more bitter could one not envisage? Quite simply, this is madness. Enter the theme of *video meliora proboque / deteriora sequor.*[8] Love is blind: every lover loves his mistress however ugly she may be. There follow quotations from the poets, amongst which, oddly enough, the end of the fourth canto of Lucretius is wanting. In a picturesque passage, Burton launches into a description of all the possible forms of ugliness:

Every lover admires his mistress, though she be very deformed of herself, ill-favoured, wrinkled, pimpled, pale, red, yellow, tanned, tallow-faced, have a swollen juggler's platter face, or a thin, lean, chitty face, have clouds in her face, be crooked, dry, bald, goggle-eyed, blear-eyed, or with staring eyes, she looks like a squis'd cat, hold her head still awry, heavy, dull, hollow-eyed, black or yellow about the eyes, or squint-eyed, sparrow-mouthed, Persian hook-nosed, have a sharp fox-nose, a red nose, China flat, great nose, *nare simo patuloque* [snub and flat nose], a nose like a promontory, gubber-tushed, rotten teeth, black, uneven, brown teeth, beetle-browed, a witch's beard, her breath stink all over the room, her nose drop winter and summer, with a Bavarian poke under her chin, a sharp chin, lave-eared, with a long crane's neck, which stands awry too, *pendulis mammis*, "her dugs like two double jugs," or else no dugs, in that other extreme, bloody-fallen fingers, she have filthy, long unpared nails, scabbed hands or wrists, a tanned skin, a rotten carcass, crooked back, she stoops, is lame, splay-footed, "as slender in the middle as a cow in the waist," gouty legs, her ankles hang over her shoes, her feet stink, she breed lice, a mere changeling, a very monster, an oaf imperfect, her whole complexion savours, an harsh voice, incondite gesture, vile gait, a vast virago, or an ugly tit, a slug, a fat fustilugs, a truss, a long lean rawbone, a skeleton, a sneaker (*si qua latent meliora puta* [think that what is not seen is better]), and to thy judgment looks like a mard in a lanthorn, whom though couldst not fancy for a world, but hatest, loathest, and wouldest have spit in her face, or blow thy nose in her bosom, *remedium amoris* [a cure for love] to another man, a dowdy, a slut, a scold, a nasty, rank, rammy, filthy, beastly quean, dishonest peradventure, obscene, base, beggarly, rude, foolish, untaught, peevish, Irus' daughter, Thersites' sister, Grobian's scholar; if he love her once, he admires her for all this, he takes no notice of any such errors as imperfections of body or mind.

The prognosis is very bad.

Love, according to Montaltus, makes the blood cold and thick. This is dementia: "Go to Bedlam for examples" (p. 187). Every village has known love-suicides. There follows a pot-pourri of poetic examples and medical cases. The curability of the disease has been debated, says Burton, "because it is so irresistible and violent a passion" (p. 189). But, according to him, it is agreed that if the disease is detected in good time one can relieve and ameliorate it by means of good remedies (p. 189). Burton announces that he will light his candle from the torches of the great, "and enlarge again upon occasion, as shall seem best to me, and that after mine own method" (p. 189), which is a precious trait of Burtonian composition.

The first rule is hygiene, a combination of exercise and diet (p. 189). One must be occupied in numerous and important affairs; one must live in poverty (pp. 190–91) and practice fasting, take baths, tire oneself out, and sweat. "Other good rules and precepts are enjoined by our physicians, which, if not alone, yet certainly conjoined may do much; the first of which is *obstare principiis* . . . " (p. 195). One must also avoid keeping the secret of one's love to oneself: *qui tacitus ardet magis uritur* (p. 195). One must move to another place, and above all denigrate the loved one by any means (p. 201).

Burton is at his best in picturesque enumerations:

> Tell him . . . that his love is false . . . or that she is a fool, a nasty quean, a slut, a vixen, a scold, a devil, or, which Italians commonly do, that he or she hath some loathsome filthy disease, gout, stone, strangury, falling sickness . . . with many other secret infirmities which I will not so much as name, belonging to women. That he is an hermaphrodite, an eunuch, imperfect, impotent, a spendthrift, a gamester, a fool, a gull, a beggar, a whoremaster, far in debt, and not able to maintain her, a common drunkard, his mother was a witch, his father hanged, that he hath a wolf in his bosom, a sore leg, he is a leper, hath some incurable disease, that he will surely beat her, he cannot hold his water . . . . (p. 201)

> Ipsa haec/ Delectant, veluti Balbinum polypus Agnae; [These very things charm him, as Agna's polypus did Balbinus;] he had rather have her than any woman in the world. (p. 156)

To be sure, he says crudely, "*Immo nec ipsum amicæ stercus fœtet*" (p. 158). Decidedly at ease in the picturesque, Burton offers us all the eccentricities to which lovers surrender themselves (pp. 162 ff.), their enslavement, their ludicrous wishes (p. 169). Here he summarizes the poetic tradition.

Paradoxically, at the very moment when he is expressing ridicule of love, Burton, with his own special type of pendulum motion, pronounces a eulogy of love. "There be some good and graceful qualities in lovers, which this affection causeth . . . it makes base fellows become generous, cowards courageous" (p. 172), etc. Love is even a teacher. Virtually parodying Marivaux, Burton tells of how Cymon was polished by love: "In brief, he became, from an idiot and a clown, to be one of the most complete gentlemen in Cyprus, did many valorous exploits, and all for the love of Mistress Iphigenia" (p. 174).

Love even lies at the origin of the arts. In the words of Erasmus, *Musicam docet amor et poesin* (p. 177). Love makes poets. All our feasts, banquets, poems, theatrical plays, comedies, elegies, odes, what have you, all the poetic genres have their source in love. Add painting to this, as Pliny's story of the young girl who traced her lover's silhouette upon the wall shows (p. 181). Even the Stoics did not neglect to make love poems (p. 183).

It is here that Burton makes a statement to which we shall return, and which is often, with good reason, excerpted. It is one of his disguised confidences. No one can encompass love in its entirety. It is necessary to have been a bit of a lover oneself: "I confess I am but a novice, a contemplator only . . . yet *homo sum* . . . not altogether inexpert in this subject" (p. 184).

Thence one procedes to a chapter on prognostics. "What fires, torments, cares, jealousies, suspicions, fears, griefs, anxieties, accompany such as are in love, I have sufficiently said . . . " (p. 185).

To cultivate two loves at once is not bad either. One must not hesitate to use good advice and persuasion. The notion of opportunity is very important, so "let passion have his course awhile" (p. 204). In the access of passion, advice is useless. Certainly the best remedy for love is systematic denigration: imagine your mistress in an attack of diarrhoea, for instance; look at her nude (pp. 205–9); and there is the example of the man who saw the cancer on his mistress' breast and was thereafter repelled. It is by no means certain whether there is not a little mysogyny in all this (pp. 214 ff.).

When persuasion fails, many seek a remedy in philters and other magical processes (p. 226). Burton enumerates some remedies which he judges foolish (p. 227). As a last resort, as a remedy at once radical and paradoxical, Burton proposes to give the melancholic lover what he wants (p. 228). Let him feast himself on it. This remedy is based on Aratæus of Cappadocia himself ("Aretaeus, an old author"—p. 229) who advocates love as a physician.[9] But circumstances do not always permit this type of expedient ("there's the rub"). Burton enumerates the possible obstacles to its realization in practice. The most potent obstacle of all, and one which touches on the paradox of love, is that the lover might not be loved: "Pan loved Echo, Echo Satyrus, Satyrus Lyda" (p. 231).

Abstinence brings many ills in its train, as one sees in the case of monks. "I am sure, from such rash vows and inhuman manner of life proceed many inconveniences, many diseases, many vices, mastupration, satyriasis, priapismus, melancholy, madness, fornication, adultery, buggery, sodomy, theft, murder, and all manner of mischiefs . . . " (p. 244). Burton condemns clerical celibacy and abstinence (pp. 244–46). Some are married, and for the others, let them burn, fire and flame; they do not care, and are not troubled with them (p. 247). Hence the necessity of the marriage bond, for a number of reasons which Burton has not the courage to enumerate, referring his reader to Voragine (p. 252). "I conclude therefore with Seneca: *cur toro viduo jaces?*" (p. 253): why bed down in an empty bed?

Let us pause here for a moment. It has been my wish to follow Burton step by step, omitting the quotations, but preserving his order and a little of his long-windedness. Of course, I have been, as he says of himself, "over-tedious." But I think this permits us some temporary reflections.

There are many questions which one does not know how to avoid. Some are more general and relate to Burton's style; others specifically concern love melancholy. Where, indeed, is the latter to be found? One must admit that the impression is mitigated with regard to the book in which we find ourselves. Is it, then, as terrible as all that? Is it such a great disease? To be sure, Burton paints some horrific pictures for us, to which we shall return. But we are often closer to fable or comedy than to tragedy. In love, there is good and evil, sweet and bitter. We are subject to this rhythm. As soon as the pendulum swings towards sweetness, Burton takes us back to the terrible, but as soon as the blade cuts too deep, he eases our anxiety. And it is here, perhaps, that Burton's longing emerges, his regret that by virtue of his office he is not in a position to take a wife, his suppressed appetite for love, and his serene ideal of conjugal love, old fogey though he be, like some character out of Molière. Bergen Evans has naturally placed great emphasis on Burton's sexual frustration,[10] and Simon confirms it: "Il nous semble incontestable que Burton ait été doué d'un appétit sexuel assez fort et sans doute exacerbé par la frustration."[11]

One senses that he would not have scorned to have been himself touched a bit by this heroical love to which even the Stoics succumbed, nor would have disdained to play with fire. When all is said and done, love is at the origin of civilization and the arts.

Paradoxically perhaps, the mass of quotations convoked for the debate on love does not provide much help in penetrating its terrifying seriousness. And it is this which we wish to point out in Burton's style. Everyone admires his culture, but I think they do so in a rather mindless way: was he, after all, as cultivated as all that? We pose this paradoxical question in order to answer it in some measure at the end of our discussion. If cultivation means assimilating, interpreting, crystallizing, then he is not cultivated. On this score Montaigne is cultived, Burton not. One never senses that he has grasped his reverie, or congealed his imagination, if I may put it that way. He is a collector of observations.

But it would be unfair to stop there. By collage and montage, he uses these observations in order to let others speak on his behalf, if others have said what he wants to say. It is doubtful if this is discretion or humility. Rather, in the manner of Democritus Junior, it might be a way of advancing in disguise while remaining visible. This would be what he calls "mine own method." Speaking of different authors who provide us different information "and yet all tending to the same purpose," he says:

"The sum of which I will briefly epitomize (for I light my candle from their torches) and enlarge again upon occasion, as shall seem best to me, and that after mine own method" (p. 189).

The method now seems clearer: to collect the most diverse authors who have written on the same subject, and to summarize them (which occupies the bulk of the book) with developments here and there according to the author's taste. The work of the author is one of compilation, summary, and fortuitous commentary.[12] Doubt arises: does he have anything to say which he is illustrating by quotations? Or does he have nothing to say but what others have already said? Who is this man, if not the orderly master of ceremonies of an assembly of phantoms who make their bow and then vanish, sometimes forever. One cannot say that Burton has ideas. He has opinions. He is not a philosopher. He is even the opposite of a philosopher. He proceeds by themes. For him, the synopsis is not merely a conventional decor;[13] it is a real plan. On the subject of the first table, J.R. Simon speaks of "une redoutable complexité" which "retient dans les mailles de sa logique irréfragable, toute la matière de la première partie" ((p. 90). But there is no "logic" in it; rather, there is an order, a harmonious deployment, a will to drain the subject dry in the mesh of a totalizing discourse.

"But," as Burton himself says, "I rove, I confess" (p. 261). It would be unjust and dishonest to call a halt here to Burton's reflections on love melancholy. The book is not finished: there is still jealousy, religious melancholy and despair, inseparable as we shall see, and indispensible for throwing light on the entire work. We will pass over jealously quickly, though Burton would "dilate and treat of it by itself, as a bastard branch or kind of love-melancholy" (p. 257). Thus he sees love, the most highly valued of the passions, as hypertrophied in one of its manifestations. Burton proceeds with the same monotonous unfolding of his matter. Is jealousy a cause or a symptom of melancholy? One finds it even amongst animals (pp. 261–62). He enumerates its causes: the stars (p. 264), the country, the climate. Are women more prone to it than men (pp. 265-66)? This is the question Montaigne posed. But Burton concludes "men and women are both bad, and too subject to this pernicious infirmity" (p. 266).[14] The enumeration of symptoms is the occasion for an interesting reflection: "Of all passions, as I have already proved, love is most violent, and of those bitter potions which this love-melancholy affords, this bastard jealousy is the greatest. . . . For besides fear and sorrow, which is common to all melancholy, [there is] anxiety of mind, suspicion, aggravation, restless thoughts . . . " (p. 280).

Here one finds fear and sorrow, the two emotions traditionally linked to melancholy since the Hippocratic aphorism,[15] but surrounded by various emotions which might be, as we see, a bit of everything. Melancholy loses the precision of its definition. Burton is sensitive to the ugliness, the grimaces of the jealous lover, to his exaggerated and contradictory postures.[16] He offers a mirror to the jealous (p. 257), which is the occasion for a picturesque description: "As a heron when she fishes, still prying on all sides, or as a cat doth a mouse, his eye is never off hers . . . " (p. 281). The prognostic for jealousy is unfortunate: "despair . . . madness" (pp. 286–88). The cure is the same as for other forms of melancholy (p. 289 ff.). Above all, idleness is to be avoided (p. 289).

But here emerges another species of the genus love melancholy: religious melancholy. "That there is such a distinct species of love melancholy, no man hath ever yet doubted" (p. 311). Here the tone changes and becomes solemn: this is a terrain to be explored. Burton takes up the accents of a Lucretius or a Manilius, but through the medium of the bad poetry of Grotius. "I have no pattern to follow as in some of the rest, no man to imitate. No physician hath as yet distinctly written of it as of the other; all acknowledge it a most notable symptom, some a cause, but few a species or kind" (pp. 311–12).

"No pattern to follow"? In fact, he cites the physicians Aretaeus,[17] Alexander, Rhazes, Avicenna, but also more recent authors such as Fuchs, Montaltus, Platter. From the point of view of the philosophers, he does not forget Plato's *Phaedrus* (p. 312). But Burton feels that he has something personal and important to say.

> Give me but a little leave, and I will set before your eyes in brief a stupend, vast, infinite ocean of incredible madness and folly: a sea full of shelves and rocks, sands, gulfs, euripes and contrary tides, full of fearful monsters, uncouth shapes, roaring waves, tempests, and siren calms, halcyonian seas, unspeakable misery, such comedies and tragedies, such absurd and ridiculous, feral and lamentable fits, that I know not whether they are more to be pitied or derided, or may be believed, but that we daily see the same still practised in our days, fresh examples, *nova novitia*, fresh objects of misery and madness in this kind that are still represented unto us, abroad, at home, in the midst of us, in our bosoms" (p. 313).

Burton becomes lyrical in his description of religious melancholy. It is certainly very close to him, and to heroical love. It does not have relevance only to a mythical past, or to history. Everyone can experience it, and experience it afresh every day; everyone can experience it in his heart. Let us recall what he said about love melancholy: he alone can speak of it who has been subject to it, Burton himself being only a sort of dilettante of this variety.

To be sure, this type of reflection enlists Burton the theologian and churchman, as in the pages on the beauty of God, which transcends all beauty (pp. 313–17). God is never loved too much for His own sake (p. 319). The "affected parts" are innumerable, and the medical expression is extended here to the whole universe and the surface of the earth (p. 318). To put some order into this infinity, Burton proposes to distinguish excessive from defective religious melancholy (p. 319). Excess is characteristic of monks, and then of other idolaters and superstitious people; it is the defect of libertines and other epicurians. Superstition is the worst of diseases. "For he that is superstitious can never be quiet . . . " (p. 320). In this case, the affected parts are "brain, heart, will, understanding, soul itself, and all the faculties of it, *totum compositum* [the whole composition], all is mad and dotes" (p. 321). Burton launches into a quite intolerant survey of non-christian religions (p. 322 ff.), but it must be admitted that Calvinists, Anabaptists and other "heretics" are not cosseted either. One can but wish for all these superstitious folk "[a sound mind] and a good physician" (p. 324). Men have made of religion "mere policy, a cloak, a human invention . . . " (p. 328). The Jesuits (p. 332) and the Pope himself (pp. 334–35) are not spared. Alongside the devil, the effects of fasting are deadly. "Monks, anchorites, and the like, after much emptiness, become melancholy, vertiginous . . . " (p. 343).

The general symptoms of these sick folk are an exclusive love for their own sect, a hatred of all other religions, stubbornness, grumbling, willingness to confront any danger, martyrdom (p. 346). Faced with these symptoms, ought one to weep with Heraclitus or laugh with Democritus? (p. 346). In truth, they manifest delerium of the imagination, but for the rest they reason correctly (*"læsum habent imaginationem . . . cætera sani"*) (p. 372). This is what Esquirol will later call monomania, and what Aretaeus had already accurately described as religious mania.[18] The prognosis for this melancholy is very bad: "folly, dotage, madness, gross ignorance, despair, obstinacy, a reprobate sense, a bad end" (p. 372). These are the seriously ill. "They are certainly far gone with melancholy, if not quite mad, and have more need of physic than many a man that keeps his bed, more need of hellebore than those that are in Bedlam" (p. 372). To cure this malady, one needs Hercules, Aesculapius, Christ himself (p. 375). In fact, as concerns the many prophets and dreamers which have been persecuted with fire and the stake, Burton thinks that the best cure, for some of them at least, would have been Bedlam (p. 379).

As for those who are ill through defect, these are the blasphemous, the unbelievers, the libertines and their ilk, "many of our great philosophers and deists" (p. 384). Ask him to what religion he subscribes, and "he scoffingly replies, a philosopher, a Galenist, an Averroist, and with Rabelais a physician, a Peripatetic, an Epicure . . . " (p. 384).

All these folk, who are in fact blatant atheists, are dangerous because they relativize the word of God: "great-witted Aristotle's works are as much authentical to them as Scriptures, subtle Seneca's Epistles as canonical as St Paul's, Pindarus' Odes as good as the Prophet David's Psalms, Epictetus' Enchiridion equivalent to wise Solomon's Proverbs . . . " (pp. 387–88). Truly, they are a race of sceptics and eclectics.

But at the same time, Burton's judgment is an important moment in the book, and one which to my knowledge has not been emphasized. We are witnessing a genuine reversal here; I can find no other way of expressing it. All of ancient culture is banished because it is pagan. All those beloved authors who had nourished reflection are condemned. They do not possess the truth. They vanish before the divine word. One must add to these agnostics those "cauterized souls," those shadowy Christians who go through the rituals, but whom the Lord knows to be rotten within (pp. 389–90).

This reversal, or if you will, this refusal to accord an absolute status to pagan pseudo-truth, leads us to despair in a movement which might be called dialectical.

After briefly posing the question of whether there might be such a thing as holy despair, Burton adopts the definition of Cicero for whom despair is a sickness of a soul without hope of bettering its situation: "*ægritudinem animi sine ulla rerum expectatione meliore*" (p. 392). It is this malady, also called the slaying of the soul (p. 394), which is the subject of the last part of the book. Its causes are, of course, the devil, together with his principal and executive agent, the melancholic humour itself. Is it not called the devil's bath (*balneum diaboli*)? (p. 395) The body, therefore, is under the domination of the soul. Sometimes, albeit rarely, melancholy and despair do not go together (p.396). In the end, despair is doubt concerning the existence of God (p. 396) or concerning his mercy (pp. 397-98). But in the last analysis, "The last and greatest cause of this malady is our own conscience, sense of our sins, and God's anger justly deserved, guilty conscience for some foul offence formerly committed" (p. 400). Inevitably, there follow the lines from Euripides' Orestes: Menelaus: "Unhappy Orestes, what malady kills you?" Orestes: "Conscience: the fact that I am conscious of the evils I have done."[19]

This conscience, which goes beyond mere moral conscience, and which has nothing to do with interior dialogue, but which exercises a tragic force through the fear of eternity, tortures the body like a cancer, to employ Burton's expression (p. 401).

Only negative theology will serve to describe the absolute quality of this despair. Here we have one of the most beautiful passages in the *Anatomy*, one which shows Burton's quality as a writer, and, in the last analysis, his sense of the tragic and the picturesque, the tragi-comic or baroque-tragic, if you will—the true Burtonian genre.

> As shoemakers do when they bring home shoes, still cry leather is dearer and dearer, may I justly say of those melancholy symptoms: these of despair are most violent, tragical, and grievous, far beyond the rest, not to be expressed but negatively as it is privation of all happiness, not to be endured. . . . What therefore, Timanthes did in his picture of Iphigenia, now ready to be sacrificed, when he had painted Calchas mourning, Ulysses sad, but most sorrowful Menelaus, and showed all his art in expressing variety of affections, he covered the maid's father Agamemnon's head with a veil, and left it to every spectator to conceive what he would himself . . . what he did in his picture, I will do in describing the symptoms of despair. . . . (p. 404)

Let us savour this encounter with the shoemaker and with Pliny. The story of Timanthes is exemplary. The absolute cannot be painted; the absolute cannot be uttered. This is the principle of apophatic or, if you wish, negative theology. Despair is what makes any malady a malaise. It leads to cursing God and blaspheming (p. 406).[20] A question of health becomes a question of salvation (p. 408). Neither medicine nor advice alone will do. The supreme remedy is the word of God (pp. 412–13). "They smell brimstone, talk familiarly with devils, hear and see chimeras, prodigious . . . blaspheme, deny God, call His power in question, abjure religion, and are still ready to offer violence to themselves, by hanging, drowning . . . (p. 424). The remedies proposed seem ludicrous, whether it be the betony of Antonius Musa or even the music by which David gave relief to Saul (pp. 429–30). Burton gives this final piece of advice: "Observe this short precept, give not way to solitariness and idleness. 'Be not solitary, be not idle' " (p. 432), wherein he invokes St. Augustine.

Writing about Burton compels one inexorably towards a particular style of writing and reflection. In short, what is one to do with all these commonplaces, all these quotations, besides repeat them, in despair of being able to add anything of one's own to an erudition so great? It seems that Burton attempted to exhaust the subject, not by his treatment of it, nor by an idea, but by strewing the territory with everything which had been said about it. Without question, the model of exposition is medical; it is even, I would say, the classical medical model followed since Antiquity.[21] Consider the example of Aretaeus, of Caelius, Alexander of Tralles etc. One begins with the definition; then come the symptoms, the causes, the affected parts, the prognosis, the remedies.

But the material organized under these rubrics is far from being exclusively medical.[22] Under "definition," for instance, we have seen that medical and philosophical definitions are placed side by side on the same plane. Symptomatology ushers in a mass of philosophical—or as we would say now, literary—and medical examples.

If one poses once again the traditional question about Burton—"Is he an author who is already archaic and outmoded, a fossil of the Renaissance, or is he already a modern," as B. Evans would claim, "a predecessor of Pinel?"—one sees that this is, to be sure, an interesting question, but one whose answer must be nuanced. It is true, as Starobinski says, that one encounters in the *Anatomy* "réunis tous les Maîtres dont le siècle suivant fera chanceler l'autorité et dont le nom même se perdra dans l'oubli," and that "cela dispensera maint lecteur hâtif de recourir aux Anciens: une bibliothèque tient en ce livre . . . c'est le festin de Sardanapale de l'érudition classique."[23] This was certainly one of the reasons for the success of this book, and an element which makes it still more precious to us now.

But what strikes me is not so much Burton's so-called classical erudition. After all, he was not much more cultivated than many of his contemporaries; like the others, he had read the Ancients. At the price of an aggravated pedantry, for which we will be forgiven for the sake of the delights of paradox, one might point out lacunae. For example, on the topic of lovers who find any ill-favoured person beautiful, or on the remedies for love, there is no reference to canto IV of Lucretius. But what makes the erudition impressive is the host of *minores* and writers of the preceding century. At bottom, here is someone who has replaced the "natural questions" such as they were posed in the sixteenth century, that is, through Aristotle and the Deipnosophists, Plutarch and the *Table Talk*, pseudo-Aristotle and the *Problemata*, with the natural questions of Fernel, Montaltus, Pratensis, Cardano etc. In this he appears modern. To be sure, modernity is not a rupture for him. In a way, it consists of being "up to date" in his bibliography, on the assumption that one can only aspire to novelty in the way one organizes perennial knowledge. We have seen how careful he is to note that he only became acquainted with Ferrand after the third edition of the *Anatomy*.

On the other hand, were I to compare Burton and Pinel as Evans has done,[24] I would be bolder, and not be satisfied with seeing a sympathy for the mentally ill in Burton which would make him a precursor of Pinel. In the history of psychopathology, this is the privilege of neither Burton nor Pinel.

But they have an important trait in common, and that is the fact that they reunite and bring into communication the domains, theoretically and juridically so remote, of medicine and philosophy. Elsewhere I have shown at length how these separate histories of medicine, specializing in the diseases of the body, and philosophy, which retained for itself the diseases of the soul, are constituted. In a way Burton, like Pinel, broke this separation by mingling the two traditions. But there are differences of stature. Burton brought in no notable reform. He was not a physician, and he did not live at the right time.

But with Burton, one cannot restrict the confluence to the medical and philsophical traditions. Everything is there, poetry, tragedy, history, what have you. One is not, as with Pinel, offered the simple and meaningful choice between the medical and the philosophical. Again, Burton did not put forth a theory of the passions as Pinel was to do.[25] On the other hand, one might say that Burton and Pinel are prone to the same criticism which would demand that they account for the legitimacy of their choice to mix together different traditions in order to establish a theory of insanity without clearly posing the question of the dualism or monism of body and soul.

There is no doubt that Burton is a dualist; once again I ask myself if the body-soul division which he adopts in distinguishing the symptoms of the soul from those of the body is anything more than a useful fiction, an explanatory strategy. The symptoms straddle each other with ease and the articulation of soul and body is not very sharply defined.

Here is a pastor who is involved in medicine. The priest is a physician of the soul. Priests and physicians "differ but in object, the one of the body, the other of the soul, and use diverse medicines to cure: one amends *animam per corpus*, the other *corpus per animam*." (I, p. 37). Melancholy affects both body and soul ("Now this being a common infirmity of body and soul": I, p. 37). He himself is a pastor by profession, a physician by inclination (I, p. 37).

If one wishes to uncover a new fact in the work of Burton, one should give some prominence to the recurring allusion to Bedlam:[26] "Go to Bedlam for examples" (p. 187). This reference to an already institutionalized experience of insanity is very interesting in the degree with which it suddenly seems to outweigh the cultural references. Even if there are some flashes of wit, and even a certain gesture of temperament or humour in these allusions to Bedlam, one must attribute this to Burton's "modernity."

To conclude, let us return to lovesickness. Love is only one passion amongst many, but it is perhaps more essential than the others. It is necessary to the cosmos and its functioning. But there is a danger that it will slide rapidly into illness. If one reviews the different divisions of love melancholy, one can say that heroical love holds us within the world of fiction and poetic imagination. I have said that I found the description of heroical melancholy a little light and frivolous; all things considered, it is not as bad as all that. Still, it is in this chapter that one can hear Burton's complaint, his bitterness at not having known love, or even in psychological terms, if one credits Evans, his sexual frustration. Jealousy, the passion of passions, aggravates the picture somewhat. But with religious melancholy, a lovesickness in itself, we are on completely different ground. In spite of the quotations from Aretaeus and others, Burton claims that he is the first to discuss religious melancholy. Why? Doubtless—and this takes us back to the preface—because he uses history. He is in a position to furnish examples drawn from the history of religions and from recent history, that of the wars of religion, and even from contemporary history. Religious melancholy arises from the soul, it is a lovesickness, a perversion of divine love. And this leads us to despair, the supreme and absolute evil. The chapter on despair is like a painter spilling ink on a canvas which he finds too cheerful. In fact, religious melancholy and despair tip the whole book over into metaphysics. The entire *Anatomy of Melancholy* is, so to speak, brought to bay upon this ultimate touchstone which makes all the rest relative, and driven to the wall of an absolute melancholy which meets with absolute evil, the denial of God. All the maladies, terrible though they be, are nothing in the face of this absolute evil which demands recourse to the methods of negative theology in order to attempt to describe it. But despair is also a lovesickness. Burton understood that lovesickness could not be confined to heroical melancholy, that one must go right up to divine love, and that man's great story is that of his relationship with God. The basis of love melancholy, indeed of any melancholy, is despair, which is like the melting-pot of all possible melancholies. Burton knew this well, and tells us so at the outset in his letter of Democritus to the reader: "So that, take melancholy in what sense you will, properly or improperly, in disposition or habit, for pleasure or for pain, dotage, discontent, fear, sorrow, madness, for part or all, truly or metaphorically, 'tis all one" (I, p. 40).

Must one think, as Starobinski does, that Burton "ne prétend pas plus dépasser son mal qu'il ne songe à dépasser ses prédécesseurs," and that "son livre est de ceux qui forment un circuit sans fin. Car la fin renvoie au commencement"?[27] Fundamentally, this it to pose the question of whether Burton changed in the course of writing his book, and if he changed himself in writing it, whether this was his intention or no. Is this organized compilation but a mere distraction? Is it a therapy which engages the human being and the writer more deeply in his book?

It is striking to read, as the conclusion to every study devoted to the *Anatomy of Melancholy*, this final piece of advice: do not live alone, do not live in idleness. Is this, then, the secret, and is it not about as disappointing on the whole as the kind of oracle one reads in one's cups? All that was necessary was to read Seneca's letters to Lucilius, or *De tranquillitate animi*, or perhaps just to have some common sense. It is by no means certain that this conclusion might not be ironic. But this irony is doubtless also a reconciliation of the self with the self, and of the self with others. The irony for a melancholic, who knows that he must keep occupied, is to take melancholy itself for his occupation, and the collection of the opinions of others upon this subject as his distraction. This conclusion, this final piece of advice, could serve as the starting point. Doubtless the immense detour was necessary to make this initial moment evident. It is the entire passage from knowledge to consciousness. Can one imagine a Burton refined by melancholy as Cymon was by love, as Burton himself describes him?

In truth, this remains an enigma; and part of the mystery lies in the fact that it is a melancholic who is writing, one who knows that he is a melancholic, and who even knows that the act of writing and cataloguing arises from his pathological state. He knows that "appropriating things generally said to his own person" is the act of a melancholic. I think that despair does not play a merely rhetorical role here: it is the dead end to which every melancholy tends, and one must pass through it in order to discover that in the end the formula is very simple: live with others and do not remain idle.

Université de Nantes

NOTES

1 Citations from Burton are from Holbrook Jackson's edition of *The Anatomy of Melancholy* (London and Toronto: J.M. Dent and Sons, 1932, 1977). Each part

is separately paginated, and unless otherwise indicated all references herein are to the third partition; thus "p. 99" stands for "p. 99 of the third partition"

2 On this sense of heroical, see J. Livingstone Lowes, "The Loverers Maladye of Hereos," *Modern Philology* 11 (1914), 291–346. Beginning with ερως, Arnold of Villanova confused it with *herus* and even with ἥρως, in his *Liber de parte operativa*, which is Burton's immediate source; cf. the note by J.R. Simon, *Robert Burton (1577–1640) et l'Anatomie de la Mélancholie* (Paris: Didier, 1964), p. 166, n. 115.

3 Cf. Jackie Pigeaud, *La maladie de l'âme. Étude sur la relation de l'âme et du corps dans la tradition médico-philosophique antique*, (Paris: Les Belles Lettres, 1981), pp. 211–42.

4 "I am of opinion that, though beauty itself be a great motive . . . yet, as it is used, artificial is of more force, and much to be preferred" (p. 88).

5 "It is true that those fair sparkling eyes, white neck, coral lips, turgent paps, rose-coloured cheeks, etc., of themselves are potent enticers; but when a comely, artificial, well-composed look, pleasing gesture, an affected carriage shall be added, it must needs be far more forcible than it was, when those curious needle works, variety of colours, purest dyes, jewels, spangles, pendants, lawn, lace, tiffanies, fair and fine linen, embroideries, calamistrations, ointments, etc., shall be added, they will make veriest dowdy otherwise a goddess, when nature shall be furthered by art" (p. 89).

6 Cf. the quotation from the *Celestina*, p. 127.

7 Author of *De cerebri morbis* (Basel, 1549).

8 This verse from Ovid is cited on p. 154.

9 On this question, see *La Maladie de l'âme*, and Jackie Pigeaud, *Folie et cures de la folie chez les médecins de l'Antiquité gréco-romaine. La manie.* (Paris: Les Belles Lettres, 1987), p. 219.

10 *The Psychiatry of Robert Burton.* (New York: Columbia U.P., 1944), p. 19.

11 Simon, *Robert Burton*, p. 511.

12 Starobinski comments perceptively on the Burtonian art of quotation in "Democrite parle," *Le Débat*, no. 29 (March 1984), 54: "L'auteur, quand il veut parler de façon plus frappante, parle avec la voix des autres. Il recourt surabondamment à ces ressources que la rhétorique nomme 'auctoritas,' 'chrie' . . . Il se dit lui-même par le texte des maîtres, qu'il détourne à son usage personnel. . . . L'accumulation immodérée des ornements empruntés (des 'emblêmes numéraires' ou des 'surpoids,' comme dit Montaigne) est l'un des aspects de la luxuriance ou se complait la Renaissance tardive; au niveau de l'écriture savante, c'est l'une des efflorescences d'un certain baroque. . . . La démarche de son 'inventio' est inséparable de celle de la 'thésaurisation.' De là le mélange de fraîcheur et de décrépitude qui, pour nous modernes, fait le charme hybride de ce livre."

13 Cf. W. Osler, "Robert Burton, the Man, his Book, his Library," *Yale Review*, new series, 3 (1913–14), reprinted in *Selected Writings* (London: Oxford U.P.,

1951), pp. 65–99, and particularly p. 95.

14 Even Hippocrates, in his *Letter to Dionysos*, was not spared (p. 269).

15 *Aphorisms* VI, 23: "When fear and sadness last a long time, it is a melancholic state."

16 "Besides those strange gestures of staring, frowning, grimming, rolling of eyes, menacing, ghastly looks, broken pace, interrupt, precipitate half-turns" (p. 280).

17 On religious mania in Aretaeus of Cappadocia, see my *Folie et cure de la folie*, pp. 67 ff.

18 See *La Manie*, p. 78 and 94. Aretaeus writes: "The mania is attached to their religious belief; concerning everything else, they retain their sound mind."

19 On these lines, and the meaning which, in our view, must be ascribed to them, cf. *La maladie de l'âme*, p. 418.

20 Sometimes it signals monomania, as we have pointed out in connection with religious melancholy: cf. the story which follows on p. 407: "An advocate of Padua, *anno* 1545, that being desperate, by no counsel of learned men could be comforted: he felt (as he said) the pains of hell in his soul; in all other things he discoursed aright, but in this most mad."

21 On the appearance of this model of exposition, see *La manie*, p. 67 ff.

22 Besides, we know, as J.R. Simon has pointed out (op. cit., p. 428), that "les auteurs médicaux cités ou mentionnés n'atteignent pas le nombre de 200."

23 J. Starobinsky, p. 54.

24 B. Evans, *The Psychiatry of Robert Burton*, p. 104.

25 On Pinel's choice of the Stoic theory of the passions, see, J. Pigeaud, "Le rôle des passions dans la pensé médicale de Pinel à Moreau de Tours," *History and Philosophy of the Life Sciences* 2 (1980), 123–40, and L"Antiquité classique et les débuts de la psychiatrie français," in *Nouvelle histoire de la psychiatrie* (Toulouse: Privat, 1983), pp. 129–45.

26 See also p. 372: "They are certainly far gone with melancholy, if not quite mad, and have more need . . . of hellebore than those that are in Bedlam." Also p. 379: as for the prophets, "I think the most compendious cure, for some of them at least, had been in Bedlam."

27 "La mélancholie de l'anatomiste," *Tel Quel* 10 (1962), 21–35.

(Article translated by Faith Wallis)